SURFACE STRUCTURE MODIFICATION AND HARDENING OF Al-Si ALLOYS

SURFACE STRUCTURE MODIFICATION AND HARDENING OF Al-Si ALLOYS

Denis A. Romonov
Stanislav V. Moskovskii
Viktor E. Gromov

CISP

CRC Press is an imprint of the
Taylor & Francis Group, an **informa** business

Translated from Russian by V.E. Riecansky

CRC Press
Taylor & Francis Group
6000 Broken Sound Parkway NW, Suite 300
Boca Raton, FL 33487-2742

© 2021 by CISP
CRC Press is an imprint of Taylor & Francis Group, an Informa business

No claim to original U.S. Government works

Printed on acid-free paper

International Standard Book Number-13: 978-0-367-53125-6 (Hardback)

Visit the Taylor & Francis Web site at
http://www.taylorandfrancis.com

and the CRC Press Web site at
http://www.crcpress.com

Contents

Introduction

The reliability of energy systems, minimizing the loss of electrical energy and saving material resources is largely determined by the reliability of electrical contacts. The effective operation of the energy and industrial equipment of the global energy system is due to the reliability of the electrical contacts. The loss of electrical energy and the occurrence of emergency situations occur due to the poor quality of the contacts and their overheating. The main reason for the failure of electrical equipment is the failure of their contact apparatus. This trend is characteristic of most industrial enterprises around the world. To restore the contact apparatus, its electrical contacts are replaced with new ones, or the contact apparatus is completely changed. As a rule, the contacts of the switches of powerful electric networks are a composite material based on a silver matrix with high electrical conductivity and an arc-resistant filler. On the international market, the cost of an ounce of silver is 15.31 USD. More than 50% of the materials spent on the production of electrical contacts remain unused during the operation of the contacts. For the electrical contacts of the switches of powerful electrical networks, only the surface erosion resistance is important. It is economically and technically feasible to develop an approach to the creation of materials when the mechanical strength is ensured by the use of economical substrates, and the special surface properties are ensured by the continuous or local formation of composite coatings on it, whose properties correspond to operational requirements. Material savings with this approach can reach 90%. Modern condensed matter physics as one of its priority areas indicates the development of methods for improving the operational characteristics of various materials is. Given all of the above, hardening of the contact surface of switches of powerful electric networks is an urgent task for the development of modern technologies.

The degree of elaboration of the topic

Scientists all over the world have been actively engaged in the problem of increasing the operational characteristics of electrical contacts operating in conditions of arc and spark erosion for the past 100 years. In 2019–2020, scientists from the USA, China, France, Turkey, Canada, Great Britain, India and other countries have been actively working in this direction. More than a dozen universities in China are working on the creation of electrical erosion materials for electrical contacts. Volumetric materials based on silver, hardened by various MAX phases, have been created by Chinese scientists from the Southeast University under the guidance of Prof. M.M. Liu and scientists from Xi'an University of Technology under the direction of Professor H. Li. Equal channel angular pressing for the production of electrical contact materials is being investigated by a team of scientists led by Professor D. Wang. The work of scientists from the UK under the guidance of Prof. R.A. Veazey is devoted to modelling the structure and properties of arc-resistant electrical contacts. To predict the life of electrical erosion-resistant contacts and manage all factors influencing it, a collaboration of scientists from Thailand (responsible Prof. S. Daocharoenporn) and the USA (responsible Prof. S. Kulkarni) has been created. The electroerosion-resistant coatings obtained to date have insufficient electrical conductivity, which reduces the life of the electrical contacts.

1

Electroerosion resistant composite materials and coatings of electrical contacts

1.1. Problem of increasing the electrical erosion resistance of the contacts of the switches of powerful electrical networks

In a survey statistical study [1], the main causes of failures and types of malfunctions in 300 cases of electrical component failures are analyzed. As a result of the analysis, it was found that most of the failures of electrical components occurred in the operation of circuit breakers and emergency generators. The main reasons for the failure were the deterioration and failure of electrical components due to a failure in the operation of their contact apparatus. This trend is characteristic of most industrial enterprises around the world.

The phenomenon of electrical erosion is the destruction of the material of the electrodes during electrical breakdown, when an electric arc or spark forms between the electrodes [2, 3]. Electrical erosion is accompanied by the transfer of material between electrical contacts. As a result of the action of numerous discharges, the contacts are gradually destroyed.

At present, compositions based on components with high electrical conductivity and components with high arc resistance are used as materials for arc-resistant contacts of switches of powerful electric networks. As components with high electrical conductivity, silver, gold, copper, etc. are usually used. As a rule, these materials are presented in the form of a matrix in which inclusions of the arc-resistant component are placed. As components with high arc resistance, tungsten, molybdenum, carbides and metal oxides are used. The combination of the properties of the matrix and the filler allows one to achieve the required level of properties.

Hardening of the surface of the material, and not the entire volume, is economically and technically feasible [4]. It is surface hardening that will save expensive materials of electrical contacts. The development of methods for improving the operational characteristics of various materials is one of the priority areas of modern condensed matter physics. Given the above, the research topic is relevant for the development of new modern technologies.

1.2. Features of the formation of bulk materials of arc-resistant electrical contacts

MAX phases with the formula $Mn + 1AXn$ (where M is a transition metal; A is an element of group IIIA or IVA; X is C and/or N; $n = 1$–3) are a group of layered ternary compounds with a high modulus of elasticity, as well as good thermal and electrical conductivity, combining the properties of both metals and ceramics [5]. As typical MAX phases, Ti_3AlC_2 [6] and Ti_3SiC_2 [7] efficiently strengthen copper-based electrical contact materials. Professor M.M. Liu et al. [8] fabricated Ag/Ti_3AlC_2 composites by hot pressing and found that they are potentially suitable for materials of sliding electrical contacts and can be used with high efficiency because they showed good mechanical and electrical properties. In [9], the authors prepared $Ag/10$ wt.% Ti_3AlC_2 is an electric contact material by powder metallurgy and its resistance to arc erosion was studied, which turned out to be comparable to the commercial Ag/CdO contacts used in contactors. As a rule, the grain size of the matrix phase and the size of the filler are of great importance for the mechanical and electrical properties of the composite.

For example, Professor H. Li et al. [10] reported that finer TiB_2 and SnO_2 reinforcing particles are more beneficial due to less mass loss and relative mass transfer of the silver base of the electrical contact material during electric arc erosion tests. But Professor N. Ray et al. [11, 12] reported that the electrical contact resistance and electrical erosion resistance of the Ag/WC electrical contact material decrease with increasing particle size of the WC. In addition, the structural anisotropy of graphite has been reported to affect the electrical conductivity and arc erosion resistance of silver–graphite electrical contact materials [13–14]. According to the authors, the influence of the silver grain size and particle size and the preferential alignment of the MAX phases with respect to the properties of Ag/MAX in the electrical contact material was not reported. Powder metallurgy followed by extrusion, drawing, and rolling were used to prepare Ag/C [15], Ag/SnO$_2$ [16], Ag/CdO [17], Ag/ZnO [17] electrical contact materials. However, these processes change the size of the sample and/or the requirements for high temperature deformation and pressure.

Equal channel angular pressing (ECAP) by the authors of [18–20] was used to prepare materials for the electric contact Ag/Ti$_3$AlC$_2$. An Ag/10 wt.% Ti$_3$AlC$_2$ composite with a relative density of 99.8% and a homogeneous microstructure was prepared by ECAP at a relatively low temperature of 200°C and a pressure of 37 MPa. Ti$_3$AlC$_2$ particles were stratified and predominantly aligned in the Ag matrix after ECAP. The preferential alignment of Ti$_3$AlC$_2$ led to the anisotropy of the electrical and compressive properties and the arc erosion resistance of the composite. The properties of the sintered compacted and ECAP sample were investigated. The Vickers hardness of the ECAP sample was about 1.5 times higher than that of the sintered pressed material. The smallest resistivity of 59.3 × 10^{-9} Ohm · m has an ECAP sample. The maximum compressive and deformation strengths were 805 ± 18.6 MPa and 43.8 ± 2.2% in the ECAP sample loaded perpendicular to the alignment of Ti$_3$AlC$_2$. An ECAP sample with a working surface parallel to the centering of Ti$_3$AlC$_2$ showed better resistance to arc erosion. The mechanisms responsible for the anisotropic microstructure and properties were proposed and discussed.

Fine-grained Cu(70–90%)–W composites were successfully obtained [21–23] using nanosized Cu/W powders under vacuum. The sintering process of Cu/W composites is explained by sintering interactions that occur both within the powders and between the powders. Microstructural analysis of Cu/W composites showed that large spherical and nanoscale tungsten particles were uniformly embedded into the copper matrix. The Cu/W interface has a semi-coherent bond and shows good contact. The relative density, hardness, electrical conductivity, and crystal size of W in Cu/W composites increased when the sintering temperature increased from 1000°C to 1090°C. It was found that with increasing copper content, the hardness and grain size of the tungsten grains of the Cu/W composites decrease, but the relative density and electrical conductivity improve. The ratio of electrical conductivity, sintering temperature, and crystal size W of the Cu/W composites was described using a regression formula.

For the Cu–Ag film contact [24–26], the good boundary properties of the salt allow gliding with a low friction coefficient, a polished worn surface, and high bearing capacity. Under current load conditions, mechanical disconnection and repeated contact of the contacting surface lead to the formation of an electric arc, and damage to the Ag film caused by the electric arc depends on the polarity of the pin and disk. For a positive Cu pin on a disk with a negative Ag film, a rainbow film and transparent LP108 on an Ag film are observed. At the same time, for the negative Cu pin against the disk of the positive Ag film, the removal of the Ag film is observed, and this leads to the suspension of a dark ion–Ag liquid. In both cases, the electric arc does not degrade the LP108. Damage caused by an electric arc and an electric arc on an Ag film can be repaired by ensuring that the contact surface matches exactly.

Three-dimensional continuous composite materials based on an Ag matrix reinforced by a Ni network were obtained by hot pressing of composite Ag–Ni powders with Ni powders deposited on the surface of Ag granules [27–29]. The formation of a three-dimensional continuous Ni network increases the load transferred from the Ag matrix to the second-phase Ni, causing the deformation of Ag and Ni during strain drawing. Joint deformation begins as orientation rotation and refinement; for example, the Ag matrix is shifted by $\{111\}$ $\langle 112\text{-}\rangle$, twins by $\{111\}$ $\langle 112\text{-}\rangle$ and $\langle 100 \rangle$, which leads to the formation of a texture in the second Ni phase along a certain direction. Finally, continuous three-dimensional nickel networks were torn and pulled into belts parallel to the axial direction of the composite wire. An increase in real deformation can increase the axial length of Ni-grids, thus increasing the hardness and conductivity of Ag–Ni materials for electrical contacts. In addition, the two-dimensional characteristics of electric networks with a high resistance profile increase the hydraulic resistance of molten Ag. Therefore, belt-reinforced Ag–Ni materials for electrical contacts exhibit low mass loss after 100 000 on/off cycles (1.8 mg, only 22.8% of the weight of the sample reinforced with round fibers).

Al_2O_3–Cu/25W_5Cr and Al_2O_3–Cu/35W_5Cr composites were fabricated by vacuum hot pressing and internal oxidation [30–32]. The electrical conductivity, relative density and Brinell hardness were measured. The effect of nano-Al_2O_3 and tungsten on the hot deformation of Al_2O_3–Cu/(W, Cr) composites was investigated using isothermal compression tests using a Gleeble-1500D thermomechanical simulator in the range from 650°C to 950°C and a strain rate of 0.001–10 s^{-1}. The deformed microstructure was characterized and analyzed using optical and transmission electron microscopy. The interaction of the hardening process, dynamic recovery, and dynamic recrystallization was illustrated. It is shown that Cr particles were extruded into strips; W particles underwent a slight deformation during hot compression. In addition, a composite with a higher tungsten content had a higher flow stress. Particles of nano-Al_2O_3 fixed dislocations and inhibited dynamic recovery and dynamic recrystallization. In addition, it is still at the stage of subcrystal formation at 850°C, 0.01 s^{-1}. Therefore, the Al_2O_3–Cu/ $35W_5Cr$ composite has typical dynamic recovery characteristics. Therefore, the Al_2O_3–Cu/(W, Cr) composites show good performance at high temperatures.

Tungsten–copper (W–Cu) contact materials are the main components of high-voltage electrical switches. However, the significant effect of arc ablation at high voltage and high current often leads to disconnection and mechanical losses, which seriously affects the safe operation of devices. In [33–35], mechanisms of the destruction of contact materials from tungsten and copper caused by significant arc ablation in the atmosphere of sulphur hexafluoride (SF$_6$) were studied. The results showed that the arc ablation of contact materials is mainly caused by evapouration and spraying of the copper component, which has a low melting point, followed by ablation and cleavage of the tungsten (W) frame structure. All this increased the surface roughness of the contact materials, and then further accelerated the volatilization of the copper component and the reaction between the contact materials and the SF$_6$ extinguishing medium. Finally, contact materials have lost their functions of extinguishing the arc and switching current. A simulated experimental work was also carried out, which confirmed the above-described mechanisms of destruction of the contact materials. Due to the instantly high temperature and high voltage occurring during the arc, the Cu and W phases in the W–Cu alloy underwent significant evapouration and mass loss.

Different configurations of the geometry of the two butt electrodes are usually used to study the electrical properties of materials, with the key being how the current flows through the sample. In studies

[36–38], finite element modelling is used to model the response of a direct electric current to an electrically homogeneous sample (based on a $SrTiO_3$ single crystal) using two butt electrode geometries based on macrocontacts over the entire surface, which is usually used to characterize bulk ceramics or large single crystals and microcontacts, which are used to characterize thin films and local intragranular and intergranular regions in ceramics. Well-known equations for macro- and microcontacts are used to calculate the electrical conductivity of a sample and are compared with eigenvalues to determine their accuracy. The geometric factor indicates the exact values of volumetric conductivity in the presence of a uniform current flow, while the equation of propagation resistance gives the most accurate values of conductivity for a heterogeneous current flow. When microcontacts are used, the reaction is dominated by a small region of high current density near the contact, providing local electrical properties. Interference can occur when areas with a high current density overlap each other, providing a less resistive path for the current to flow, thereby reducing the applicability of the propagation resistance equation. For microcontacts at short distances, the electrical conductivity is overestimated. The accuracy of the propagation resistance equation increases with increasing distance between the contacts and makes an error within 10% when they are separated eight times along the radius of the microcontact. The convergence of the error to values below 10% is becoming increasingly difficult and requires excessively large (and problematic for the experiment) separation distances. For example, to obtain a result with an error below 5%, separation is required that exceeds 28 times the radius of the microcontact. Retention occurs when the size of the sample limits the ability of the current to propagate from the microcontact, thereby increasing the resistance. Since the shape and size of the sample can limit the flow of current, a geometric factor can sometimes be used to determine the exact conductivity. In some cases, interference can balance the limitation to obtain randomly accurate conductivity values.

In studies [39–41], algorithms of computational multibody systems are used to develop detailed models of railway vehicles to predict wear resulting from the dynamic pantograph/contact chain interaction. Wear is predicted using algorithms of computational multi-body systems for various motion scenarios, which include matching the curve with a constant speed and acceleration and deceleration along the tangent to the path. The influence of vehicle vibration in these various driving scenarios on the contact force is additionally used to study the wear rate of the contact wire. The wear model used in this study takes into account electrical and mechanical stresses. The nonlinear finite element formulation of absolute nodal coordinates, which is suitable for implementation in algorithms of computational multibody systems, is used to model a flexible contact system, thereby eliminating the need to use incremental rotation procedures and joint modeling methods. To obtain effective solutions, both the overhead contact line and the connecting wire are modeled using a cable element of absolute nodal coordinates with insufficient bias. The pantograph elastic contact/contact network composition used in this study allows separation between the pantograph panel head and the contact wire and takes into account the friction effect due to sliding between the pantograph panel head and the contact cable. The approach proposed in the study [39–41] can be used to assess the electrical contact resistance, the contribution of sparking resulting from the separation of the head / contact chain, mechanical and electrical wear, and the influence of the lifting force of the pantograph mechanism on the wear rate. Numerical results are presented and analyzed for studying the wear rates for different scenarios of motion.

The method proposed in articles [42–44] is based on the first principles of the density functional theory for calculating the electronic structure of SnO_2 and rare-earth elements alloyed with SnO_2. The energy zone and state density of unalloyed SnO_2 and SnO_{2-x} (La, Ce, and Y) were calculated using the Origin Pro 9.0 software for quantitative calculation. Carrying out an experimental test of $AgSnO_2$ and $AgSnO_{2-x}$ (La, Ce and Y), contact materials prepared by sol-gel and powder metallurgy methods, as well as contact resistance and arc energy, were measured using a simulated electric contact test. In the simulation results, the relative electrical conductivity of SnO_{2-x} (La, Ce, and Y) Y-doped in comparison with pure SnO_2 is greatest. In the experimental results, the minimum and maximum values and the range of variation of the arc energy and contact resistance after $AgSnO_{2-x}$(La, Ce, and Y) are reduced. The effect of Y-alloyed $AgSnO_2$ is more obvious and has the highest density. The final simulation and experiment results are in good agreement. Y-alloyed with $AgSnO_2$ has the best electrical characteristics, followed by La alloyed $AgSnO_2$.

Studies [45–47] focus on the wear, friction, and electrical characteristics of the newly developed disk contact design for sliding electrical contacts. Various types of graphite and copper as combinations of materials, various operating parameters of the contact and, in particular, different directions of the electric current, that is, the polarity of the disk, were investigated in real contact conditions on a special tribological test setup. Electrographite and polymer-bound graphite worked in the coupled contact, against copper and against each other. A pair of polymer-bound graphite / polymer-bound graphite showed the best results for almost all the parameters studied, while a mixed, heterogeneous combination of polymer-bound graphite/electrographite had the worst performance. In addition, all couples containing electrographic material showed unstable contact behavior and generally gave the worst overall performance. The wear of self-conjugate graphite pairs was less than the wear of graphite/ copper couples. The effect of polarity on graphite/graphite material combinations was negligible, while in graphite/copper combinations it was found that the direction of electric current significantly affects disk wear. The wear of a positive graphite disk was 30% lower than that of a negative graphite disk, while the wear of a positive copper disk was 8 times greater than the wear of a negative copper disk. Differences in the boundary contact film were observed in graphite / copper contacts depending on the polarity of the surface, which means that sliding contacts with the current flowing from the graphite disk to the copper disk showed less wear than contacts where the current flows from the copper disk to the graphite disk .

Copper-based materials are widespread industrial products that are widely used in the fields of powder metallurgy, electrical contacts, heat exchangers, etc. However, the ease of surface oxidation limits the durability and efficiency of copper-based components. The authors of [48–50] developed a powder metallurgy process for the manufacture of graphene/copper composites using copper powders, which were first deposited on graphene layers by thermal chemical vapour deposition (CVD). Graphene/copper composites enclosed in a bonded graphene network could then be obtained by vacuum hot pressing. After thermal oxidation (up to 220°C) in humid air for several hours, the authors [48–50] found that the degree of surface oxidation of the samples was much lower than that of their pure Cu analog, and the samples [48–50] showed a smaller increase contact resistance of the interface when used as materials of electrical contacts. As a result, graphene/copper composites showed a significant improvement in oxidation resistance (about 5.6 times) compared to their pure copper counterpart, thus offering potential applications as new materials for electrical contacts.

Multilayer Cu/Ni–P/Au systems are used as electrical contacts [51–53]. The upper layer of Au is thin and porous. These pores deliver a corrosive medium to the lower layer, which causes corrosion using a galvanic coupling mechanism. Therefore, filling these pores is necessary to increase the life of electronic devices. The pores can be sealed by electrodeposition of poly (methyl methacrylate), which reduces the porosity index (about 97%) and increases the corrosion resistance (about 10 times) of electrical contacts after 10 cycles of electropolymerization. However, an inhomogeneous polymer film was formed during a larger number of polymerization cycles (> 50), which reduced the corrosion resistance.

In papers [54–56], an attempt was made to evaluate the operability of arc contacts as a vital component of the interruption chamber in SF_6 high-voltage circuit breakers with a tension filter. The relationship between the eroded mass caused by interruption of the short-circuit current and various thermal voltage indicators, such as transferred electric charge, square of the current strength and arc energy, were investigated by conducting many experiments with different current amplitudes and arc lifetime. It is shown that none of the known indicators can determine only mass erosion caused by interruption of current. Therefore, to evaluate mass erosion, equations have been proposed that include two of certain parameters. The method using arc energy and the transferred electric charge has the highest accuracy in estimating mass loss [54–56]. However, given the complexity of measuring arc voltage, you can also use another method that uses current and arc lifetime. In addition, the development of erosion during the life cycle of arc contacts is studied. It is shown that the roots of the arc tend to form on new non-eroded sections of the contacts during current interruption, which leads to different erosion rates between the first several and subsequent interruptions due to changes in the contact morphology after the first several switching operations.

The susceptibility of the pin socket to vibration loads is one of the achievements of electrical engineering. Electrical engineering alone is not enough to solve this complex problem. Multiphysics analysis is expected to be the solution to analyze this electromechanical pin-socket dynamic structure. Studies [57–59] develop dynamic contact multiphysical analysis with the formalism of tensor network analysis. The multiphysical model combines the relative speed and position of the pin in combination with instantaneous contact resistance implemented in an RC network. An innovative method has been developed that allows one to determine the signature of vibrational voltage by the signal-to-noise amplitude. The relevance of the model of multiphysical tensor analysis of networks is illustrated by the example of a 10 mm long socket with uniaxial vibrational voltage of an arbitrary waveform with a passband of 20 kHz. It has been shown that contact resistance can fluctuate more than a thousand times. The vibration-stress state of the pin-socket depending on the parameters of the RC network is also discussed. The proposed multiphysical analysis can be potentially applied to the study of electromagnetic compatibility and signal integrity of assembled electronic equipment and printed circuit boards under conditions of vibrational stresses.

With the rapid development of ultra-high voltage technology (over 500 kV), it is becoming increasingly difficult to meet the high demands of traditional electrical contact materials for ultra-high voltage switches. Copper/graphene composite coatings on a pure copper substrate were successfully fabricated using the simple cathodic electric codeposition method [60–62]. The morphology, structure, coating composition, and porosity of composite copper / graphene coatings were studied. The Vickers hardness of the copper / graphene composite coating increases by about 25% compared to pure copper coating. Adding graphene to a composite coating with a low coefficient of friction of approximately 0.2 increases wear resistance. The thermal conductivity of the copper / graphene composite coating prepared in a galvanic solution with a graphene content of 10 g / l reaches 285.2 W / (m · K) at room temperature, which is 61.9% more compared to a pure copper coating. The average interrupt current of 3.6 A of the copper / graphene composite coating is superior to that of the Cu20W80 alloy, indicating improved resistance to arc ablation. The copper / graphene composite coating provides new opportunities for replacing traditional materials for electrical contacts of ultra-high voltage circuit breakers.

To study the electrical characteristics of $AgTiB_2$ contact materials with various Ni additives, arc erosion tests were performed 20 000 times at a voltage of 24 V and a direct current of 16 A [63–65]. The morphology and chemical composition of the arc eroded contact surface was characterized by scanning electron microscopy and energy dispersive X-ray spectrometry, the mass change after testing for arc erosion was determined, and the arc energy and arc duration on the working and bursting arc were determined. The mechanisms of arc erosion are analyzed and discussed. The results show that the mode of arc erosion varies from anodic erosion to cathodic erosion with the addition of Ni. The contact material Ag–4 wt.% TiB_2 with the addition of 2 wt.% Ni has optimal characteristics along with the smallest weight loss, while especially high arc energy and total mass loss are formed at 4 wt.% and 8 wt.% Ni. In addition, the mechanism of arc erosion was discussed based on contact characteristics, thermal properties, and ionization energy of materials. It is believed that excessive addition of Ni is not beneficial for improving arc erosion resistance, since Ni has a great potential for ionization and the possibility of evapouration due to its small difference in the change in enthalpy compared to ionization energy.

The materials of the electrical contact Al_2O_3–Cu/(25)W(5)Cr and Al_2O_3–Cu/(35)W(5)Cr were prepared by vacuum sintering by hot pressing and internal oxidation [66–68]. Relative density, electrical conductivity, and Brinell hardness were measured. The microstructure was analyzed using scanning electron microscopy and transmission electron microscopy. The JF04C electrical contact tester was used to study the electrical contact characteristics of composites. The morphology of arc erosion was analyzed using scanning electron microscopy and a three-dimensional profilometer. Material transfer, as well as the characteristics of the electrical contact, were studied during the operations of closing and opening contacts at 30 V DC from 10 to 30 A. Nano-Al_2O_3 particles fixed the dislocations. The material was transferred from the cathode to the anode. During the melting, evapouration, and atomization of copper during sparking, W particles collect and form needle-shaped skeletons. At the end of experiments [66–68], liquid droplets, needle-like structures, craters and bulges formed on the surfaces of electrodes after arc erosion. In addition, their content and morphology are affected by the tungsten content. When the tungsten content of the dispersed copper matrix increases from 25 to 35 wt.%, The welding power decreases during stable operations. In addition, when the arc duration exceeds 8.86 ms, the Al_2O_3–Cu/(35)W(5)Cr contact material has a shorter average arc duration than Al_2O_3–Cu/(25)W(5)Cr at the same energy arcs.

1.3. Hardening of electrical contacts by spraying electroerosion-resistant coatings

To ensure high electrical erosion resistance and electrical conductivity, at least two components are required, one of which has high electrical conductivity, and the other has electrical erosion resistance. Obtaining such composite coatings is a complex task, since it is necessary to ensure acceptable adhesion of the coating to the substrate and cohesion of the particles of the composite coating. At the Plasma Focus installation, electroerosion-resistant coatings of the W–Cu system were obtained [69–71]. Tungsten penetrates into the copper substrate to a depth of not more than 25 microns, while its concentration does not exceed 10 at. % However, for contacts of switches of powerful electric networks, pseudo-alloy materials based on the W–Cu system with a higher concentration of tungsten are required.

Condensed from the vapour phase composite materials obtained by high-speed electron beam evapouration and subsequent condensation have a layered structure [72, 73]. The thickness of a single layer is from units to hundreds of micrometers and is set by the operating parameters of the installation. At present, materials based on electroerosion-resistant systems W–Cu, Mo–Cu and Cr–Cu, C–Cu have been obtained [74, 75]. These condensed materials have a lamellar structure with a hierarchy of macro-, micro- and submicron levels. In condensed materials based on copper and chromium, solid solutions of supersaturated chromium are formed and decomposed. the influence of temperature and volume fraction of refractory particles on the kinetics of their growth during liquid-phase sintering of Cr–Cu composites in the temperature range 1150–1350 °C in vacuum (2–4) 10^{-3} Pa is considered. It was found that the kinetics of growth of medium-sized particles is described by an almost cubic law, and the decrease in their number is determined by an almost inverse relationship: the apparent activation energy ($Q = 113 \pm 10$ kJ/mol) has an order comparable to diffusion in liquid metals. According to the Lifshitz–Slezov–Wagner theory, diffusion coalescence indicates the growth of particles controlled by diffusion. The experimental growth constants are an order of magnitude higher than those calculated in the framework of the classical Lifshitz-Slezov-Wagner theory. An increase in the growth rate constant with a volume fraction of refractory particles varying from 0.4 to 0.7, and a change in the particle size distribution function after sintering for 90 min at 1200°C are consistent with the Ardell model, which modifies the Lifshitz–Slezov–Wagner theory taking into account the effect, the volume fraction of particles according to the kinetics of their growth. The coatings obtained in this way have low adhesion and for this reason are not suitable for practical use. The article

[76] presents and discusses the actual state and prospects of using powerful electron beam technology for the manufacture of metal as well as non-metallic composite materials, mainly for electrical contacts and electrodes.

A technology has been developed for producing condensed gradient composite materials of the Cu–W system using high-speed electron beam evapouration–condensation [77]. Changes in the structure, electrical conductivity, hardness, mechanical properties, tensile fracture of a condensed Cu–W material at ambient temperature and elevated temperatures depending on the tungsten content and heat treatment are studied. New morphological features of the condensed composite material have been discovered that cause a change in the properties of the material. The relationships and correlation dependencies between the tungsten content, structure, strength and hardness of the composite are established.

Production technology, structure, electrical conductivity, friction coefficient, hardness, strength and ductility in the temperature range of 290–870 K of copper–carbon composites with layered structures and carbon content from 1.2 to 7.5 mass. % of sliding electrical contacts of current collectors obtained by electron beam evapouration and vacuum condensation were studied by the authors [78]. A thermodynamic activation analysis of the hardness and strength of the composites was carried out. Correlations between hardness and strength of composites are established.

Scientists at the Siberian State Industrial University are studying the structure and properties of electroerosion-resistant coatings of various systems obtained by the electric explosion method. Thanks to the modernized installation [79] over the past 10 years, it has been possible to obtain coatings with unique properties. These include composite coatings of immiscible components of the W–Cu and Mo–Cu systems with a layered or dispersion-strengthened structure [80–82]. The addition of carbon to the W–Cu and Mo–Cu systems makes it possible to increase the hardness of coatings due to the formation of molybdenum and tungsten carbides [83, 84]. An increase in the hardness of electroerosion-resistant coatings can be achieved by synthesizing titanium borides in a copper matrix [85, 86] or using ready-made titanium diboride powder [87].

Prediction of the properties of formed coatings was based on various physical and mathematical models [88–92]. These models are based on the occurrence of various instabilities during the EES process, such as Rayleigh–Taylor, Marangoni, Richtmeyer–Meshkov,

Kelvin–Helmholtz, etc. In the structure of electroexplosive coatings of all the systems under study, rounded regions with a diameter of 10–30 µm, having well distinguishable thin (from 1 to 2–3 µm) border with the surrounding coating material. The distances between the regions of dynamic rotations, although they do not have a constant value, can be estimated on average as ~10–50 µm. The appearance of such formations during EES can be explained as a first approximation from the position of 'dynamic rotations' developed by the school of Academician V.E. Panin. The surface structure is stable due to the formation of a system of confined localization sites of embedded atoms. In the places of localization during solidification, deformation of the crystal lattice occurs. Apparently, these are manifestations of the rotational mode of formation of distortions of the structure after its occurrence and solidification. The closeness of the considered distortions and their typicality in the observation field are the properties that form the strength of the developed coatings. It should also be borne in mind that EES is a complex, fast-flowing process associated with the formation of a liquid phase on a substrate. In the works of V.D. Sarychev, A.A. Buneev and other researchers it was shown that vortices are formed near the molten metal due to the development of thermocapillary instability. Thermocapillary instability – an increase in the amplitude of oscillations of the liquid surface in a nonuniformly heated liquid due to the Marangoni effect. In addition to the above, other forces act in the molten metal; for example Marangoni, who showed that fluid would flow from areas with a lower surface tension to higher. The surface tension depends on temperature and this imposes additional force on the movement. A generalization of theoretical ideas about EES and experimental studies was carried out in [93–96].

It is possible to improve the properties of electroexplosive coatings using EBT [97–101]. As a result of exposure to EBT, electroexplosive coatings are nanostructured, their volume is homogenized. The influence of EBT on the structure and properties of electroerosion-resistant coatings was generalized in [102–104].

1.4 The purpose and objectives of the study

A literature review allows us to state that a variety of methods for the formation of bulk electroerosion-resistant composite materials and coatings have various characteristic features. A large number of bulk electroerosion-resistant composite materials was obtained, however, the formation of similar coatings is associated with a number of unsolved technological problems. In this regard, the aim of this work was to identify the laws and physical nature of the formation of the structure and properties of electroerosion-resistant electroexplosive coatings during the spraying process and subsequent electron-beam processing. To achieve the goal, the following tasks were set and solved:

1) to develop methods for electric explosive spraying of electroerosion-resistant coatings of various systems;

2) to develop methods for electroexplosive spraying of wear- and electroerosion-resistant coatings of various systems with subsequent electron-beam processing;

3) to establish the influence of the parameters of electric explosive spraying and subsequent electron-beam processing on the surface topography, the structure of the coatings in depth and the features of their structural-phase states;

4) to determine the wear and erosion resistance, nanohardness of sprayed coatings;

5) to determine the erosion resistance and tribological properties of the coatings after electron-beam processing in modes that provide a complex of high functional properties;

6) to test the operational properties of sprayed coatings at industrial enterprises.

2

Equipment, materials and research methods

2. The rationale for the choice of materials for conducting electric explosion spraying of composite coatings

It is known that, for example, silver-based composite materials hardened by cadmium, zinc, copper, and tin monoxides are highly resistant to electrical discharge erosion. Therefore, it is of interest from both a practical and scientific point of view the formation of composite electrical coatings of the CdOAg, SnO_2–Ag, CuO–Ag, and ZnO–Ag systems in order to protect copper arc-resistant electrical contacts [105]. The type of coating was selected on the basis of previously obtained conclusions on the production and industrial use of bulk materials.

The choice of M00 brand copper for the substrate material on which coatings for electrical purposes was applied is due to the fact that it includes a set of properties that determine a large area of its application in the electrical industry. These are such properties: high heat sink rate into the volume of the material, high electrical conductivity, corrosion resistance in various environments, good mechanical properties at various temperatures. Copper is used for the production of wires, electrical cables, windings of electric machines, various transformers, copper strips, tires, tapes, collector plates, machine components and parts, electrical contacts of various assorments, etc. [105].

Table 2.1. The chemical composition of the substrate for the formation of coatings (wt.%)

Electrotechnical copper, grade M00												
Cu	Fe	Ni	S	P	As	Pb	Zn	Ag	O	Sb	Bi	Sn
rest	0.001	0.001	0.001	0.001	0.001	0.001	0.001	0.001	0.0005	0.0005	0.0005	0.0005

For EES, a composite electrically explosive material (CEM) was used [106], which is a two-layer silver foil with samples of CdO, SnO_2, CuO, or ZnO powders enclosed in it. In this case, the mixing of the KEVM foil with powder particles and the interaction of the powder particles occurred with the formation of new hardening phases during the formation of the plasma flow. The choice of CdO, SnO_2, CuO or ZnO as reinforcing particles is due to the fact that these compounds have high values of hardness, elastic modulus, are well wetted by a silver melt and are widely used in the industrial production of arc-resistant electrical contacts.

In recent years, the interest in obtaining nanomaterials, including nanocrystalline and nanocomposite coatings on the surface of metals, has grown markedly [107]. Owing to their unique structural and phase characteristics, they possess enhanced properties – hardness, fracture toughness, thermal stability, etc. Such materials find new areas of their practical use [108, 109]. In this regard, it is of interest to realize the possibility of the formation of such coatings by the EBS method by introducing ultrafine particles of a particular substance into the explosion region of the conductor of the powder.

Using the example of phase diagrams of two- and three-component systems, let us consider chemical compounds whose synthesis can be expected after electron beam treatment (EBT) of electric explosive coatings of the CdO–Ag, SnO_2–Ag, CuO–Ag, and ZnO–Ag systems [110–113].

The state diagram of the Ag–Cu system is eutectic. The eutectic reaction L$\leftrightarrow$(Cu) + (Ag) is observed at 40 at% Cu and occurs in the temperature range of 780°C. The solubility of Cu in (Ag) at low temperatures is small (0.35 at.%), But starting from 200°C the solubility of Cu in (Ag) increases and reaches a maximum value of 13.6 at.% at a temperature of 780°C (temperature eutectic). The solubility of Ag in (Cu) in the low-temperature region (up to 400°C) is negligible and increases at temperatures above 400°C. At eutectic temperature, it reaches a maximum value of ~4.9 at.% [110].

On the state diagram of the Cu–Sn system, the existence of nine phases (solid solution based on (Cu), β, δ,γ($Cu_{31}Sn_8$), ξ, ε

(Cu_3Sn), η, η', (Sn)), which are formed as a result of crystallization, structural phase transformations and chemical reactions in different temperature and concentration ranges: melt crystallization ((Cu), α, β, γ and η); solid state structural transformations (phases ζ, ε and δ); three peritectic reactions (L+$\alpha\leftrightarrow\beta$, L+$\delta\leftrightarrow\gamma$, L+$\varepsilon\leftrightarrow\eta$); one eutectic reaction (L$\leftrightarrow$Sn+η at a temperature at 227°C); four eutectoid decomposition reactions ($\beta\leftrightarrow\alpha$+$\gamma$ at a temperature at 586°C; $\gamma\leftrightarrow\alpha$+$\delta$ at a temperature at 520°C; $\zeta\leftrightarrow\delta$+$\varepsilon$ at 582°C; $\delta\leftrightarrow\alpha$+$\varepsilon$ at 350°C.); catatectic reaction ε+L at 640°C); structural transformation ($\gamma\leftrightarrow\varepsilon$ at 676°C); peretectoid reactions (the formation of phases ζ and δ), phase transition order–disorder ($\eta\leftrightarrow\eta'$) [111].

On the diagram of the Ag–Sn system, the presence of two peritectic reactions is established, as a result of which two phases ξ and ε are formed. In the region of high Sn concentrations, the eutectic reaction L$\leftrightarrow$Sn+ε was established. In the Ag–Sn system, the existence of a sufficiently wide region of solid solution (~10 at.% Sn) based on (Ag) was established, due to the good solubility of Sn in silver. At the same time, the solubility of Ag in (β-Sn) is weak, of the order of 0.09 at.% Ag [110].

The isothermal sections of the ternary Ag–Cu–Sn system at different temperatures are shown in Fig. 2.1 [112, 113]. It can be seen that ternary compounds with limited regions of homogeneity are formed only on the basis of binary compounds on the sides of the isothermal triangle Cu–Sn and Ag–Sn. It is characteristic of the ternary system Ag–Cu–Sn that inside the isothermal triangle it is not possible to form single-phase regions from ternary compounds $Ag_{1-x}Cu_{1-y}Sn_{x+y}$. Basically, the region of the isothermal triangle is filled with two-phase and three-phase regions, which are formed from two-phase compounds in binary systems Cu–Sn and Ag–Sn.

The formation of four compounds in the Cd–Cu system was established: Cu_2Cd, Cu_4Cd_3, Cu_2Cd_3, and $CuCd_3$ [110, 111]. The compound Cu_5Cd_8 is formed congruently at a temperature of 563°C. Other compounds (β, δ, γ) are formed by peritectic reactions at temperatures of 549, 547 and 397°C, respectively. At temperatures of 544 and 314°C and contents of 47.3 and 97.9% (at.) Cd, respectively, eutectic transformations occur. The solubility of Cd in Cu is retrograde and amounts to 2.56% (at.) At 650°C, 0.33% (at.) At 1055°C and 0.26% (at.) at 300°C . The solubility of Cu in Cd is 0.12% (at.) At a temperature of 300°C.

During the crystallization of the Ag–Cd [110, 111] system, solid solutions are formed on the basis of the initial components (Ag)

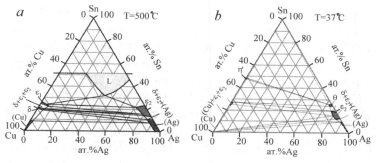

Fig. 2.1. Isothermal sections of the state diagram of the ternary Ag–Cu–Sn system at different temperatures: [112, 113]. a – 500°C; b – 37°C.

and (Cd), as well as three compounds: the β-phase (solid solution based on AgCd), the γ-phase (solid solution based on AgCd), which undergoes polymorphic transformation with a decrease in temperature into the γ'-phase at temperatures of 436 and 470°C for alloys rich in Ag and Cd, respectively, and the ε-phase (solid solution based on AgCd$_3$). These compounds are formed by peritectic reactions and have wide areas of homogeneity. So, for (β-phase, the concentration of Cd at a temperature of 736°C is 42% (at.), at a temperature of 640°C 57% (at.), at a temperature of 470°C 51.2% (at.), and at a temperature of 440°C 48.5% (at.). For the γ (γ') phase, the concentration of Cd at a temperature of 640°C is 60% (at.), and at 592°C 62.85% (at.). For the ε-phase, the Cd concentration is 65.7 and 81.4% (at.) at temperatures of 592 and 343°C, respectively. The system also exhibits the formation of ζ- and β'-phases from peritectoid reactions. These phases also have regions of homogeneity The ζ-phase is homogeneous in the composition range of 50–56.5% (at.) Cd in the temperature range 440–470°C, and at temperatures of 240 and 230°C, the concentration of Cd is 49.5 and 54.0% (at.). For β'-phase, the concentration of Cd is 48.5% (at.) at a temperature of 240°C and 50% (at.) at a temperature of 230°C. According to differential thermal analysis and hardness measurements, the formation of Ag$_{11}$Cd takes place (8.05% (by weight) Cd, Ag$_3$Cd [25.78% (by weight) Cd] and Ag$_2$Cd (34.26 % (by mass) Cd) as a result of the ordering of the (Ag)-based solid solution at temperatures below 700, 380, and 450°C, respectively.

There are six phases in the Cu–Zn [110] system. The phase (Cu) crystallizes from the liquid in the temperature range from the solidification temperature of copper to 902°C and at concentrations up to 36.8% (at.) Zn. In the solid state in the region (Cu), transformations are established that indicate the formation of a compound with the formula Cu_3Zn, which exists in two modifications: α_1 and α_2. The phases β, γ, δ, ε, (Zn) are formed by peritectic reactions. The region of β-phase is limited by the concentration range of 36.1% (at.) Zn at a temperature of 902°C, 56.5% (at.) Zn at 834°C; 48.2% (at.) Zn at 468°C and 44.8% (at.) Zn at 454°C. In the temperature range 454–468°C, the β-phase is ordered: $\beta \leftrightarrow \beta'$. The β'-phase decays according to the eutectoid reaction $\beta' \leftrightarrow$ (Cu) + γ'''(NT) at a temperature of 255°C. The eutectoid decomposition of the β'-phase occurs at temperatures above 100°C. The γ-phase has a wide homogeneity region, and its maximum extent at at a temperature of 558°C is 13% (at.%), the γ-phase exists in four modifications, but the γ''-phase is stable up to a temperature of 250–280°C; the γ-phase is stable above 280°C, which transforms into temperatures of 550–650°C in the γ'-phase, above 700°C, there is a high-temperature modification of γ. The δ-phase exists in a narrow temperature range of 700–558°C and in the interval and at a temperature of 558° C, $\delta \leftrightarrow \gamma'' + \varepsilon$ decays. The region of the ε-phase is within the concentration range of 78 at.% Zn at a temperature of 597°C and 87.5% (at.) Zn at a temperature of 423°C. The ε-phase is stable to room temperature. The solubility of Zn in (Cu) initially increases from 31.9% (at) at a temperature of 920°C to 38.3% (at.) at a temperature of 454°C, and then decreases to 34.5% (at.) at temperatures 150°C and to 29% (at.) at 0°C.

The metals of the Ag–Zn [110] diagram dissolve infinitely in each other in the liquid state, form limited regions of solid solutions in each other (Ag) and (Zn) and three intermediate phases β, γ, ε. The β-phase is formed by the peritectic reaction L + (Ag) $\leftrightarrow$ β at a temperature of 710°C and a content of 36.7% (at.) [26.0% (by mass)] Zn and has a large homogeneity region, which is located in the concentration range 36.7–58.6% (at.) Zn at temperatures of 710–661°C and 45.6–50.4% (at.) Zn at temperatures of 258–274°C, respectively. At temperatures of 258–274°C, the $\beta \leftrightarrow \zeta$ transformation takes place in the β-phase. Upon quenching from the β-region, a metastable β'-phase with ordered bcc structure is formed in the alloys. After cold deformation, the β'-phase turns into a ζ-phase with a hexagonal structure, and after cold deformation and ageing at 20°C, the ζ-phase turns into a β'-phase. The γ (Ag_5Zn_8) phase is formed by the peritectic reaction L + $\beta \leftrightarrow \gamma$ at a temperature of 661°C and a content of 61.0 (at.) [48.7% (by mass)] Zn, with a homogeneity interval of 61.0–64.0 % (at.) Zn at temperatures of 661–631°C and

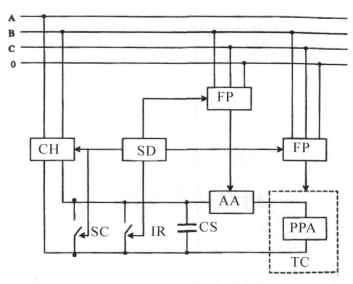

Fig. 2.2. Functional electrical diagram of a laboratory electric explosive installation EVU 60/10 [114]. SD – starting device; CS – capacitive storage; FP – foreline pump; AA – arc arrester; CH – charger; PPA – pulsed plasma accelerator; SC – short circuit; TC – technological chamber; IR – insulated rod.

58.5–62.7% (at.) Zn at a temperature of 274°C. The system also has a peritectic transformation L + ε (Zn) at a temperature of 431°C and a content of 95.0% (at.) [92% (by mass)] Zn. At a temperature of 710°C, 32.1% (at.) Zn dissolves in Ag, and at a temperature of 258°C 40.2% (at.) Zn. The solubility of Ag in (Zn) decreases from 5.0% (at.) Ag at 431°C to 10% (at.) Ag at 150°C.

2.2. Electric explosion installation EVU 60/10 M

For the formation of multiphase plasma jets and the study of EES processes in this work we used an electric explosive installation of EVU 60/10 M [114]. Structurally, it consists of three main parts (Fig. 2.2): a charger, which includes an autotransformer, a step-up transformer and a rectifier; capacitive energy storage; plasma accelerator. The installation works in automatic mode. Protection of the installation from exceeding the specified charging voltage and from malfunctioning allows the discharge to the short circuit, and the residual charge is removed by an insulated rod.

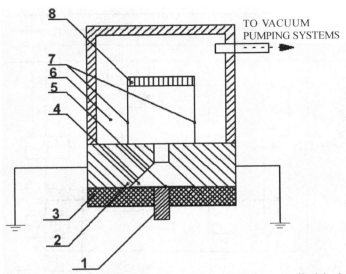

Fig. 2.3. Diagram of a pulsed plasma accelerator. 1 – inner cylindrical electrode, 2 – outer ring electrode, 3 – insulator, 4 – discharge chamber, 5 – conductor, 6 – vacuum process chamber, 7 – sample holders, 8 – processed sample

The plasma accelerator (Fig. 2.3) consists of a coaxial-end system of current-supplying electrodes – the inner electrode 1, the outer electrode 2, disconnected by the insulator 3, the discharge working chamber 4, which concentrates the explosive products and passes into the nozzle. An electric explosion occurs if a high current density passes through the conductor 5 when the capacitive energy storage is discharged. Explosive products rush into the vacuum process chamber 6 with a pressure of 100 Pa. The sample holders 7 produce a position of the sample 8 fixed at a certain distance from the nozzle.

The products of an electric explosion are a multiphase system that includes both a plasma component and condensed particles of different dispersion. When a jet is formed, its front forms a plasma component, while condensed particles, having greater inertness, are located in the rear of the jet. This allows the spraying of composite coatings. Leakage to the surface and reflection from it of a supersonic front of the jet is accompanied by the formation of a shock-compressed layer with high temperature and pressure. This ensures that the surface is heated to a melting point and higher in a short time of pulsed plasma exposure. The main parameters of the installation of the EVU 60/10 are shown in Table 2.2.

Table 2.2. Main parameters of the electric explosive installation EVU 60/10

Parameter, measurement unit	Value of parameter a
Energy intensity, kJ	60
Own discharge frequency, kHz	10
The maximum value of the charge, kV	5
Resolution discreteness of the charge voltage, kV	0.1
Maximum productivity at maximum charge voltage, cycle/h	10
Average power consumption at a charge no more, kW	0.55

2.3 Vacuum pulsed electron-beam installation SOLO

The general view of the SOLO installation, intended for pulsed modification of the surface of materials by an electron beam, is shown in Fig. 2.4, its main parameters are shown in Table 2.3 [115]. When an electron beam hits the surface to be treated, it produces superfast heating (during a pulse) to the melting temperature of the substrate material. Rapid cooling then occurs due to the removal of heat into the deeper cold layers of the substrate. As a result of ultrafast hardening, a finely dispersed, up to nanocrystalline, improved structure of the processed material is formed in the surface layer with a thickness of several units to several tens of micrometers,

Fig. 2.4. General view of SOLO equipment for pulsed surface modification of materials with the electron beam.

the surface is cleaned, and low-melting impurities are annealed. In addition, in the liquid phase in vacuum due to surface tension forces smoothing of the surface relief occurs (polishing).

The Solo installation can be used for electron-beam polishing of the surface of metal and metal–ceramic products, pulsed quenching of the surface from the molten state, conditioning the surface by removing low-melting components and other processes requiring concentrated energy flows in the form of a pulsed electron beam. When optimizing the regimes of pulsed EBT, the processes of nanostructuring of the surface layer of materials and products are realized.

Table 2.3. Main parameters of equipment

Dimesions of equipment	1350×2150×2000 mm
Vacuum chamber size	600×500×400 mm
Beam current	20–250 A
Electron energy	5–25 keV
Pulse duration	50–200 μs
Pulse repetition rate	0.3–20 Hz
Maximum power consumption, depending on the accelerating voltage of the source	2.5–10 keV
Operating pressure	0.01–0.05 Pa
Working gas	argon, nitrogen
Beam autograph diameter	2–5 cm
Manipulator dimensions (scan area)	200×200 cm

2.4. Processing modes, methods of structure research, phase and elemental composition and properties of electroexplosive coatings

Processing modes. The samples that were sprayed were copper plates with dimensions of $20 \times 20 \times 3$ mm. For EES, the main processing parameters are the pulse time τ and the absorbed power density $q = 5.5$ GW/m² under thermal exposure of the irradiated surface, as well as the pressure $p = 12.5$ MPa of the plasma in the shock-compressed layer, which is formed near the surface. The necessary conditions for the implementation of the EES were set by the magnitude of the charging voltage of the energy accelerator storage device, the diameter of the nozzle channel and the distance from its cut to the sample, which were 1.8 kV, 20 and 20 mm, respectively. To justify the choice of q values used in the processing, the temperature of the irradiated surface was calculated using the model of heating with a flat heat source [116].

In the work, composite coatings with a filled structure were formed. The composite filled structure is formed by a metal matrix, which is hardened by its high-strength fine dispersed refractory particles insoluble in it.

Coatings were formed at the absorbed power density value, which ensured the premelting state of the treatment surface (Table 2.4). EBT of electroerosion-resistant coatings of all systems was performed in the modes with the number of pulses 10, pulse time 100 µs, with a variable surface energy density of 45, 50, 55 and 60 J/cm^2 and with the number of pulses 20, pulse time 200 µs, and surface energy density 60 J/cm^2 (Table 2.4).

Sections for metallographic studies were prepared as follows: samples were cut out on an automatic cutting machine with a diamond wheel, then they were ground, polished and chemically etched. The preparation of thin sections for metallographic investigations in the general case included cutting samples on a cutting machine with a diamond wheel, grinding, polishing, and chemical etching. Before grinding, the samples were fixed in a mandrel and filled with epoxy resin. Grinding was carried out with emery papers with decreasing dispersion of abrasive particles. The quality of grinding was controlled under a microscope at a magnification of 50–100 times. After grinding on the papers, polishing was carried out with chromium oxide powder on the cloth. Before microscopic inspection, with an increase of 200...400 times, the sections were thoroughly washed. Polishing was completed when visible traces of machining were eliminated, and additional processing did not increase the quantity and clarity of the details of the structure observed on the thin section.

Chemical etching of the sections was carried out with a solution of the following composition: HCl – 2.5 ml, FeCl$_3$ – 3 g, C$_2$H$_5$OH – 100 ml. The etching time ranged from 3 to 5 s. After etching, the samples were thoroughly washed in running water and ethanol, and then dried.

Coatings with a layered structure were formed at a value of absorbed power density, which ensured the pre-melting state of the treatment surface (Table 2.5). Coatings with a composite filled structure were formed at a value of absorbed power density providing mixing of the components (Table 2.6). An exception is the deposition of composite filled coatings using a computer at a q value that ensures the premelting state of the treatment surface.

EBT of the electroerosion-resistant coatings of all systems was performed in the modes with the number of pulses 10, pulse time 100 μs, with a variable surface energy density of 45, 50, 55 and 60 J/cm² and with the number of pulses 20, pulse time 200 μs, and surface energy density 60 J/cm² (Table 2.7).

Table 2.4. Parameters of formation of coatings

Coating	EES parameters		EBT paramters		
	q, GW/m²	m, mg	E_s, J/cm²	t, μs	N, pulses
CdO–Ag		50×250	45	100	10
			50	100	10
			55	100	10
			60	100	10
			60	200	20
SnO$_2$–Ag		50×250	45	100	10
			50	100	10
			55	100	10
			60	100	10
			60	200	20
CuO–Ag	5.5	50×250	45	100	10
			50	100	10
			55	100	10
			60	100	10
			60	200	20
ZnO–Ag		80×250	45	100	10
			50	100	10
			55	100	10
			60	100	10
			60	200	20

Comment. E_s – surface energy density; t – pulse duration; N – number of pulses; pulse repetition frequency 0.3 Hz, optimum EBT conditions indicated by the colour.

Table 2.5. Parameters of EES of coatings from non-mixed components with a layered structure

Treatment parameters		Sprayed materials	
q, GW/m	m, mg	Foil	Powder
4.1	170	Mo	–
3.7	150	Cu	–
4.1	350	Mo	–
3.7	300	Cu	–
4.1	5/800	Cu	Mo
3.7	175	Cu	–
4.1	5/900	Cu	W
7.6	175	Cu	–

Note. The indicated modes provide heating of the surface to the melting temperature. The numerator indicates the mass of the foil, the denominator indicates the mass of the sample powder.

Research methods. The mass of the components of the computer was monitored using a Shimadzu AUX 120 analytical balance. To measure the thickness of the coatings, the sizes of the structural components, to study the phase distribution in depth, and photograph the sections, we used a Carl Zeiss Axio Observer A1m metallographic microscope. This device allows one to get an image of small objects and their details at various magnifications up to 2000 times. The surface structure of the samples and thin sections was studied by scanning electron microscopy using Carl Zeiss EVO50 and Phillips SEM 515 devices with EDS X-Act and EDAX energy dispersive X-ray spectral analysis attachments according to the methods described in [117, 118]. The analysis of the defective substructure and phase composition of the surface layer of the coating melting upon EBT was carried out by transmission electron diffraction microscopy (EM-125 device). Foils were made of plates located at a distance of 25–30 μm from the irradiation surface and cut parallel to the surface of the coating. X-ray diffraction analysis was performed on an ARLX'TRA diffractometer in copper radiation with a wavelength of $\lambda_a = 0.15406$ nm. Also, coatings were investigated by atomic force microscopy (Solver NEXT device).

The tribological properties (friction coefficient and wear resistance) of the coatings were studied in the geometry of a disk pin using a TNT-S-AX0000 tribometer (CSEM, Switzerland) at a temperature of 25°C. A VK-8 hard alloy ball with a diameter of 3

Table 2.6. Parameters of EES coatings with a composite filled structure

Coating	Treatment parameters		Sprayed materials		
	q, GW/m^2	m, mg	Foil	Powder	????
From non-mixed components of W, Cu, Mo and Cu	2.0	150	Mo	–	
	7.6	250	Cu	–	
	6.0	150	Mo	–	
	10.00	250	Cu	–	
	4,5	5/800	Cu	–	
	6,5	175	Cu	Mo	
	4,5	5/900	Cu	W	
	8,1	175	Cu	–	
	4,1	800/800		–	Mo/Cu
	4,1	800/800		–	W/Cu
TiB$_2$–Cu system using powder charges of Ti diboride	4.1	124/125			TiB$_2$/C
Mo–C–Cu, W–C–Cu and Ti–B–Cu systems formed in electric explosion synthesis	5.5	100/10/110			Mo/C/Cu
	6.5				
	7.6				
	5.5	199/6.5/10 6.5			W/C/Cu
	6.5				
	7.6				
	5.5	90.41	Ti	B	–
	6.5				
	7.6				

Note. The colour indicates the modes that ensure heating of the surface to the melting temperature. Sprayed substances and their masses are indicated through the oblique.

mm was used as a counterbody, the track diameter was 6 mm, the rotation speed was 2.5 cm/s, the load was 3 N, the distance to stop was 38.6 m, and the number of revolutions was 3000. The wear criterion was the specific volume of the material wear track, which was determined using a MicroMeasure 3D Station laser optical profilometer and calculated by the formula:

$$V = \frac{2\pi RA}{F\,L},$$

where R is the radius of the track, A is the cross-sectional area of the wear groove, F is the magnitude of the applied load, L is the distance traveled by the ball.

Tests for the electrical discharge resistance of coatings under conditions of arc erosion were carried out on the contacts of electromagnetic starters of the CJ20 grade. In accordance with the requirements of the AC-3 test mode for switching wear resistance, alternating current and inductive load were used when working in a three-phase circuit. The low voltage values were 400/230 V, the frequency was 50 Hz for currents up to 320 A and $\cos\varphi = 0.35$ and the number of switching cycles was 6000 according to the circuit shown in Figs. 2.5 and 2.6. The number of on-off cycles to complete destruction was ~8000.

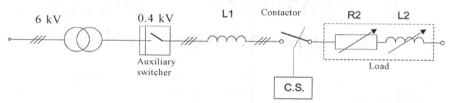

Fig. 2.5. Principle diagram of switching the testing system.

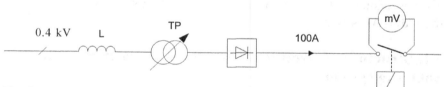

Fig. 2.6. Principle diagram the system for measuring the contact resistance for 100 A alternating current in tests for electroerosion resistance of arc erosion.

3

Electroerosion resistant electric explosive coatings for electromagnetic starters and medium and heavy relays

This chapter is written on the basis of scientific articles [119–122], which discuss issues related to the study of electroexplosive coatings of the SnO_2–Ag system and scientific articles [123, 124], which discuss issues related to the study of electroexplosive coatings of the CdO–Ag system.

3.1. Structure of electroerosion-resistant coatings of the SnO_2–Ag system

The transformation of the volume structure of the surface layer was analyzed by studying chemically etched transverse sections. It is clearly seen (Figure 3.1) that the coating thickness is from 50 to 60 microns.

A typical electron microscopic image of the surface layer of copper subjected to electroexplosive modification is shown in Fig. 3.2. It is clearly seen that the copper layer adjacent to the coating has a fragmented structure, which may indicate a high level of deformation of the sample surface during coating formation.

The electron microscopic image of the coating formed during the electric explosion modification of the copper contact is shown in Fig. 3.3. The obtained images indicate that the resulting coating has a nanocrystalline structure with crystallite sizes varying within (20–40) nm.

Fig. 3.1. A characteristic image of the cross-sections of electroexplosive coatings of the SnO$_2$–Ag system. Scanning electron microscopy

Fig. 3.2. Electron microscopic image of the structure of the SnO$_2$–Ag system. The arrows indicate: a coating layer adjacent to the surface of copper (1), and an adjacent layer of copper (2).

The elemental composition of the surface layer of the coating layer (Fig. 3.4 *b*) was determined by X-ray spectral analysis. Energy spectra and analysis conditions are shown in Fig. 3.4 *a*. Quantitative results of the analysis of the elemental composition of the coating material are presented in Table 3.1. From Table 3.1 it is seen that the coating is 39.18 silver. The redistribution of the silver and tin content in the coating is caused by the fact that the EES was carried out on the surface of the electrical contact. This contact has a smaller area in comparison with the diameter of the pulsed plasma jet used

Fig. 3.3. Electron microscopic image of the SnO$_2$ – Ag system coating. *a* – nanocrystalline structure; *b* – crystallites.

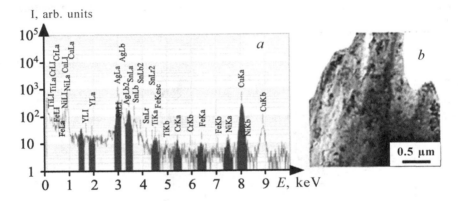

Fig. 3.4. The results of x-ray spectral analysis of the foil. *a* – energy spectra; *b* - coating area.

for EES. For this reason, the utilization of the material was 0.7. At the same time, the coefficient of material utilization during EES is 0.98 in the case when the area of the treated surface corresponds to the area of a pulsed plasma jet.

As a result of studies performed in this way, it was found that the analyzed coating is a multi-element material, the main metal elements of which are copper, silver and tin. Consequently, during electroexplosive coating formation, mixing of the substrate and coating elements to a depth of 10 μm is observed. The phase composition and defective coating substructure were analyzed by diffraction electron microscopy. Following the results presented in [110, 111, 125, 126], it can be concluded that Ag–Sn and Sn–Cu based compounds can be formed in the Ag–Sn–Cu system; it is also

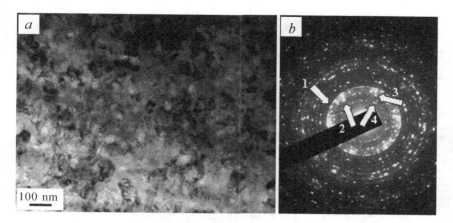

Fig. 3.5. Electron-microscopic image of the coating area formed on the copper sample by the electroexplosive method (*a*) and the corresponding microelectron diffraction pattern (*b*). The arrows in the microelectron diffraction pattern indicate the reflections in which dark-field images of the foil section (*a*) are obtained, shown in Fig. 3.6. Namely, reflex 1 – [004] Ag_3Sn; reflex 2 – [100] Ag_4Sn; reflex 3 – [002] Cu_6Sn_5; reflection 4 – [110] SnO_2.

possible the presence of solid solutions based on silver, tin and copper. The presence of these elements in the coating and oxide phases should not be ruled out.

A typical electron microscopic image of the coating structure (Fig. 3.5 *a*) and a microelectron diffraction pattern (Fig. 3.5 *b*) corresponding to this structure are shown in Fig. 3.4. It is clearly seen that the microelectron diffraction pattern has a ring structure, which clearly indicates that the coating belongs to the class of nanocrystalline materials [127–129]. Taking into account the nonequilibrium conditions of the transformations that occur during the electroexplosive formation of the coating and the possible presence of several phases simultaneously in the studied area of the foil, the microelectron diffraction patterns were indicated by determining the phase affiliation of each of the five nearest diffraction rings individually. Indication of the microelectron diffraction pattern shown in Fig. 3.5 *b* revealed reflections of the following phases: SnO_2, Ag_3Sn, $Cu_{10}Sn_3$, Cu_3Sn, Cu_6Sn_5, Ag_4Sn and CuO. Figure 3.6 shows dark-field images of the phases most often found in the studied coating. Analyzing the results of studies of the phase composition of the coating, it can be noted that the particles of tin oxide SnO_2, the image of which is shown in Fig. 3.6 *d*, have a rounded shape; Particle sizes range from 15 nm to 40 nm. Particles of Ag_3Sn, Ag_4Sn

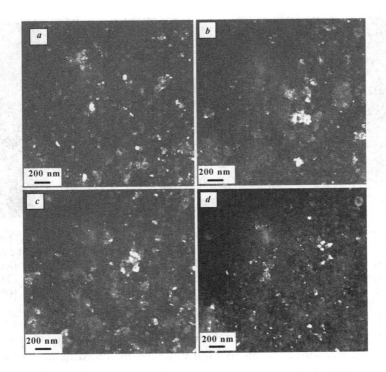

Fig. 3.6. Electron-microscopic dark-field images of the coating area, the bright field of which is shown in Fig. 3.5 *a*. Dark fields were obtained in the reflections indicated by arrows on the microelectron diffraction pattern of Fig. 3.4 *b*: (*a*) – [004] Ag_3Sn; (*b*) – [100] Ag_4Sn; (*c*) – [002] Cu_6Sn_5; (*d*) – [110] SnO_2.

and Cu_0Sn_5 compounds, the image of which is shown in Fig. 3.6, *a–c*, respectively, are relatively larger (20–50 nm) and often form regions (80–120) nm in size.

The methods of electron diffraction microscopy were used to study the elemental and phase composition, defective substructure, and morphology of the phases of the coating formed on the surface of copper samples by the electric explosion method. The formation of a multi-element multiphase coating having a nanocrystalline structure is revealed. By indexing microelectron diffraction patterns, it was established that the main phases of the coating are SnO_2, Ag_3Sn, $Cu_{10}Sn_3$, Cu_3Sn, Cu_6Sn_5, Ag_4Sn and CuO. It was found that the volume of copper adjacent to the coating has a fragmented structure, which may indicate a high level of deformation of the surface layer of the sample during the electric explosion method of coating formation.

Also, studies of copper electrical contacts after EES and EBT were carried out by scanning electron microscopy (Fig. 3.7), X-ray phase analysis (Figs. 3.8–3.12).

Figure 3.7 *a* shows the cross-sectional structure of the surface layer of the electroexplosive composite coating of the SnO_2–Ag system without exposure to EBT; Figure 3.7 *b* shows the cross-sectional structure of the surface layer of the electric explosive composite coating of the SnO_2–Ag system after exposure to EBT.

Scanning electron microscopy studies have shown that, when an EES is applied on the surface of a copper electrical contact by an electric explosion of a composite electrically exploded conductor with an absorbed power density of 5.5 GW/m², a coating with a filled structure is formed when SnO_2 inclusions with the dimensions from 0.5 to 4.0 μm are located in the silver matrix (Fig. 3.7 *a*).

Pulse-periodic EBT of the surface of an electric explosive coating with a surface density of absorbed energy of 40–60 J/cm², pulse duration of 100–200 μs, and number of pulses of 10–30 leads to smoothing of the surface relief until a mirror shine is formed. The thickness of the modified layers after EBT varies from 20 to 40 μm and increases slightly with increasing electron beam energy density. Electron beam processing, accompanied by remelting of the coating layer, leads to the formation of a composite filled [130] structure (Fig. 3.7 *b*). Defects in the form of micropores and microcracks are not observed in it. The sizes of inclusions of SnO_2 in silver range from 0.1 to 0.2 microns. Pulse-periodic EBT of the surface layer leads to the formation of a more dispersed and uniform structure in it.

The phase composition of the obtained after EBT coatings consists of the following components: $Cu_{40.5}Sn_{59.5}$, $Ag_{0.877}Sn_{0.123}$, Sn, SnO_2, Cu, $Cu_{41}Sn_{59}$, $Ag_{0.902}Cu_{0.098}$, $Cu_{1.2}Sn$, $Ag_{0.88}Cu_{0.12}$, Cu_3Sn, CuO, CuSn and Ag.

The $Cu_{40.5}Sn_{59.5}$ phase, with a mass fraction of 27%, is observed only at W_s = 0.3 MW/cm². Moreover, the parameter *a* of the crystal lattice is 18.011 nm.

At the same time, the $Ag_{0.877}Sn_{0.123}$ phase is observed at a power density of 0.3 and 0.6 MW/cm². The volume fraction of the considered phase is 12% at both power density values. The parameter *a*, equal to 2.956 nm, also remains constant. Parameter *c* changes from 4.752 nm at 0.3 MW/cm² to 4.753 at 0.6 MW/cm².

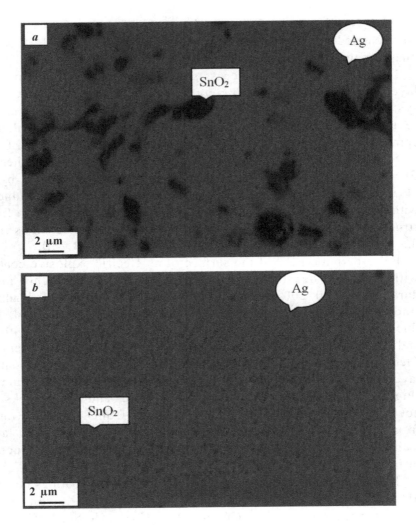

Fig. 3.7. The structure of the cross section of the surface layer of electric explosive composite coating of SnO_2–Ag systems. SEM in backward-reflected electrons. *a* – without exposure to EBT; *b* – after EBT.

The initial value of the mass fraction of Sn at W_s = 0.3 MW/cm² is 12%. This indicator is the largest. With a further increase in the power density, the mass fraction decreases to 4% and remains at the same level for other values of the power density, except for W_s = 0.5 MW/cm², at which Sn is not observed.

The initial value of the parameter *a* of the crystal lattice of the Sn phase at W_s = 0.3 MW/cm$_2$ is 3.678 nm. This value remains maximum and does not change at a power density of 0.45 MW/cm².

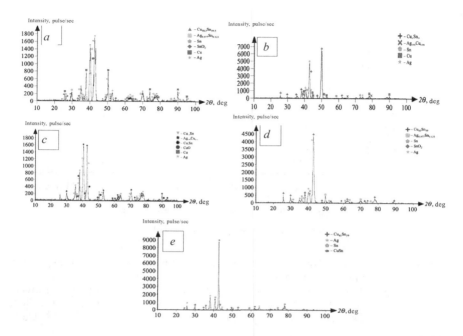

Fig. 3.8. Plots of radiographs of electrical contact after explosive spray coating system SnO2-Ag and electron beam processing in various modes. *a – d* – EBT in modes 1–5, respectively

With a subsequent increase in power density to $W_s = 0.55$ MW/cm², the parameter value drops to its minimum of 3.1297 nm. The final value increases to 3.1391 nm at $W_s = 0.6$ MW/cm².

The parameter c of the crystal lattice of the phase under consideration invariably remains equal to 3.362 nm with power density indices of 0.3 MW/cm² and 0.45 MW/cm². Then this indicator monotonically decreases to a minimum value of 3.109 nm at $W_s = 0.6$ MW/cm².

In turn, the SnO_2 phase is observed only at 0.3 and 0.6 MW/cm², and its mass fraction varies from 29% to 18%. The lattice parameter a varies from 4.748 nm at $W_s = 0.3$ MW/cm² to 4.972 nm and $W_s = 0.6$ MW/cm².

At $W_s = 0.3$ MW/cm², the initial value of the mass fraction of the Cu phase is 5%. The indicator reaches its maximum of 10% at $Ws = 0.45$ MW/cm². The final mass fraction at $W_s = 0.5$ MW/cm² is equal to the initial one and is 5%.

With a power density of 0.3 MW/cm², the initial value of the parameter a is 3.617 nm. This value is maximum and remains

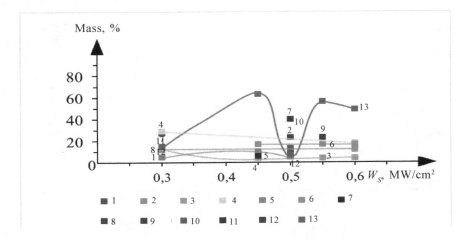

Fig. 3.9. Dependence of the volume fraction of the phases (V) of electroexplositon coating of the SnO_2–Ag systems on the electron beam power density (W_s). The phase composition of the obtained after EBT coating consists of the following components: $1 - Cu_{40.5}Sn_{59.5}$, $2 - Ag_{0.877}Sn_{0.123}$, $3 - Sn$, $4 - SnO_2$, $5 - Cu$, $6 - Cu_{41}Sn_{59}$, $7 - Ag_{0.902}Cu_{0.098}$, $8 - Cu_{1.2}Sn$, $9 - Ag_{0.88}Cu_{0.12}$, $10 - Cu_3Sn$, $11 - CuO$, $12 - CuSn$ and $13 - Ag$.

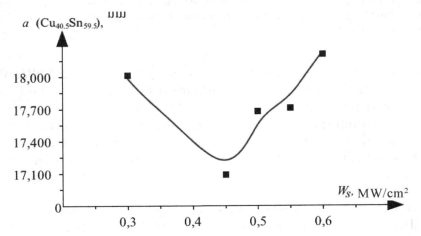

Fig. 3.10. The dependence of the parameter a of the crystal lattice from power density for phase $Cu_{40.5}Sn_{59.5}$.

unchanged at $W_s = 0.45$ MW/cm^2. When the power density reaches 065 MW/cm^2, the parameter a decreases to a minimum of 3.613 nm.

The $Cu_{41}Sn_{59}$ phase is observed at power density indices of 0.45, 0.55, and 0.6 MW/cm^2. Its mass fraction does not invariably amount to 17% at all power density values.

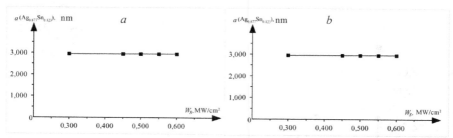

Fig. 3.11. Dependences of the parameters of the crystal lattice on the power density for the $Ag_{0.877}Sn_{0.123}$ phase. *a* is the lattice parameter *a*; *b* is the parameter of the crystal lattice *c*.

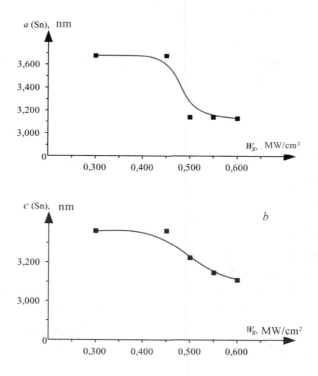

Fig. 3.12. The dependence of the parameters of the crystal lattice on the power density for phase Sn. *a* is the lattice parameter *a*; *b* is the parameter of the crystal lattice *c*.

Parameter *a* has a maximum value of 18.011 nm at W_s = 0.45 MW/cm². Then, with an increase in power density to 0.55 MW/cm², the considered indicator decreases to its minimum of 17.98 nm and remains at W_s = 0.6 MW/cm².

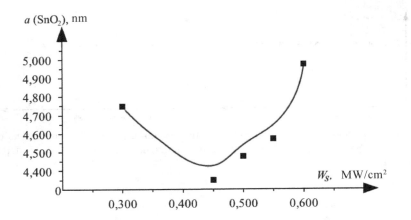

Fig. 3.13. The dependence of the parameter a of the crystal lattice on the power density for the SnO_2 phase.

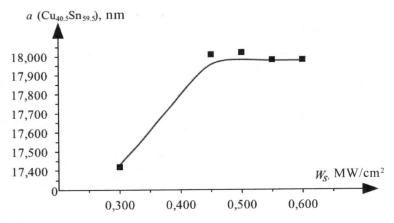

Fig. 3.14. The dependence of the parameter a of the crystal lattice on the power density for the $Cu_{41}Sn_{59}$ phase.

The $Ag_{0.902}Cu_{0.098}$ phase is observed only at $W_s = 0.45$ MW/cm² and has a mass fraction of 27%. The parameter a of the crystal lattice is 2.956 nm, $c = 4.752$ nm.

The phases $Cu_{1.2}Sn$, $Ag_{0.88}Cu_{0.12}$, Cu_3Sn, CuO are observed only at $W_s = 0.5$ MW/cm², the mass fractions of these phases are 23%, 12%, 13%, and 40%, respectively.

The crystal lattice parameters a and c of the $Cu_{1.2}Sn$ phase are 4.24246 nm and 5.13989 nm, respectively.

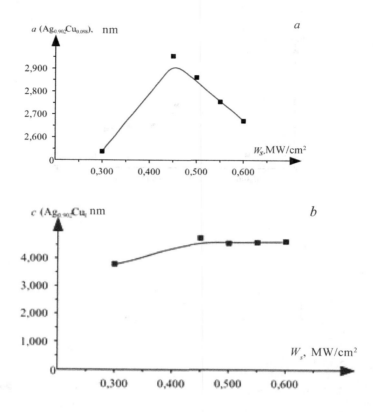

Fig. 3.15. The dependence of the parameters of the crystal lattice on the power density for phase $Ag_{0.902}Cu_{0.098}$. a is the lattice parameter a; b is the parameter of the crystal lattice c.

For the $Ag_{0.88}Cu_{0.12}$ phase, the parameter a is 2.9285 nm, and c is 4.7853 nm.

The parameters a and c for the Cu_3Sn phase are 6.1166 nm and 3.362 nm, respectively.

The CuO phase has crystal lattice parameters a, b, and c that are 4.723 nm, 3.397 nm, and 5.041 nm, respectively.

The CuSn phase, with a mass fraction of 23%, is observed only at W_s = 0.55 MW/cm². The parameter a of the crystal lattice is 4.208 nm, the parameter c is 5.104 nm

At the initial time at W_s = 0.3 MW/cm², the mass fraction of the Ag phase is 15%. With a subsequent increase in power density to 0.45 MW/cm², the mass fraction reaches its maximum of 63%. The decline following it ends with a minimum of 7% at W_s = 0.5

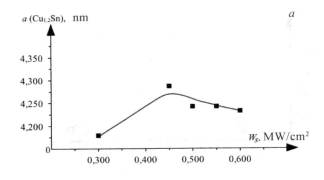

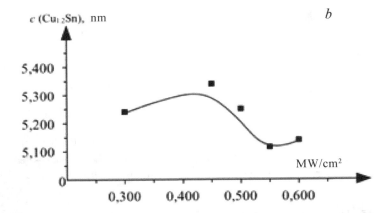

Fig. 3.16. The dependence of the crystal lattice parameters on the power density for the $Cu_{1,2}Sn$ phase. *a* shows the lattice parameter *a*; *b* the parameter of the crystal lattice *c*.

MW/cm², followed by an increase in the mass fraction to 56% at W_s = 0.55 MW/cm². With a power density of 0.6 MW/cm², the final indicator is 49%.

At the same time, the parameter a of the Ag crystal lattice at all values of the power density is 4.0863 nm.

3.2. Structure of electroerosion-resistant coatings of the CdO – Ag system

The Ag–CdO coating, formed on the surface of a copper electrical contact by the electric explosion method, has a nanocrystalline structure (Figure 3.21, a, b). The crystallite size varies from 20 nm to 50 nm. The copper layer adjacent to the coating has a polycrystalline

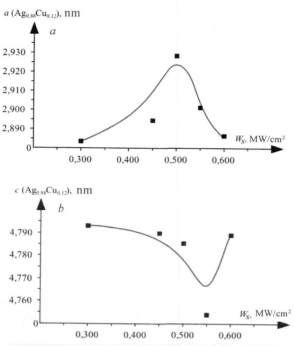

Fig. 3.17. The dependence of the parameters of the crystal lattice on power density for $Ag_{0.88}Cu_{0.12}$ phase. a is the lattice parameter a; b is the parameter of the crystal lattice c.

structure. The crystallite size varies from 200 nm to 400 nm (Figure 3.21, c). It can be assumed that the submicrocrystalline grain structure of the copper layer adjacent to the coating was formed both as a result of high-speed crystallization and of the process of dynamic recrystallization, initiated by the thermomechanical effect of the plasma flow generated during the electric explosion of the conductor, on the surface of the copper electrical contact [131].

As one moves away from the interface between the coating and the substrate, the defective copper substructure changes significantly (Fig. 3.22). In the layer located at a distance of 90 µm from the boundary with the Ag–CdO coating, a fragmented substructure characteristic of highly deformed copper is observed in the bulk of grains (Fig. 3.22 a). A dislocation substructure formed by randomly distributed dislocations is revealed in the volume of fragments. The scalar dislocation density is $0.8 \cdot 10^9$ cm^{-2}. In a layer located at a

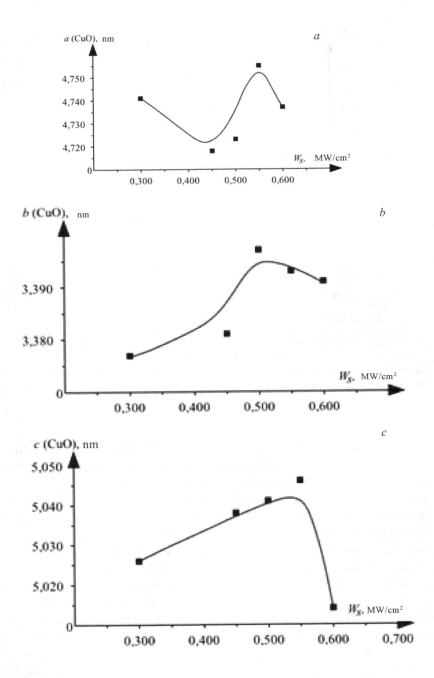

Fig. 3.18. The dependence of the crystal lattice parameters on the power density for the CuO phase.

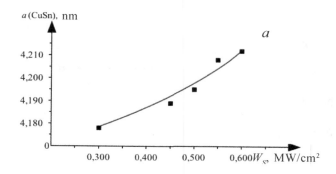

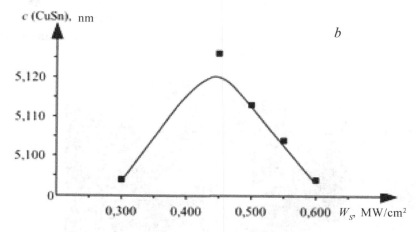

Fig. 3.19. The dependence of the parameters of the crystal lattice on the power density for the CuSn phase. *a* is the lattice parameter *a*; *b* is the parameter of the crystal lattice *c*.

distance of 170 μm, a strip dislocation substructure and a disoriented cellular substructure are observed (Fig. 3.22 *b*). When moving away from the interface of the Ag–CdO/copper substrate coating system at a distance of 220 μm, a cellular dislocation substructure and (Fig. 3.22 *c*) and orientational chaos substructure (Fig. 3.22 *d*) are observed in the volume of copper grains. Following the results presented in Refs. [132–134], it can be stated that the electroexplosive formation of a coating of Ag–CdO composition is accompanied by a significant deformation effect on the sample surface. As one moves away from the surface of the sample, the degree of deformation of the material decreases.

The phase composition of the material was analyzed by diffraction electron microscopy using the dark-field analysis technique and the

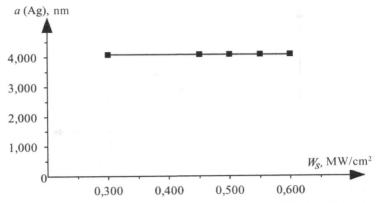

Fig. 3.20. The dependence of the parameter *a* of the crystal lattice of the Ag phase on the power density.

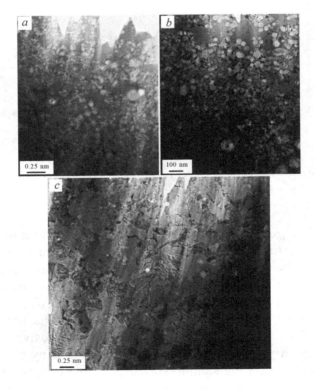

Fig. 3.21. Structure of the Ag–CdO coating and the copper layer adjacent to the interface between the coating and the substrate. *a* – nanocrystalline coating structure; *b* – coating nanocrystallites; *c* – substrate crystallites.

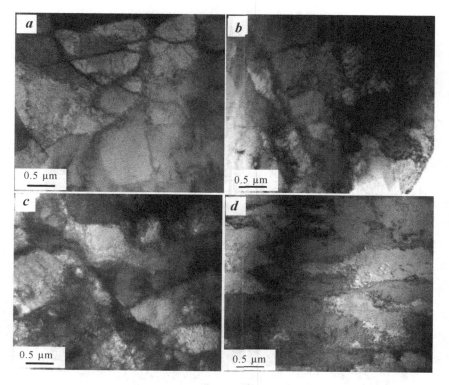

Fig. 3.22. The structure of the copper substrate in layers located at a distance of ≈90 μm (*a*); ≈170 μm (*b*); ≈220 μm (*c, d*) from the boundary with the Ag–CdO coating; *a* – fragmented substructure; *b* – strip and disoriented cellular substructures; *c* – cellular dislocation substructure; *d* – a substructure of orientational chaos.

microelectron diffraction indexing technique. Figure 3.23 shows the results of electron microscopic microdiffraction analysis of the phase composition of the coating formed on copper by the electroexplosive method.

It is clearly seen that the microelectron diffraction pattern (Fig. 3.23 *b*) obtained from the coating area, the electron microscopic image of which is shown in Fig. 3.23 *a*, is circular, which confirms the above conclusions about the nanocrystalline structure of the coating [127–129].

Indexing of a microelectron diffraction pattern (Fig. 3.23 *b*) shows that the coating is multiphase. Reflections of the following phases are detected on the microelectron diffraction pattern: Cu; Cd_3Cu_4, Ag_2O_3, CdO_2, as well as CuO. The dark-field analysis

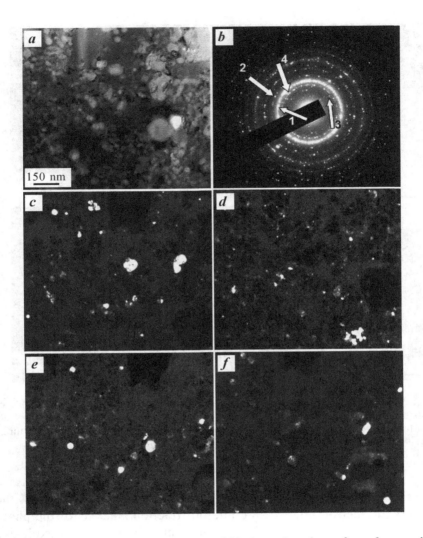

Fig. 3.23. The structure of the coating Ag–CdO, formed on the surface of copper by the electric explosion method. a – bright field image; b – microelectron diffraction pattern; arrows indicate reflexes in which dark fields ($c - f$) are obtained, respectively; c–f – dark-field images obtained in reflections of [111] Cu + [973] Cd_3Cu_4 (reflex 1), [002] Cu + [151] Ag_2O_3 (reflex 2), [200] CdO_2 (reflex 3), [953] Cd_3Cu_4 (reflex 4), respectively.

method allowed us to determine the shape and size of crystallites of the detected phases. It has been established that phase crystallites are predominantly rounded (globular) in shape; the size of copper crystallites varies from 20 nm to 50 nm; sizes of Cd_3Cu_4 inclusions – in the range (30–40) nm; sizes of CdO_2 inclusions – in the range

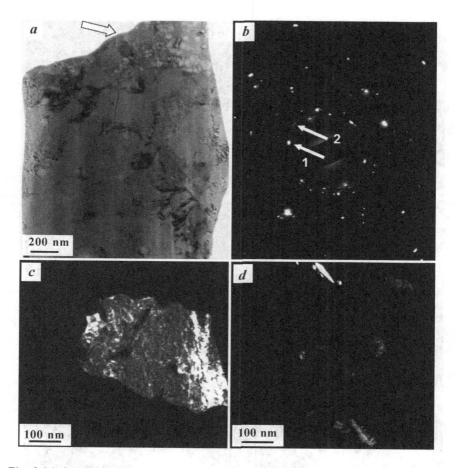

Fig. 3.24. Structure of a copper substrate located at the border coated with Ag–CdO. On (*a*) the arrow indicates the coating area, adjacent to the substrate. *a* – bright field image; *b* – microelectron diffraction pattern, the arrows indicate the reflexes in which the dark fields (*c, d*) are obtained, respectively; *c, d* – dark-field images obtained in reflections of [111] Cu (reflex 1), [600] Ag_5Cd_8 + [11 11 1] Cd_3Cu_4 (reflex 2), respectively.

(15–50) nm; sizes of inclusions of Ag_2O_3 are in the range of (5–10) nm.

The copper layer adjacent to the coating is also multiphase (Fig. 3.24). Indexing of the microelectron diffraction pattern (Fig. 3.24 *b*) obtained from a given volume of material made it possible to identify reflections of the following phases: Cu; Ag_5Cd_8 and Cd_3Cu_4. The size of copper crystallites varies from 200 nm to 400 nm (Fig. 3.24 *a, c*). Inclusions of particles of the second phases are located

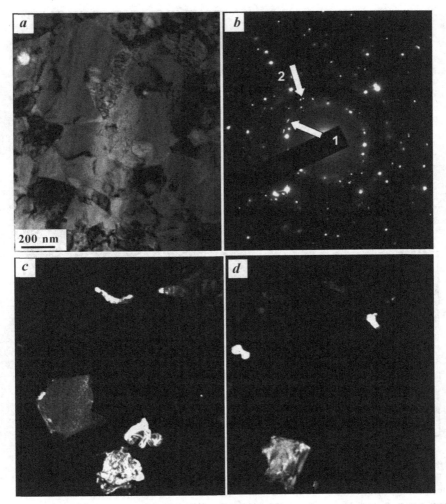

Fig. 3.25. The structure of the copper substrate located at a distance of (15–20) microns from the Ag–CdO coating boundary. *a* – bright field image; *b* – microelectron diffraction pattern, the arrows indicate the reflexes in which the dark fields (*c, d*) are obtained, respectively; *c, d* – dark-field images obtained in reflections of [002] Cu + [102] Cd + [202] CuO (reflex 1), [600] Ag_5Cd_8 + [002] Cu (reflex 2);

mainly along the grain boundaries of copper and have a globular shape or the shape of thin interlayers (Fig. 3.24 *d*). The sizes of such inclusions vary from 40 nm to 60 nm. Significantly less frequently, inclusions having a plate (needle) shape are detected (Fig. 3.24 *d*). Inclusions of this types are detected in the volume of copper grains and are located at the grain boundaries (most likely, grow from the grain boundaries).

A typical electron microscopic image of the structure of the volume of copper located at a distance of (15–20) μm from the boundary with the Ag–CdO coating is shown in Fig. 3.25. Dark-field analysis shows that this layer of material is also multiphase. Indexing of the corresponding microelectron diffraction pattern (Fig. 3.25 *b*) revealed the reflexes of copper, cadmium, CuO and Ag_5Cd_8. The inclusions of the second phases have a globular shape and are located mainly along the grain boundaries of copper (Fig. 3.25 *c*, *d*). The sizes of inclusions vary from 20 nm to 60 nm. It should be noted that in the volume of grains of the copper layer adjacent to the coating (Figs. 3.24 and 3.25), a dislocation substructure is detected mainly in the form of randomly distributed dislocations. The scalar dislocation density is $0.5 \cdot 10^9$ cm^{-2}. The low dislocation density is most likely due to the processes of high-speed crystallization [131] and dynamic recrystallization [135–138] that take place in this copper layer.

The methods of electron diffraction microscopy were used to study the phase composition, defective substructure, and phase morphology of the Ag–CdO/copper substrate coating system formed on the surface of a copper electrical contact by the explosive method. The formation of a multi-element multiphase coating having a nanocrystalline structure is revealed. It has been established that the main phases of the coating are Cu, Cd_3Cu_4, Ag_2O_3, CdO_2, Cd_3Cu_4. It was found that the volume of copper adjacent to the coating has a submicrocrystalline grain structure, which can indicate both the occurrence of high-speed crystallization in this layer and the process of dynamic recrystallization. The effect of dispersion hardening of a copper layer adjacent to the coating due to the formation of nanoscale phases of the composition Ag_5Cd_8, Cd_3Cu_4, Cd, and CuO was revealed. It was shown that the electroexplosive formation of a coating of Ag–CdO composition is accompanied by thermo-deformational action on the surface of copper samples with the formation of a gradient of dislocation substructures.

It was found that with increasing distance from the surface of the sample, the degree of deformation of the material decreases.

Also, studies of copper electrical contacts after electroexplosive spraying by scanning electron microscopy (Fig. 3.26), x-ray phase analysis (Fig. 3.27) were conducted.

The phase composition of the coating obtained after EBT consists of the following components: CuO, $Ag_{0.908}Cu_{0.89}$, Cu_2O, Ag_2O_3, Ag_2O, Cu, $Cu_{0.98}Cd_{0.02}$, $Ag_{0.48}Cd_{0.52}$.

The CuO phase is observed only at a power density of 0.3 MW /cm^2, its mass fraction is 0.01%. The crystal lattice parameter a is 4.345 nm, and the coherent scattering region (CSR) is 44.29 nm.

At the initial time, at a power density of $W_s = 0.3$ MW/cm^2, the mass fraction of the $Ag_{0.908}Cu_{0.89}$ phase is 38.45%. With an increase in power density to $W_s = 0.3$ MW/cm^2, the fraction of the $Ag_{0.908}Cu_{0.89}$ phase reaches a maximum value of 54.66%. It is followed by a

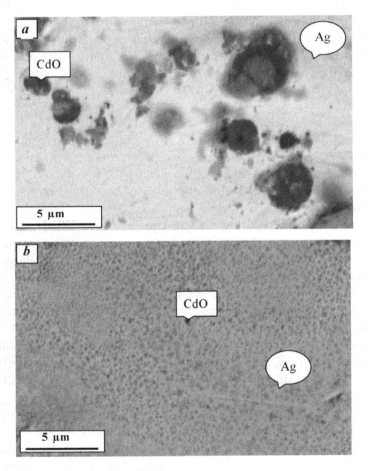

Fig. 3.26. Structure of the cross section of the surface layer of electric explosive composite coating of the CdO–Ag systems. SEM in backward-reflected electrons. a – without exposure to EBT; b – after EBT.

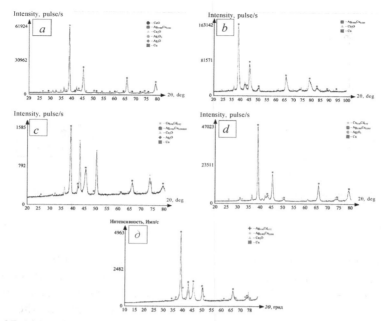

Fig. 3.27. Plots of radiographs of electrical contact after electroexplosive spraying CdO–Ag coating system and electron beam processing in various modes. a–d – EBT in modes 1–5, respectively

decline to the minimum value of the considered phase, corresponding to 19.97% at $W_s = 0.6$ MW/cm^2.

At $W_s = 0.3$ MW/cm^2, the initial value of the parameter a of the Ag$_{0.908}$Cu$_{0.89}$ crystal lattice is 4.0029 nm. With an increase in power density to $W_s = 0.45$ MW/cm^2, this indicator increases to its maximum, equal to 4.0216 nm. With a subsequent decline, the considered indicator reaches its minimum of 3.9955 nm at 0.55 MW/cm^2. The final value of parameter a at $W_s = 0.6$ MW/cm^2 increases to 4.0121 nm.

At the same time, at $W_s = 0.3$ MW/cm^2, the initial value of the CSR is 34.88 nm. Then, at $W_s = 0.45$ MW/cm^2, the CSR reaches its minimum of 17.47 nm, however, with a further increase in power density to $W_s = 0.5$ MW/cm^2, this parameter reaches its maximum, equal to 42.37 nm. Then, at $W_s = 0.55$ MW/cm^2, the CSR value drops to 22.93 nm. The final value after a slight increase, at $W_s = 0.6$ MW/cm^2, is 22.93 nm.

For the Cu$_2$O phase, the initial value of the mass fraction at $W_s = 0.3$ MW/cm^2 is maximum and equals 26.56%. As the power density increases to at $W_s = 0.5$ MW/cm^2, the mass fraction decreases to

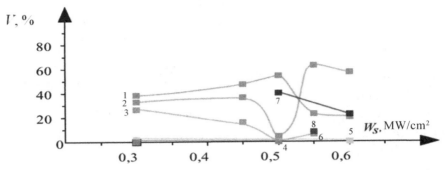

Fig. 3.28. Dependence of the volume fraction of phases (V) of the electroexplosive coating CdO–Ag systems on electron beam power density (W_s). 1 – CuO; 2 – $Ag_{0.908}Cu_{0.89}$; 3 – Cu_2O; 4 – Ag_{2O3}; 5 – Ag_2O; 6 – Cu; 7 – $Cu_{0.98}Cd_{0.02}$; 8 – $Ag_{0.48}Cd_{0.52}$.

its minimum, equal to 0.75%. The final mass fraction is 6.15% at W_s = 0.55 MW/cm². At W_s = 0.6 MW/cm², Cu_2O is not observed.

At W_s = 0.3 MW/cm², the initial value of parameter a for this phase is 4.2733 nm. Subsequently, with an increase in the power density to 0.45 MW/cm², the parameter under consideration reaches its minimum equal to 4.2653 nm. As a consequence, parameter a increases to its maximum of 4.356 nm at W_s = 0.55 MW/cm².

At the same time, at W_s = 0.3 MW/cm², the initial value of the CSR is maximum, and its value is 65.97 nm. With a subsequent increase in power density to 0.45 MW/cm², the CSR value is 17.76 nm. Subsequently, at W_s = 0.5 MW/cm², an increase in the considered parameter is observed to 29.44 nm. After it, at W_s = 0.55 MW/cm², there is a decrease and the final CSR value is 9.19.

The mass fraction of the Ag_2O_3 phase at the initial moment, at W_s = 0.3 MW/cm², is 1.95%. The second phase is observed at W_s = 0.6 MW/cm², and its mass fraction is 0.01%. Parameter a at 0.3 MW/cm² is 4.7499 nm, at 0.6 MW/cm² its value increases to 4.816 nm. The CSR varies from 14.03 nm at 0.3 MW/cm² to 23.74 nm at 0.6 MW/cm².

The Ag_2O phase is initially observed at W_s = 0.3 MW/cm², and its mass fraction is 0.05%. For the second and last time, the phase under consideration is observed at 0.5 MW/cm² with a mass fraction of 0.01%. The parameter a for both values of the power density remains unchanged at 4.819 nm, but the CSR changes from 16.71 nm at 0.3 MW/cm² to 36.55 nm at 0.5 MW/cm².

The initial mass fraction at W_s = 0.3 MW/cm² Cu is 32.98%. A subsequent increase in the power density W_s = 0.45 MW/cm² is

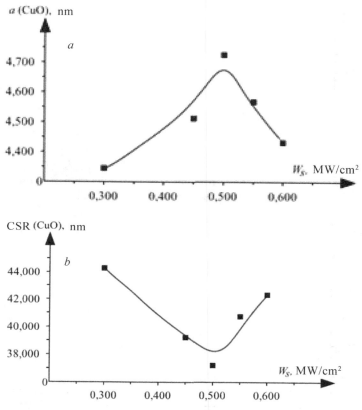

Fig. 3.29. Dependences of the crystal lattice and CSR parameters on the power density for the CuO phase. *a* is the lattice parameter *a*; *b* – CSR.

accompanied by an increase in the mass fraction to 36.66%, followed by a decrease in the mass fraction of Cu to a minimum of 4.35% at $W_s = 0.5$ MW/cm². After that, the Cu content reaches its maximum of 63.06% at $W_s = 0.55$ MW/cm². The final value of the mass fraction of Cu is 57.37 at $W_s = 0.6$ MW/cm².

At the same time, at $W_s = 0.3$ MW/cm², the parameter *a* is minimal and equal to 3.6188 nm. With a subsequent increase in power density to $W_s = 0.5$ MW/cm², the value of parameter *a* reaches its maximum of 3.713 nm, followed by a decrease to the final value of 3.6363 nm at 0.6 MW/cm².

At the same time, the initial value of the CSR at $W_s = 0.3$ MW /cm² is 8.27 nm. With a subsequent increase in density to $W_s = 0.5$

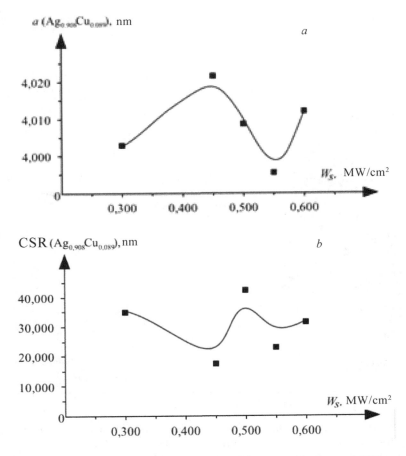

Fig. 3.30. The dependence of the parameters of the crystal lattice and CSR on power density for the $Ag_{0.908}Cu_{0.89}$ phase. *a* is the lattice parameter *a*; *b* – CSR

MW/cm², the CSR value reaches its maximum of 17.44 nm, followed by a decline to a minimum value of 8.02 nm at 0.6 MW/cm².

Initially, at W_s = 0.5 MW/cm², the mass fraction of the $Cu_{0.98}Cd_{0.02}$ phase is 40.23%. The second time the phase appears at W_s = 0.6 MW/cm², its mass fraction is 22.65%. Parameter *a* at W_s = 0.5 MW/cm² is 3.636 nm, when the power density reaches 0.6 MW/cm², the parameter in question increases to 3.9955 nm. At the same time, the CSR at W_s = 0.5 MW/cm² is 22.93 nm; with an increase in the power density to W_s = 0.6 MW/cm², the CSR decreases to 11.02 nm.

The $Ag_{0.48}Cd_{0.52}$ phase is observed only at a power density equal to W_s = 0.55 MW/cm², moreover, its mass fraction is 8.05%, the

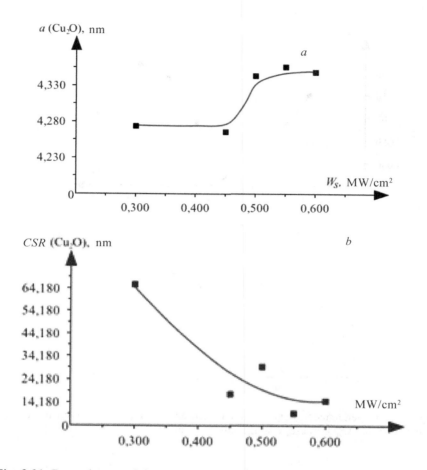

Fig. 3.31. Dependences of the parameters of the crystal lattice and CSR on power density for the Cu$_2$O phase. *a* is the lattice parameter *a*; *b* – CSR.

crystal lattice and CSR parameters are 3.0189 nm and 34.96 nm, respectively.

3.3, Properties of electroerosion-resistant coatings of SnO$_2$–Ag and CdO–Ag systems

Let us analyze the dependence of contact resistance (R) on the number of on/off cycles (N) when testing the coatings of the CdO-Ag system for electrical discharge resistance under conditions of arc erosion (Fig 3.37 *a*). At the beginning of the experiment, the value of R contacts is 10.5, 7.4, and 9.6 μΩ for phases L$_1$, L$_2$,

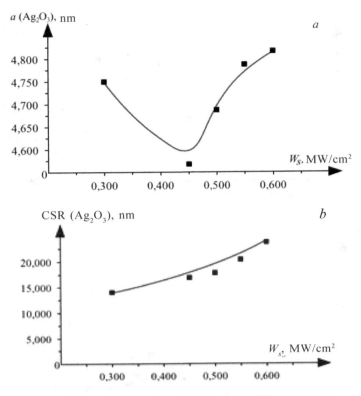

Fig. 3.32. Dependences of the crystal lattice and CSR parameters on the power density for the Ag_2O_3 phase. a is the lattice parameter a; b – CSR.

and L_3, respectively. After the first on/off cycles are carried out, the resistance increases to a maximum value of 16 μOhm with the number of on / off cycles equal to 1023 for the L_1, L_3 μOhm phase with the number of on/off cycles equal to 1234 for the L_2 phase, 9.2 μOhm with the number on/off cycles equal to 1906 for phase L_3. This indicates that at the present stage of the experiment, intensive evaporation of the fusible silver matrix begins under the influence of an electric arc. The contact surface is enriched with particles of CdO powder, which has a lower electrical conductivity (10^{-8} S/ m) compared with silver (62.5 MS/m) [138]. For this reason, the contact resistance in this section of the graph increases. When the maximum values of R are reached in all three phases with a further increase in N, the electrical resistance decreases again. This is due to the fact that due to the evaporation of silver, the contact surface is enriched

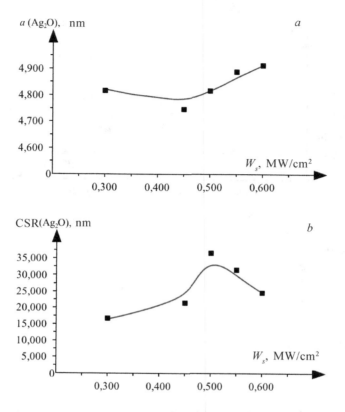

Fig. 3.33. Dependence of the crystal lattice and CSR parameters on the power density for the Ag$_2$O phase. *a* is the lattice parameter *a*; *b* – CSR.

to the maximum with refractory CdO particles, which have low electrical conductivity. Upon reaching $N \approx 1000...2000$, mechanical accumulation of CdO particles on the contact surface occurs. Then, with an increase in the number of on/off cycles, the resistance decreases to the minimum value. For phase L$_1$, the resistance value is 4.1 μOhm with the number of on/off cycles equal to 4907, for phase L$_2$ the resistance value is 3.4 μOhm with the number of on/ off cycles equal to 5009, for phase L$_3$ the resistance value is 3 μOh with the number of on cycle on/off equal to 5028. With a further increase in the number of on/off cycles, an increase in resistance begins. The final resistance values for phases L$_1$, L$_2$, L$_3$ are 6.7, 4, 5.6 μΩ with the number of on/off cycles 6023, 5983, 6098, respectively. The tests showed that the formed coatings of the CdO–Ag system satisfy the testing of starters for electroerosive stability [139].

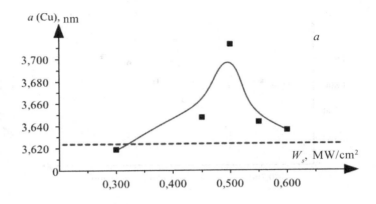

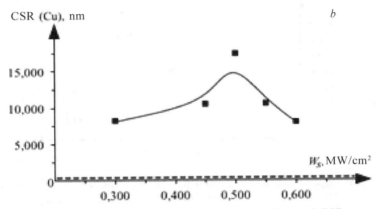

Fig. 3.34. Dependences of the parameters of the crystal lattice and CSR on power density for the Cu phase. *a* is the lattice parameter *a*; *b* – CSR.

In the case of the SnO_2–Ag system (Fig. 3.45 *b*), the L_2 phase is characterized by a monotonic increase in the value of R, which varies from 3 μΩ with the on/off number equal to 231 to 12 μΩ at 6042 cycles. For phase L_1, the R value changes from 6 μOhm with the number of on/off cycles equal to 250 to 16 μOhm at 6023 cycles, however, in the interval from 2178 to 3059 test cycles, the value does not change and equals 8 μOhm. For phase L_3, the value of R increases from 4 μOhm with the on/off number equal to 100 to 13 μOhm at 6076 cycles, however, in the interval from 1987 to 2987 on/off cycles, the resistance decreases from 6 μOhm to 5.4 μOhm.

Thus, the increase in electrical resistance during tests of electric explosive coatings of the CdO–Ag and SnO_2–Ag systems for electrical discharge resistance is caused by evaporation of a low-melting silver

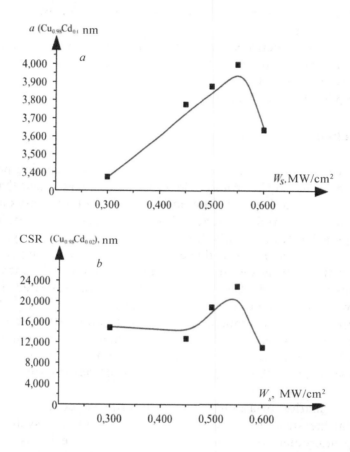

Fig. 3.35. Dependences of the parameters of the crystal lattice and CSR on the power density for the $Cu_{0.98}Cd_{0.02}$ phase. a is the lattice parameter a; b – CSR.

matrix under the influence of an electric arc and enrichment of the coating surface with cadmium or tin oxide particles. Electrical contacts hardened by electric explosive coatings of the CdO–Ag and SnO_2–Ag systems are capable of mechanically cleaning the surface of metal oxide particles. The formed coatings satisfy the testing of starters for electrical discharge resistance [139].

An analysis of the results of wear resistance tests (Table 3.1) shows that the coatings formed on the surface of the copper electrical contact are characterized by high wear resistance values (exceed the wear resistance of the substrate by more than 2.9 times for the CdO–Ag system and 2.6 times for the SnO_2–Ag system) and close values of the friction coefficient.

Tests for nano- and microhardness showed the following values for coatings of the CdO–Ag and SnO_2–Ag systems. Nano- and microhardness of electroexplosive coatings after EBT amounted to 290...450 HV. The hardness of the copper substrate was 150 HV. The hardness of the formed coatings exceeds the value of the hardness of the copper substrate 1.9...3 times.

3.4. Conclusions

1. For the CdO–Ag system it was found that the main coating phases after EBT are Cu, Cd_3Cu_4, Ag_2O_3, CdO_2, Cd_3Cu_4. It was found that the volume of copper adjacent to the coating has a submicrocrystalline grain structure, which indicates both the occurrence of high-speed crystallization in this layer and the process of dynamic recrystallization. The effect of dispersion hardening of a copper layer adjacent to the coating due to the formation of nanoscale phases of the composition Ag_5Cd_8, Cd_3Cu_4, Cd, and CuO was revealed. It has been shown that the electroexplosive formation of a coating of Ag-CdO composition is accompanied by thermal deformation action on the surface of a copper sample with the formation of a gradient of dislocation substructures. It was found that with increasing distance from the surface of the sample, the degree of deformation of the material decreases.

2. The formation of a multi-element multiphase coating having a nanocrystalline structure was revealed in the SnO_2–Ag system. By indicating microelectron diffraction patterns, it was established that the main phases of the coating are SnO_2, Ag_3Sn, $Cu_{10}Sn_3$, Cu_3Sn, Cu_6Sn_5, Ag_4Sn and CuO. It was found that the volume of copper adjacent to the coating has a fragmented structure, which may indicate a high level of deformation of the surface layer of the sample during the electric explosion method of coating formation.

Table 3.1. The results of the test samples for wear resistance

Sample	Friction coefficient, μ	Wear coefficient 10^{-6}, $mm^2/N \cdot m$
Cu	0.248	35
CdO–Ag	0.22	12
SnO_2–Ag	0.21	13

Note. The higher the wear rate, the lower the wear resistance of the material.

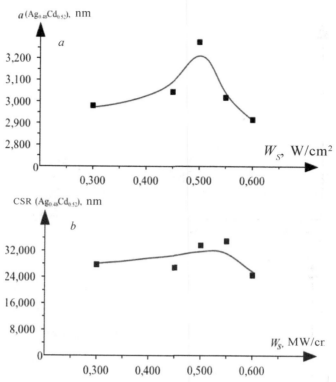

Fig. 3.36. Dependences of the parameters of the crystal lattice and CSR on power density for the $Ag_{0.48}Cd_{0.52}$ phase. *a* is the lattice parameter *a*; *b* – CSR.

3. Nano- and microhardness of electric explosive coatings of the CdO–Ag and SnO_2–Ag systems after EBT exceed the value of the copper substrate hardness by 1.9...3 times and amounts to 290... 450 HV. The wear resistance of the formed coatings exceeds the wear resistance of the substrate by more than 2.9 times for the CdO–Ag system and 2.6 times for the SnO_2–Ag system. The friction coefficient for the coatings of the CdO–Ag system was 0.220, and for the SnO_2–Ag system 0.21. These values are close to the friction coefficient of the copper substrate, which amounted to 0.248.

4. The formed coatings of the CdO–Ag and SnO_2–Ag systems satisfy the erosion resistance tests of starters under conditions of arc erosion. Electrical contacts hardened by electric explosive coatings of the CdO–Ag and SnO_2–Ag systems are capable of mechanically cleaning the surface of the metal oxide particles.

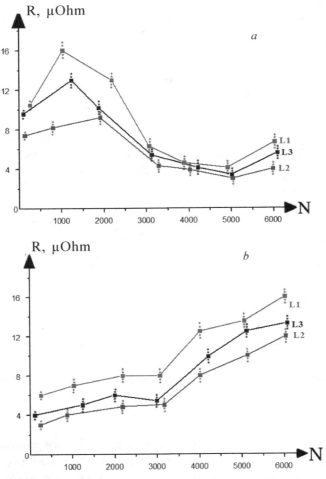

Fig. 3.37. Typical dependence of contact resistance (R) of the number of on/off cycles (N) during electric explosion tests on the erosion resistance of coatings in conditions of arc erosion. a – CdO–Ag coating; b – SnO$_2$–Ag coating; L$_1$, L$_2$, L$_3$ are phase contacts.

4

Electroerosion resistant electric explosion coatings for heavy loaded DC and AC contacts

This chapter is written on the basis of scientific articles [140–144], which discuss issues related to the study of electroexplosive coatings of the CuO–Ag system and scientific articles [145–150], which discuss questions related to the study of electroexplosive coatings of the ZnO–Ag system. Methods for producing electroerosion-resistant coatings of CuO–Ag and ZnO–Ag systems are protected by invention patents [151, 152].

4.1. Structure of electroerosion-resistant coatings of the CuO–Ag system

Using scanning electron microscopy, the structure and elemental composition of the transverse section of the coating/substrate system formed by the electric explosion method were studied. A typical image of the cross-sectional structure of the coating of the composition of CuO–Ag is shown in Fig. 4.1. An analysis of the results shows that the formed coating is a composite material that is uniform in structure (Fig. 4.1 a, b). According to the morphology of the structure and the etching contrast, the formed coating consists of a light silver matrix and dark CuO inclusions with sizes varying from 0.3 to 0.5 μm (Fig. 4.1 b). The elemental composition of the coating was analyzed by X-ray spectral analysis. The research results are presented in Fig. 4.1. c–d. Analyzing the results presented in Fig. 4.1 c–d, it can be noted that the concentrations of copper (Figure

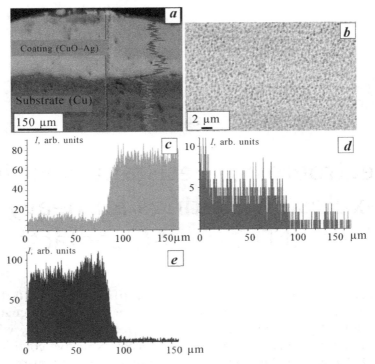

Fig. 4.1. Structure of the electric explosion coating of the CuO-Ag system. The atomic concentrations of the elements are determined along the line indicated on *a*. *a* – general view of the coating; *b* – composite filled structure; *c* – *d* are the concentration profiles of copper, oxygen, and silver atoms, respectively. Copper concentration determined by characteristic X-ray radiation $K\alpha1$; oxygen concentration – according to $L\alpha1$;

4.1, *c*), oxygen (Fig. 4.1 *d*) and silver (Fig. 4.1 *e*) in the coating vary slightly in thickness. This fact also indicates the structural homogeneity of the resulting coating.

Atomic force microscopy was carried out in a coating layer located at a distance of 10 μm (Fig. 4.2) from the coating surface, as well as at the interface between the coating and the copper substrate (Fig. 4.3). Since the electroexplosive coating is formed by a silver matrix and particles of CuO powder located in it, small particles of CuO powder can be tinted from the matrix when preparing a thin section.

In this case, pores are formed at the place of the precipitated particles (dark areas in Fig. 4.2 *a, b*) with a depth of 30 to 100 nm and a width of 2 to 5 nm (Fig. 4.2 *c*). Particles of CuO are

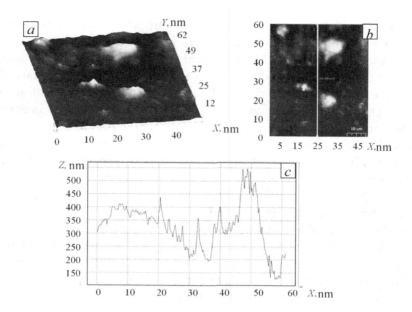

Fig. 4.2. Coating structure of the CuO–Ag system, identified by atomic force microscopy. *a* – distribution of unevenness of the relief in height in 3D format; *b* – the position of the secant (top view); *c* – distribution of roughness along the base length.

dispersed up to 2...5 nm during an electric explosion in the course of the formation of a pulsed plasma jet of products of an electric explosion of conductors.

Separate large particles of various shapes with sizes from 10 to 15 nm are also detected. These CuO particles do not crumble from the silver matrix when preparing the thin section, they are sharply highlighted in colour (they are lighter in comparison with the matrix). They are randomly arranged in a silver matrix. As can be seen from Fig. 4.2 *a*, *b*, large particles have a complex structure the characteristic structural units of which they are composed are spheres (globules) with a diameter of 2 to 5 nm (these are small spherical particles described above). The ratio of the silver matrix, large and small particles of CuO powder is 0.6:0.15:0.25. If we take into account that large particles of CuO consist of smaller globular particles of CuO, then the ratio of silver matrix and inclusions of CuO powder is 0.6:0.4. This ratio is proportional to the content of CuO powder and silver foil used for electric explosion spraying. The average surface roughness of the coating surface of the CuO-Ag system is 100 nm.

Thus, it was possible to identify an important structural element - the CuO globule, a spherical particle with a diameter of 2 to 5 nm. There is a multilevel hierarchical structure of the coating of the CuO–Ag system based on the same type of spherical CuO particles with a diameter of 2 to 5 nm. The single structural unit of which the CuO inclusions located in the silver matrix consist of is a very important argument in favour of the fractal mechanism for the formation of an electric explosive coating. Such particles constitute the first hierarchical level of the structure of the electroexplosive coating of the CuO–Ag system. The second hierarchical level consists of large particles of various shaped globules with sizes from 10 to 15 nm, which, in turn, form a sediment of irregularly shaped micron particles, detected by scanning electron microscopy.

At the interface between the coating and the copper substrate (Fig. 4.3 *a, b*), dark depressions from 10 to 15 nm in size are distinguishable. The large CuO particles, which were discussed above, crumbled out of them. In addition, surface periodic structures (SPS) appear in the silver matrix at the coating/substrate interface. The secant, perpendicular to these structural formations (Fig. 4.3 *b,*

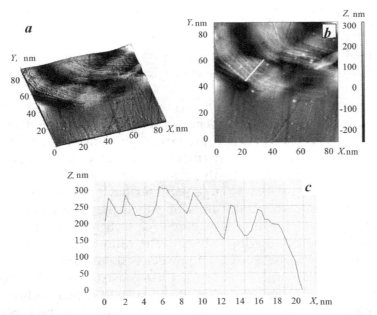

Fig. 4.3. The structure at the boundary of the CuO–Ag coating with the copper substrate, revealed by atomic force microscopy. *a* – distribution of the relief surface along the heght in 3D format; *b* – position of the secant line (top view); *c* – distribution of roughness along the basic line.

c), suggests that the wavelength in them is on average 3 nm. The structures are the residual nanorelief of the surface.

After the end of the impact of a pulsed plasma jet of electrical explosion products of conductors on the substrate and cooling of the surface, the induced relief is fixed in the form of SPS (surface periodic structures). The specific processes of their formation can be evaporation, surface melting and displacement of the melt by excessive vapour pressure, thermocapillary phenomena and thermochemical reactions, thermal deformations, the appearance and development of various instabilities, such as Rayleigh–Taylor, Kelvin–Helmholtz, Marangoni [153] and others. On the whole, the phenomenon is universal in nature and represents an example of self-organization in a system where initially there are no distinguished directions and structures [154]. The energy regimes for the production of SPS correspond to the heating of the material to a temperature approximately equal to the melting temperature (lower limit), but not higher than the developed evaporation temperature [154]. It is this mode that was used for electroexplosive spraying in the present work.

Surface profilometry (Fig. 4.3 *a*) showed that the roughness parameter of the electroexplosive coating of the CuO–Ag system is 73 nm. The maximum protrusion of the profile in this case reaches 536.85 nm, and the depression 497.5 nm. Comparing the roughness parameters at the interface of the electric explosive coating with the substrate (Fig. 4.3) with the roughness parameter in the coating layer located at a distance of 10 μm (Fig. 4.2), it can be noted that they differ by 28%. In Figure 4.3, 35% of the photograph is taken by the substrate, and 65% by the coating. This makes it possible to conclude that the roughness of the substrate is lower than the roughness of the coating. This is logical, since due to the inclusions of CuO deposited from the silver matrix, the parameter of coating roughness increases.

The assembly mechanism of such a complex multilevel CdO in a silver matrix can be represented as follows. The single size r_1 of spherical CdO particles of the first hierarchy level can be explained in terms of the model of diffusion-limited aggregation by the mechanism of diffusion-limited aggregation 'particle–cluster' [155]. The plasma components of a multiphase jet of products of electric explosion of conductors distributed in a certain effective volume over some effective space of a substrate interface of the same size are assembled into a cluster, which then turns into a sphere with a diameter of 2 to 5 nm [155]. It should be noted that the size of the effective volume in which the formation of blanks

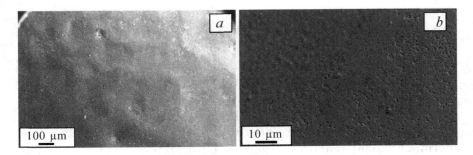

Fig. 4.4. The characteristic surface of the electroexplosive coating of the CuO–Ag system after treatment with an electron beam. SEM. *a* - general view; *b* - structural components

of spherical particles of the first level of the hierarchy will depend on the composition of the exploding conductors and temperature. The formation of CdO clusters occurs only at the initial stage of the action of a pulsed plasma jet on the substrate. At the next stage of growth, the particle–cluster aggregation mechanism ceases to act, but the cluster sizes increase. Growth begins at the same time and ends synchronously after the exhaustion of the presence of CdO in the plasma state, the clusters turn into particles of almost the same size (under the discussed conditions, these are spheres with a diameter of 2 to 5 nm). Particle sizes are not large enough for gravitational forces to dominate. In other words: there is a metastable state in which spheres with diameters from 2 to 5 nm are maintained in suspension mainly due to Brownian motion and forces of intermolecular interaction with other components of the molten metal. Under the influence of Brownian forces, the spheres continue a chaotic movement, which stimulates their agglomeration. Self-assembly of particles of the first hierarchical level leads to the formation of a second hierarchical level of globules of size r2 from 10 to 15 nm. The formation of this hierarchical level occurs mainly by the cluster–cluster mechanism. Further, such globular particles can be enlarged by sticking to particles in the micrometer range.

An electron beam falling on the treated surface of the electric explosive coating of the CuO–Ag system produces ultrafast heating (during the pulse) to the melting temperature of the substrate material. Rapid cooling then occurs due to the removal of heat into the deeper cold layers of the substrate.

The composite electroexplosive coating of the CuO–Ag system after treatment with an electron beam consists of components that are a heterogeneous structure consisting of a mixture of more than two

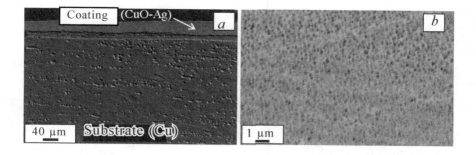

Fig. 4.5. Structure of the electric explosion coating of the CuO–Ag system after electron beam processing. *a* – general view; *b* - structural components. Direct section. SEM.

phases (Fig. 4.5), and one phase (copper oxides) has a significantly higher refractoriness than silver [156]. When one of the phases goes into a liquid state in such a heterogeneous structure, this phase is retained in the pores of the refractory phase by surface tension forces. According to the morphology of the structure and the etching contrast, the formed coating consists of a light silver matrix and dark inclusions of copper oxides with sizes varying from 0.1 to 0.2 μm (Fig. 4.5 *b*). In contrast to [140], it was found that EBT (electron beam treatment) leads to a decrease in the size of copper oxides to values from 1.5 to 5.0 times smaller than those without EBT.

Using X-ray phase analysis methods (Fig. 4.6), it was established that the phase composition of the coating of the CuO–Ag system after EBT represents the following phases: Ag, Cu_2O, $Cu_{64}O$ and Cu. The lower copper suboxide $Cu_{64}O$ is formed even at room temperature and forms the thinnest film on the surface of an electroexplosive coating. However, with an oxide film thickness> 40 nm, diffusion of oxygen to the copper surface is hindered and oxidation of the oxide to CuO occurs. This reaction proceeds quickly at temperatures above 300°C. EBT, on the other hand, provides the melting of the surface layer of the electric explosive coating of the Ag–CuO system to the entire coating thickness of 40 μm, heating it to a temperature of more than 1000°C. Partial oxidation of the surface layer of the metal also occurs when it melts in air, and the Cu_2O oxide formed in this process dissolves in the melt. When an electron beam acts on an electric explosion coating of the CuO–Ag system, the following chemical reactions proceed in parallel:

$$4Cu + O_2 \rightarrow 2Cu_2O;$$
$$2Cu_2O + O_2 \rightarrow 4CuO;$$
$$4CuO \rightarrow 2Cu_2O + O_2;$$
$$Cu + CuO \rightarrow Cu_2O.$$

Let us analyze the dependence of the volume fraction of the phases of the electroexplosive coating of the CuO–Ag system on the power density of the electron beam (Fig. 4.6). The initial content of the volume fraction of the Ag phase at $W_s = 0.3$ MW/cm^2 is 59.75% and is maximum for this phase. With an increase in power density to 0.5 MW/cm^2, the volume fraction of Ag monotonically decreases to its minimum value of 49.99%. Then there is an increase in the volume fraction of Ag. The volume fraction of Ag increases to 55% at an electron beam power density of 0.6 MW/cm^2. In this case, the Ag crystal lattice parameter a (Fig. 4.7 a) increases from 0.40792 nm at 0.3 MW/cm^2 to 0.40971 nm at 0.55 MW/cm^2. Then, at a power density of 0.6 MW/cm^2, the value of this parameter decreases to 0.4057 nm. The coherent scattering region (CSR) for Ag (Fig. 4.7 b) with a minimum power density of 0.3 MW/cm^2 is 14.36 nm and decreases to 13.8 nm at 0.45 MW/cm^2, after which the CSR increases to its maximum of 25.32 nm at 0.55 MW/cm^2. The minimum CSR for Ag, equal to 11 nm, is achieved at 0.6 MW/cm^2.

The volume fraction of the Cu_0O phase (Fig. 4.6) increases from the initial value of 20.93% at 0.3 MW/cm^2, which is the minimum, to its maximum value of 37.79% at 0.55 MW/cm^2. With a power

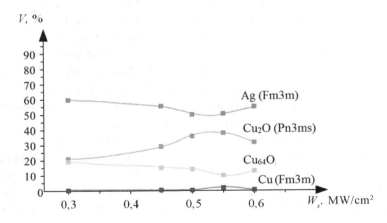

Fig. 4.6. Dependence of the volume fraction of phases (V) of an electroexplosive coatings of the CuO–Ag system on the electron beam power density (W_s).
"

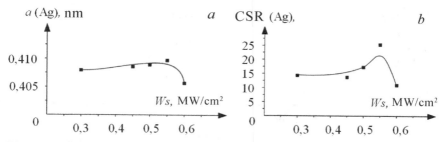

Fig. 4.7. Ag (Fm3m) phase dependences on the electron beam power density. *a* – dependence of the parameter *a* of the crystal lattice; *b* – dependence of coherent scattering regions.

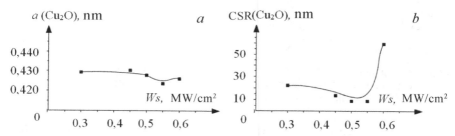

Fig. 4.8. Dependences of the parameters of Cu_2O (Pn3ms) on the electron beam power density. *a* is the dependence of the parameter *a* of the crystal lattice; *b* is the dependence of coherent scattering regions.

density of 0.6 MW/cm², the volume fraction is 31.67%. The value of the crystal lattice parameter *a* of the Cu_2O phase (Fig. 4.8 *a*) at the minimum power density is 0.42919 nm. The maximum value of this parameter is 0.43026 nm at 0.45 MW/cm².

With an increase in the power density to 0.55 MW/cm², the parameter *a* decreases to its minimum, equal to 0.42353 nm. With a power density of 0.6 MW/cm², parameter *a* is 0.42603 nm. The value of the CSR of the Cu_2O phase at 0.3 MW/cm² is 22.3 nm (Fig. 4.8 *b*), then with an increase in the absorbed power density, the value of the CSR decreases to its minimum of 9.02 nm at 0.5 MW/cm². After that, there is a sharp increase in the indicator to a maximum value of 59.6 nm at 0.6 MW/cm².

The $Cu_{64}O$ phase is characterized by a decrease in the volume fraction (Fig. 4.6) from the maximum value of 19.07% at 0.3 MW/cm² to a minimum of 9.89% at 0.55 MW/cm². With an increase in absorbed power density to 0.6 MW/cm², the volume fraction increases to 13%. The lattice parameter *a* of the $Cu_{64}O$ phase (Fig. 4.9 *a*) has a minimum value of 0.97717 nm at 0.3 MW/cm², followed

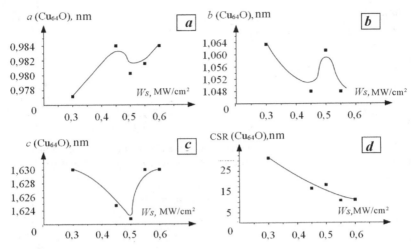

Fig. 4.9 Dependences of $Cu_{64}O$ parameters on the electron beam power density. a– c – dependences of the parameters a, b, c of the crystal lattice, respectively; d – dependence of the coherent scattering regions (CSR).

by an increase to its maximum of 0.984 nm at 0.45 MW/cm². After that, this parameter decreases to 0.98027 nm at 0.5 MW/cm². With a further increase in the absorbed power density to 0.6 MW/cm², parameter a again reaches its maximum at 0.984 nm. The crystal lattice parameter b of the $Cu_{64}O$ phase (Fig. 4.9 b) has a maximum value of 1.06341 MW/cm² with a minimum absorbed power density of 0.3 MW/cm². With its growth, the value of b decreases to its minimum of 1.048 MW/cm² at 0.45 nm, the subsequent increase in the index b reaches 1.06137 nm at 0.5 MW/cm². Later, the value of b drops to its minimum again at 0.55 MW/cm² and remains so at 0.6 MW/cm². The parameter c of the crystal lattice of the $Cu_{64}O$ phase (Fig. 4.9 c) has a maximum value of 1.63 nm at 0.3 MW/cm². After this, a decrease in b occurs and a minimum of 1.62283 nm is achieved at 0.5 MW/cm². At a value of 0.55 MW/cm², the value of parameter c again reaches a maximum and remains so at 0.6 MW/ cm². The maximum value of the CSR of the $Cu_{64}O$ phase (Fig. 4.9 c) is 31.26 at 0.3 MW/cm². It is followed by a drop to 16.63 nm at 0.45 MW/cm², followed by an increase to 18.3 nm at 0.5 MW/cm², followed by a drop to a minimum of 11.17 nm at 0.6 MW/cm2. The dependence is approximated by an almost linear function.

The Cu phase (Fm3m) has a volume fraction of 0.25% (Fig. 4.6) at 0.3 MW/cm² and increases its value to 0.3 at 0.45 MW/cm², then it drops to the minimum value of 0.22% at 0.5 MW/cm². When the power density reaches 0.55 MW/cm², the proportion of Cu increases

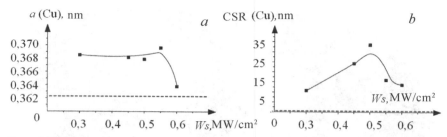

Fig. 4.10. Dependences of the parameters Cu (Fm3m) on the power density of the electron beam. The red dashed line indicates the values of these parameters for copper used as a substrate. *a* is the dependence of the parameter *a* of the crystal lattice; *b* is the dependence of coherent scattering regions.

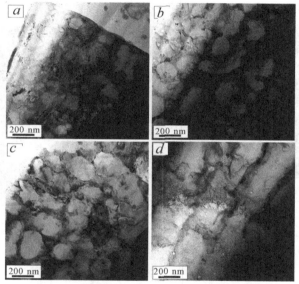

Fig. 4.11. Structure of copper modified by the electric explosion method and electron-beam processing: *a* – surface layer, *b* – a layer located at a distance of 10 μm from the surface, *c* – at a distance of 20 μm, *d* – at a distance of 35 μm from the surface of the modification.

to its maximum of 1.77%. At 0.6 MW/cm^2, the volume fraction indicator decreases to 0.33%. For the Cu phase (Fm3m), the initial value of the parameter *a* of the crystal lattice at 0.3 MW/cm^2 is 10.72 nm (Fig. 4.10 *a*). The subsequent increase in parameter *a* ends at 0.45 MW/cm^2 and amounts to 16.63 nm. Then the parameter *a* increases to its maximum, equal to 33.62 nm at 0.5 MW/cm^2. The parameter *a* reaches its minimum at 11.17 nm at 0.6 MW/cm^2. The CSR for the Cu (Fm3m) phase (Fig. 4.10 *b*) increases from its minimum of 10.72

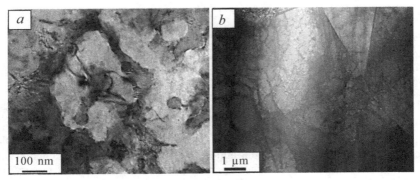

Fig. 4.12. Electron microscopic image of copper subjected to electroexplosive spraying and electron-beam processing. *a* – structure of the surface layer; *b* – the structure of the layer located at a distance of ≈60 μm from the surface of the modification

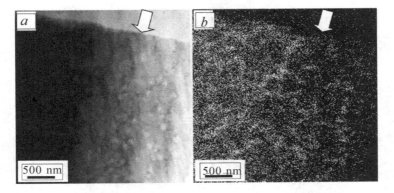

Fig. 4.13. Electron microscopic images of the structure of the surface layer of copper subjected to EES and EBT. *a* – STEM-image; *b* – image of the structure of the photo *a* obtained in characteristic x-ray emission of silver atoms.

nm at 0.3 MW/cm² to a maximum of 33.62 nm at 0.5 MW/ cm², followed by a drop to 16.14 nm at 0.6 MW/cm². Both the parameter and the CSR of the Cu (Fm3m) phase have larger values than those for the copper electrical contact used as a substrate for the formation of an electric explosion coating.

Similar dependences of changes in the parameters of the crystal lattice and regions of coherent phase scattering depend on changes in the physicochemical parameters of the crystalline substance and the specific energy of its crystal lattice. These dependences are explained by the fact that with an increase in the volumetric (mass) specific energy of the crystal lattice, the physicochemical parameters of the crystalline substance change, whose growth (hardness, melting point, thermal conductivity, etc.) or decrease (gram-atom heat capacity, thermal expansion coefficient)) is determined by the cohesion energy of ions in crystals [157]. In addition, deformations of the structural parameters of the detected phases are associated with elastic stresses in the initial electroexplosive coating of the CuO–Ag system on a copper electrical contact substrate, as well as with stresses arising from the irradiation of a material with a high-intensity electron beam [158]. As a result of the action of the electron beam, the distortion of the initial crystal cells of the electroexplosive coating, associated with the displacement of atoms along an eigenvector along a certain crystallographic direction, becomes energetically most beneficial [159].

The phase and elemental composition, the state of the defective substructure of the copper sample modified by the electroexplosive method, were analyzed by the transmission electron diffraction microscopy of thin foils. The performed studies show that in the surface layer with a thickness of ≈30 μm, a high-speed cellular crystallization structure is formed, regardless of the distance to the irradiation surface, the characteristic electron-microscopic images of which are shown in Fig. 4.11 a–c. The cell size varies from 150 nm to 300 nm. The cells are separated by interlayers, the thickness of which varies from 10 nm to 70 nm. A dislocation substructure is revealed in the volume of cells in the form of randomly distributed dislocations (Fig. 4.12 a). Scalar dislocation density is ≈1 · 10^{10} cm^{-2}. In the transition layer, the structure of dendritic crystallization is revealed, a characteristic image of which is shown in Fig. 4.11.

At a distance of more than 40 μm from the surface of the modification, a thermal influence layer is revealed that has a polycrystalline structure and is a solid solution based on copper.

In the volume of copper grains, a cellular–mesh dislocation substructure is observed, a characteristic image of which is shown in Fig. 4.12 b. The cell size varies from 350 nm to 700 nm. The scalar dislocation density is 0.9 · 10^{10} cm^{-2}.

The distribution of silver atoms in the modified copper layer was studied by X-ray microanalysis of thin foils. The research results are shown in Figs. 4.13 and 4.14. Analyzing the results presented in Fig. 6, it can be concluded that in the structure of high-speed cellular crystallization formed in the surface layer, the cell volume is formed by copper atoms, silver atoms are located mainly along the cell boundaries, forming extended interlayers (Fig. 4.13 b).

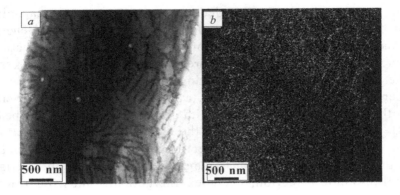

Fig. 4.14. Electron microscopic images of the structure of the surface layer of copper subjected to EES and EBT. The analyzed layer is located at a depth of ≈30 μm. *a* – STEM image; *b* – image of the structure of the plot *a*, obtained in the characteristic x-ray emission of silver atoms.

In the structure of dendroid crystallization, silver atoms are located mainly along the borders of dendrites, forming discontinuous lines of separately located particles (Fig. 4.14 *b*). Particle sizes vary from 20 nm to 30 nm. In the volume of copper grains forming the heat-affected zone, silver atoms were not detected by X-ray spectral analysis.

Studies of electroexplosive coatings of the CuO–Ag system after EBT are confirmed by the results of X-ray diffraction analysis (Fig. 4.15).

The results obtained suggest that the formation of a multielement multiphase submicron-nanoscale state in the surface layer will lead to an increase in the strength (nanoscale hardness) and tribological (wear resistance) properties of copper subjected to EVN.

4.2 Structure of electroerosion-resistant coatings of the ZnO–Ag system

The defective substructure of the electroexplosive coating of the ZnO–Ag system was studied by analyzing transverse etched sections (Fig. 4.16). It is established that the EES of copper is accompanied by the formation of a multilayer structure. The thickness of the surface layer (Fig. 4.16 *a*, layer 1) having a submicrocrystalline (150 to 230 nm) structure (Fig. 4.16 *c*) varies over a wide range and varies from 30 μm to 60 μm. The surface layer is separated from the

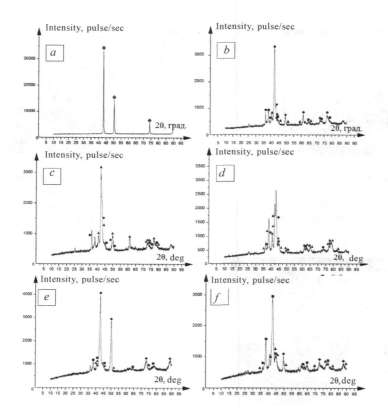

Fig. 4.15. Areas of radiographs of copper without coating and after electrical explosion spray coating system CuO–Ag and electron beam processing (EBT) in various modes. The symbols indicate the phases Cu (♦), Ag (■), Cu64O (▲), and Cu2O (●). *a* – without coating; *b – f -* after EBT in modes 1–5, respectively

thermal influence layer by a transition layer with a thickness of (1.0-1.3) μm (Fig. 4.16 *b*, layer 2). It should be noted that the transition layer contains a large number of micropores (Fig. 4.16 *a, b*).

X-ray spectral analysis methods have been used to study the elemental composition of the modified layer of copper electrical contact. The research results presented in Figure 4.17 indicate that silver is the main element of the surface layer. In the transition layer, the concentration of silver atoms decreases rapidly and in the main volume of the copper electrical contact, silver atoms are detected in a minimal amount.

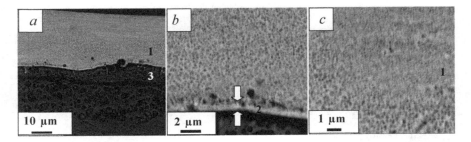

Fig. 4.16. The structure of the transverse section of a copper sample subjected to electric explosion spraying. *a* – general view of the coating; *b* – structure formed at the boundary of the coating with a substrate; *c* – electron microscopic image of the structure of the surface layer; 1 – surface layer; 2 – transition layer; 3 – thermal influence layer.

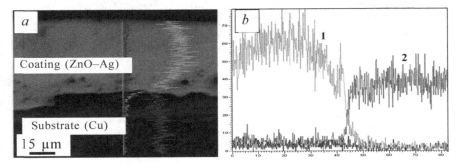

Fig. 4.17. Distribution of silver and copper atoms in a copper electrical contact subjected to EES of the coating of the ZnO–Ag system. *a* – general view of the coating with the imposition of profiles; *b* – concentration profiles of silver atoms (curve 1) and copper (curve 2).

The phase and elemental composition, the state of the defective substructure of the copper electrical contact subjected of the coating of the ZnO–Ag system subjected to EES, were analyzed by transmission electron diffraction microscopy of thin foils. The performed studies show that in the surface layer with a thickness of up to 60 µm, a structure of high-speed cellular crystallization is formed, regardless of the distance to the irradiation surface and its characteristic electron microscopic images are shown in Fig. 4.17 *a, b*. The cells have a rounded shape (Fig. 4.18 *a*). The cell size ranges from 150 nm to 400 nm. The cells are separated by interlayers (Fig. 4.18 *b*), the thickness of which varies from 15 nm to 50 nm. A dislocation substructure in the form of randomly distributed dislocations is revealed in the volume of the cells (Fig.

Fig. 4.18. TEM structure of the electroexplosive coating of the ZnO–Ag system. *a,*
b – surface layer, *c* – transition layer, *d* – thermal influence layer.

4.18 *b*). Scalar dislocation density is $\approx 2.1 \cdot 10^{10}$ cm^{-2}. The transition layer has a dendritic crystallization structure from the side of the electroexplosive deposition layer (Fig. 4.18 *c*, layer 1) and a plate type structure from the side of the thermal influence layer (Fig. 4.18 *c*, layer 2). The layer of thermal influence of the copper electrical contact has a grain–subgrain structure (Fig. 4.18 *d*). A dislocation substructure in the form of randomly distributed dislocations is observed in the volume of copper grains (Fig. 4.18 *d*). The scalar dislocation density is $\approx 1.3 \cdot 10^{10}$ cm^{-2}. It should be noted that the electron microscopic image of the structure of the thermal influence layer contains a large number of bending extinction contours [160] (Fig. 4.18 *d*), which indicates a high level of torsion curvature of the material due to internal stress fields [161].

The distribution of silver, zinc, and oxygen atoms in an electric explosion coating was studied by X-ray microanalysis of thin foils. The research results are shown in Figs. 4.19 and 4.20. Analyzing the results presented in Fig. 4.19, we can conclude that in the structure of high-speed cellular crystallization formed in the surface layer, the cell volume is formed mainly by silver atoms (Fig. 4.19 *b*), zinc atoms (Fig. 4.19 *c*) and oxygen (Fig. 4.19 *d*) are located mainly along the boundaries of the cells, forming extended interlayers.

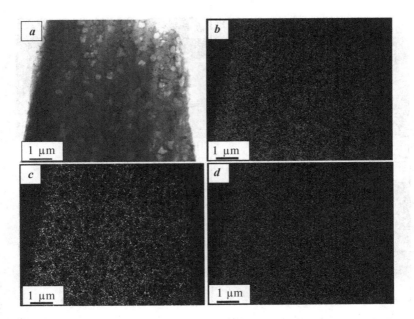

Fig. 4.19. Electron microscopic STEM-image of the structure of the electric explosion coating of the ZnO–Ag system. *a* - the analyzed area; *b–d* – images of the analyzed region obtained in the characteristic X-ray emissions of silver, zinc and oxygen atoms, respectively.

Table 4.1. The relative content of chemical elements in the surface layer of the electroexplosive coating of the ZnO–Ag system. Fit factor 0.1921

Element	E, keV	Mass. %	Amount	Error.%	At.%
Ag (L)	2.984	51.83	101179.97	0.01	63.89
Zn (K)	8.630	31.43	33371.70	0.01	22.82
O (K)	0.525	16.74	18340.04	0.26	13.29
Total	–	100.00	–	–	100.00

The relative content of atoms forming the surface layer of the sprayed electroexplosive coating is given in Table 4.1. Analyzing the results presented in Table 4.1, it can be noted that the main elements of the surface layer are silver, zinc and oxygen, which is to be expected.

In the structure of the transition layer (layer with dendroid crystallization), silver and zinc atoms are located mainly along the boundaries of dendrites (Fig. 4.20 *c, d*). In the volume of copper grains that form the heat-affected zone, silver and zinc atoms are detected in small quantities by X-ray spectral analysis methods.

Table 4.2. The relative content of chemical elements in the transition layer of copper, modified by the electric explosion method

Element	E, keV	Mass. %	Amount	Error.%	At.%
Cu (K)	8.040	86.84	179363	0.00	91.4
Ag (L)	2.984	8.6	9663.6	0.01	5.33
Zn (K)	3.443	4.28	4812.1	0.01	2.41
O (K)	0.525	0.28	595	0.61	0.86
Total	–	100	–	–	100

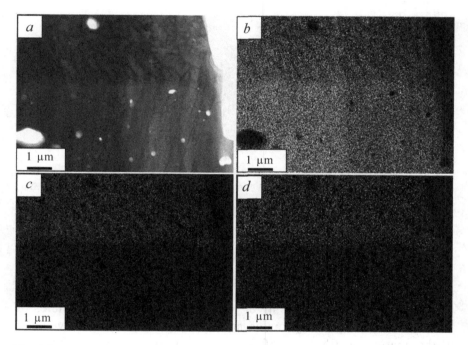

Fig. 4.20. Electron-microscopic STEM-image of the structure of the electric explosion coating of the ZnO–Ag system. a – the analyzed area; $b – d$ – images of the analyzed region obtained in the characteristic X-ray emissions of copper, silver and zinc atoms, respectively.

The relative content of atoms forming the transition layer of the electroexplosive coating of the ZnO–Ag system is shown in Table 4.2. Analyzing the results presented in Table 4.2, it can be noted that the concentration of silver and zinc atoms in the transition layer is significantly lower than in the surface layer, which is in good agreement with the results of X-ray spectral analysis obtained by scanning electron microscopy (Fig. 4.17).

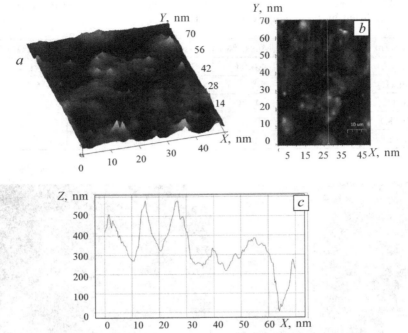

Fig. 4.21. The coating structure of the ZnO–Ag system, identified by atomic force microscopy. a – distribution of unevenness of the relief in height in 3D format; b – the position of the secant (top view); c – distribution of roughness along the base length.

By atomic force microscopy, individual ZnO particles of various shapes with a size of 10–15 nm were randomly located in a silver matrix (Fig. 4.21 a). Spherical Zn particles 2–5 nm in size were also found. The fractions of the silver matrix, large and small particles of ZnO in the coating are estimated at 60, 15, and 25%. The unevenness of the coating profile was 550.6 nm, and the troughs were 300.5 nm deep. At the coating/substrate interface on the coating side there are surface periodic structures with an average period of 3 nm (Fig. 4.22).

As a result of the combined treatment, including the EES of the ZnO–Ag system coating and its subsequent EBT, a coating is formed in which four layers are distinguished, which differ in the state of the structure. These are the following layers: the surface layer obtained by two-stage processing of EES + EBT (layer 1 in Fig. 4.23); the boundary between the surface layer of EES + EBT and the layer of EES not affected by EBT (indicated by a dashed line in Fig. 4.23);

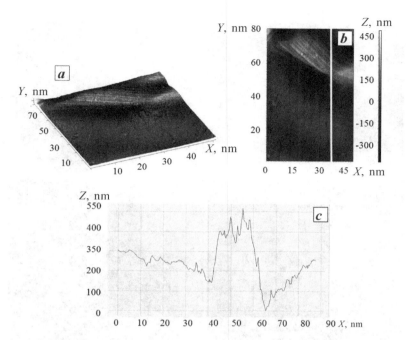

Figure 4.22. Structure at the boundary of the ZnO–Ag coating with a copper substrate, identified by atomic force microscopy. a – distribution of unevenness of the relief in height in 3D format; b – the position of the secant (top view); c – distribution of roughness along the base length.

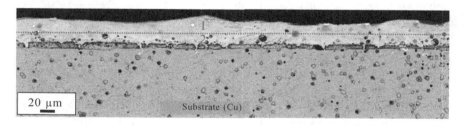

Fig. 4.23. Structure of the electroexplosive coating of the ZnO–Ag system after treatment with an electron beam. Direct thin section. SEM. 1 – surface layer obtained by two-stage processing of EES + EBT; 2 – a layer of electroexplosive coating, not affected by EBT; the dashed line indicates the boundary between layers 1 and 2; the arrow indicates the boundary of the electroexplosive coating with a copper substrate.

a layer of electroexplosive coating not affected by EBT (layer 2 in Fig. 4.23) and the boundary of the electroexplosive coating with a copper substrate (indicated by the arrow in Fig. 4.23).

Let us consider the structure of each of the layers of the electroexplosive coating of the ZnO–Ag system after EBT.

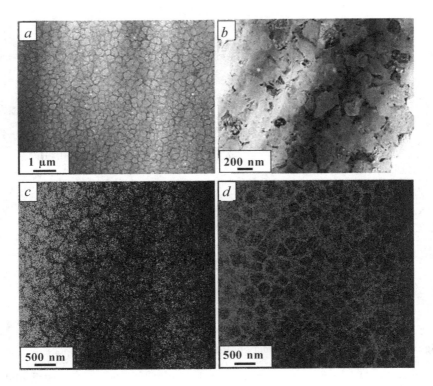

Fig. 4.24. Electron microscopic image of the structure of the electroexplosive coating system ZnO–Ag. *a, b* – bright-field images; *c, d* – images obtained in characteristic x-ray radiation of the silver and zinc atoms, respectively.

The surface layer obtained by two-stage processing of EES + EBT (layer 1 in Fig. 4.23). Studies performed by transmission electron diffraction microscopy of thin foils showed that the surface layer obtained by two-stage processing of the EES + EBT of the ZnO–Ag system at a distance of ≈15 μm from the surface has the structure of high-speed cellular crystallization (Fig. 4.24 *a*). The cells have a rounded shape. The cell size varies from 170 nm to 300 nm. The cells are separated by interlayers of the second phase (Fig. 4.24 *b*). The transverse dimensions of the interlayers vary from 35 nm to 73 nm. Using X-ray microspectral analysis, it was found that the volume of the cells is enriched with silver atoms (Fig. 4.24 *c*); the layers are enriched with zinc atoms (Fig. 4.24 *d*). The relative silver atom content of the foil portion shown in Fig. 4.24 is 55.1 at.%; zinc 30.6 at.%.

Figure 4.25 shows the results of a phase analysis of the structure of cellular crystallization of an electroexplosive coating. Analysis of the microelectron diffraction pattern (Fig. 4.25 c) obtained from the foil plot, the image of which is shown in (Figure 4.25, a), allowed to reveal reflections of silver, zinc, zinc compounds with oxygen. Reflexes of the detected phases are located on the microelectron diffraction pattern (Fig. 4.25 c) close to each other, which does not allow us to confidently identify the phase arrangement in dark-field images. It can only be noted, based on the results of X-ray microspectral analysis (Fig. 4.24), that the crystallization cells formed by the silver-based solid solution contain nanosized (≈20 nm) particles of the second phases. The cells are separated by extended interlayers, which also have a nanostructured structure and are formed by phases based on zinc and oxygen (Fig. 4.24, b).

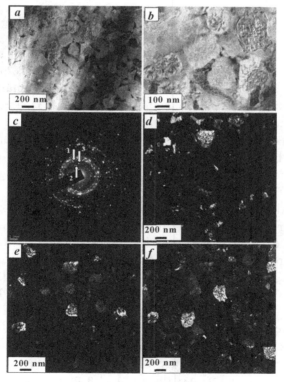

Fig. 4.25. Electron microscopic image of the structure of the cellular crystallization of the electroexplosive coating of the ZnO–Ag system. *a, b* – bright-field images; *c* – microelectron diffraction pattern; *d – f* – dark-field images obtained in the reflections of [111] Ag (*d*), [110] ZnO (*e*), [0 16 2] Ag$_5$Zn$_8$ (*f*); on (*c*) arrows indicate reflexes in which dark-field images 1 – (*d*); 2 – (*e*); 3 – (*f*) were obtained;.

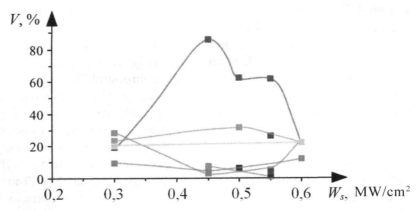

Fig. 4.26. Dependence of the volume fraction of phases (V) of the electroexplosive coating of the ZnO–Ag system on the electron beam power density (W_s). ∎ – Ag; ∎ – Cu; ∎ – CuZn; ∎ – ZnO; ∎ – Ag_5Zn_8; ∎ – Cu_2O; ∎ – Ag_2O; ∎ – $Cu_{0.67}Zn_{0.33}$; ∎ – AgZn.

The method of X-ray diffraction analysis was used to study the crystal lattice parameters and the values of coherent scattering regions (CSR) of phases formed in the surface layer obtained by two-stage processing EES + EBT (layer 1 in Fig. 4.23). Let us analyze the dependence of the volume fraction of the phases of the electric explosive coating of the ZnO–Ag system on the power density of the electron beam (Fig. 4.26). The phase composition of this layer consists of the following phases: Ag, ZnO, Cu, CuZn, Ag_5Zn_8, Cu_2O, Ag_2O, $Cu_{0.67}Zn_{0.33}$, AgZn.

The initial value of the volume fraction of Ag (Fig. 4.26, ∎ is the blue marker) is 19.16% and is the smallest at 0.3 MW/cm². With an increase in power density, the volume fraction increases to a maximum value of 85.97% at 0.45 MW/cm². After, the volume fraction of Ag decreases to a final value of 21.98% at 0.6 MW/cm².

The initial value of the crystalline parameter a is 0.40475 nm at 0.3 MW/cm² (Fig. 4.27 a) and decreases to its minimum 0.40461 nm at 0.45 MW/cm². At 0.55 MW/cm², the parameter a is 0.40549 nm. At 0.6 MW/cm², the maximum value of the parameter $a = 0.4058$ nm is observed. The dependence of the crystalline parameter a on W_s for the Ag phase (Fm3m) has the form of a power-law function. The CSR of the Ag phase (Fm3m) (Fig. 4.27 b) almost linearly increases with increasing W_s.

The volume fraction of the Cu phase (Fig. 4.26, ∎ - orange marker) is 28.31% at 0.3 MW/cm² and decreases to a minimum of

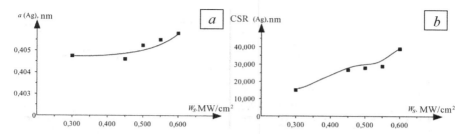

Fig. 4.27. Ag phase dependences (Fm3m) on the electron beam power density. *a* is the dependence of the parameter *a* of the crystal lattice; *b* – dependence of coherent scattering regions.

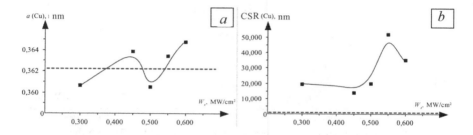

Fig. 4.28. Dependences of the parameters of the phase Cu (Fm3m) on the electron beam power density. *a* is the dependence of the parameter *a* of the crystal lattice; *b* – dependence of coherent scattering regions.

2.93% at 0.45 MW/cm². At a power density of 0.5 MW/cm², the Cu phase is not observed. When the power density changes from 0.55 MW/cm² to 0.6 MW/cm², the volume fraction varies from 21.98% to the final value of 5.02%.

In this case, the parameter *a* of the crystal lattice of copper (Fig. 4.28 *a*) at a power density of 0.3 MW/cm² is 0.360 nm. With an increase in power density to 0.45 MW/cm², the value of parameter *a* increases to 0.36387 nm, after which at 0.5 MW/cm² parameter *a* reaches its minimum, equal to 0.36053 nm. With a subsequent increase in power density, parameter *a* increases to its maximum, which is the final value and is equal to 0.36478. The CSR of copper (Fig. 4.28 *b*) at 0.3 MW/cm² is 19.57 nm, then with an increase in the power density, the CSR decreases to its minimum, 13.95 nm. With an increase in power density to 0.55 MW/cm², the CSR increases to its maximum, equal to 51.95 nm. At 0.6 MW/cm², the CSR decreases to 35.18 nm.

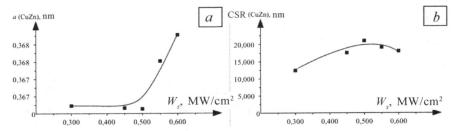

Fig. 4.29. Dependences of the phase parameters CuZn on the electron beam power density. *a* is the dependence of the parameter *a* of the crystal lattice; *b* is the dependence of coherent scattering regions.

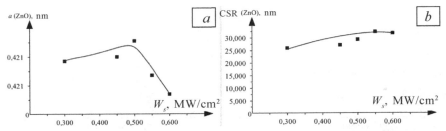

Fig. 4.30. Dependences of the parameters of the ZnO phase (Fm3m) on the electron beam power density. *a* is the dependence of the parameter *a* of the crystal lattice; *b* is the dependence of coherent scattering regions.

The volume fraction of the CuZn phase at 0.3 MW/cm^2 is 23.32% (Fig. 4.26). At 0.45 and 0.55 MW/cm^2, the CuZn phase is not observed. The largest value of this phase is 31.42% at 0.5 MW/cm^2 and decreases to the final value of 5.02% at 0.6 MW/cm^2.

The parameter a of the crystal lattice of the CuZn phase (Fig. 4.29 *a*) with the W_s changing from 0.3 to 0.5 MW/cm^2 remains constant and amounts to 0.36613 nm. After increasing W_s to 0.55 and 0.6 MW/cm^2, the parameter *a* of the crystal lattice of the CuZn phase sharply increases to a maximum value of 0.36828 nm. The minimum CSR value of the CuZn phase (Fig. 4.29 *b*) is 15.08 nm observed at 0.3 MW/cm^2. The maximum CSR value of 38.97 nm is observed at 0.6 MW/cm^2.

For the ZnO phase (Fm3m), the initial and minimum volume fractions are 19.99% at 0.3 MW/cm^2 (Fig. 4.26), and the final and largest are 21.93% at 0.6 MW/cm^2. The impact of the EB does not lead to a significant change in the volume fraction of the ZnO phase.

The lattice parameter *a* of the ZnO phase (Fm3m) (Fig. 4.30 *a*) increases from 0.42097 nm when W_s varies from 0.3 to 0.5 MW/cm^2. With a further increase in W_s, the parameter *a* of the crystal

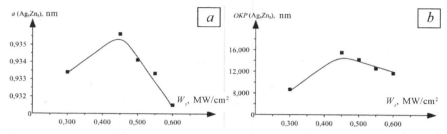

Fig. 4.31. Dependences of the parameters of the Ag_5Zn_8 phase on the power density of the electron beam. *a* is the dependence of the parameter *a* of the crystal lattice; *b* is the dependence of coherent scattering regions.

lattice of the ZnO phase (Fm3m) drops sharply to a minimum value of 0.42074 nm. The minimum value of the CSR of the ZnO phase (Fm3m) (Fig. 4.30 *b*) is observed at 0.3 MW/cm² and equals 25.98 nm, and the maximum is 31.82 nm at 0.6 MW/cm². The dependence of the change in CSR on W_s is approximated by a linear function.

For the Ag_5Zn_8 phase, the initial value of the volume fraction is 9.22% at 0.3 MW/cm² (Fig. 4.26). With an increase in power density, the volume fraction drops to its minimum 3.82% at 0.45 MW/cm². At 0.6 MW/cm², the volume fraction of the Ag_5Zn_8 phase is maximum and amounts to 12.13%.

The initial value of the parameter *a* of the crystal lattice of the Ag_5Zn_8 phase at 0.3 MW/cm² is 0.9334 nm (Fig. 4.31 *a*). Subsequent growth of the parameter reaches its maximum of 0.93561 nm at 0.45 MW/cm². It decreases after an increase in the parameter *a* of the crystal lattice of the Ag_5Zn_8 phase. The crystal lattice parameter of the Ag_5Zn_8 phase reaches its minimum of 0.9315 nm at 0.6 MW/cm². The initial value of the CSR of the Ag_5Zn_8 phase (Fig. 4.31 *b*) is also a minimum of 8.67 nm at 0.3 MW/cm². A gradual increase in this parameter reaches its maximum value of 15.51 nm at 0.45 MW/cm². The final CSR value of the Ag_5Zn_8 phase is 11.73 nm at 0.6 MW/cm².

The initial and minimum volume fraction of the Cu_2O phase (Fm3m) is 7.28% (Fig. 4.26) at 0.45 MW/cm², and the final and smallest is 1.07% at 0.55 MW/cm².

The maximum value of the parameter *a* of the crystal lattice of the Cu_2O phase (Fm3m) is 0.42694 nm and is observed at 0.45 MW/cm² (Fig. 4.32 *a*). The minimum value of 0.42353 nm is observed at 0.55 MW/cm². The maximum CSR value of the Cu_2O phase is observed at 0.45 MW/cm² is 21.52 nm, and the minimum 18.92 nm at 0.55 MW/cm² (Fig. 4.32 *b*).

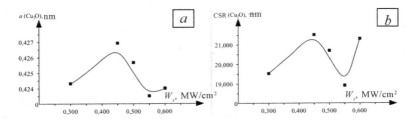

Fig. 4.32. Dependences of the parameters of the phase Cu_2O (Fm3m) on the electron beam power density. *a* is the dependence of the parameter *a* of the crystal lattice; *b* is the dependence of coherent scattering regions.

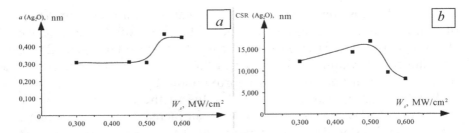

Fig. 4.33. Dependences of the parameters of the Ag_2O (Pm3) phase on the electron beam power density. *a* is the dependence of the parameter *a* of the crystal lattice; *b* is the dependence of coherent scattering regions.

The initial and maximum value of the Ag_2O phase (Fig. 4.33) is 6.05% at 0.5 MW/cm^2, and the final and largest is 2.01% at 0.55 MW/cm^2.

The lattice parameter *a* of the Ag_2O (Pm3) phase (Fig. 4.33 *a*) remains constant at a change in W_s from 0.3 to 0.5 MW/cm^2 and amounts to 0.30626 nm. After an increase in W_s to 0.55 and 0.6 MW/cm^2, a sharp increase in the parameter *a* of the crystal lattice of the Ag_2O (Pm3) phase occurs to a maximum value of 0.47017 nm. The maximum value of the CSR of the Ag_2O (Pm3) phase (Fig. 4.33 *b*) is observed at 0.5 MW/cm^2 and equals 16.78 nm, and the minimum 9.62 nm at 0.6 MW/cm^2.

The maximum volume fraction of Cu0.67Zn0.33 is 26.34% (Fig. 4.34) at 0.55 MW/cm^2, while the crystal lattice parameter *a* is 0.36695 nm, and the CSR is 20.42 nm. A similar situation is observed with the AgZn phase. Its volume fraction is 3.92% at 0.55 MW/cm^2. The crystal lattice parameter *a* is 0.31672 nm, and the CSR is 15.96 nm.

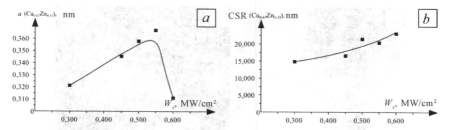

Fig. 4.34. Dependences of the parameters of the phase $Cu_{0.67}Zn_{0.33}$ on the electron beam power density. *a* is the dependence of the parameter *a* of the crystal lattice; *b* is the dependence of coherent scattering regions.

Such changes in the crystal lattice and CSR parameters (Figs. 4.28–4.34) of the detected phases are associated with a change in the dominant thermodynamic processes, active phase transformations, possible fragmentation of individual phases, the formation of new internal boundaries in them as a result of the growth of thermal stresses that occur during the processing of an electric explosive coating by an electron beam . As a result of the action of EBT, layers 1 and 2 in Fig. 4.23, as well as their boundary, begin to behave 'asynchronously'; most likely, the temperature lag of the processes of structural rearrangements is manifested here. The increase in the CSR parameter of individual phases is associated with the 'healing' of small-angle boundaries due to the facilitation of intergranular slippage and the emergence of dislocations on the surface. The formation of liquid-phase layers and a decrease in their viscosity, as well as a decrease in mechanical stresses in the solid-phase framework, contribute to these processes. The size of the CSR in the formed coating substantially depends on structural transformations under thermal effects caused by EBT. Changes in CSR sizes and the parameters listed correlate. The CSR sizes turn out to be a very sensitive signal for monitoring changes occurring in the coating structure [159–161]. These results are in logical connection with the technological parameters of EBT. These issues require special research.

The boundary between the surface layer of EES + EBT and the layer of EES not affected by EBT (indicated by a dashed line in Fig. 4.23). The region of the material located at the interface between the surface layer of EES + EBT and the EES layer not affected by EBT has a lamellar structure formed by silver plates separated by zinc interlayers. This is evidenced by the results of X-ray microspectral

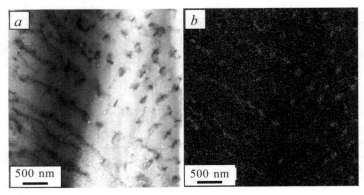

Fig. 4.35. Electron microscopic image of the structure at the interface between the surface layer of EES + EBT and the layer of EES not affected by EBT. *a* – bright field image; *b* – image obtained in the characteristic X-ray radiation of silver atoms.

analysis, presented in Fig. 4.35. The silver concentration of this portion of the foil is 90.5 wt. % (92.9 at.%), zinc 5.4 wt.% (3.3 at.%).

The results obtained by X-ray spectral analysis were confirmed by microdiffraction electron microscopic examination of the structure of the foils. The results presented in Fig. 4.36 show that ZnO particles are located both at the interfaces of silver plates and in the volume of silver plates. In the first case, the particles have sizes (60–80) nm; in the second (10–20) nm.

The layer of electroexplosive coating not affected by EBT (layer 2 in Fig. 4.23). By means of transmission electron microscopy, it was found that the ZnO–Ag electroexplosive coating not affected by EBT obtained at the copper electrical contact has the structure of high-speed cellular crystallization (Fig. 4.37 *a*). The cells have a rounded shape. The cell sizes vary from 250 nm to 380 nm.

Using X-ray microanalysis of thin foils, the relative content of zinc atoms in the volume of a layer with a cellular substructure is 22.8 at.%; oxygen atoms 10.2 at.% The cell volume is enriched with silver atoms, zinc atoms are arranged in the form of interlayers separating crystallization cells, oxygen atoms are distributed almost uniformly in the volume of the studied layer (Fig. 4.38).

A characteristic image of the structure of cellular crystallization of an electric explosion layer not affected by EBT, revealed by bright-field and dark-field methods, is shown in Fig. 4.39.

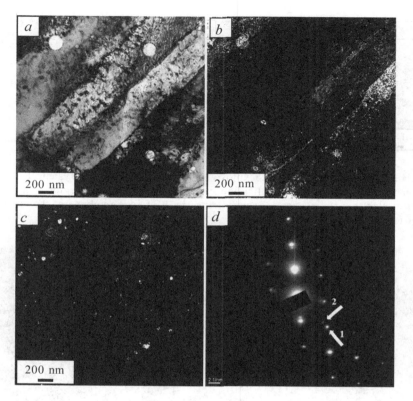

Fig. 4.36. Electron-microscopic image of the structure at the interface between the surface layer of EES + EBT and the layer of EES not affected by EBT. *a* – bright field image; *b, c* – dark-field images obtained in reflexes of [022] Ag (reflex No. 1 on the microelectron diffraction pattern) and [220] ZnO (reflex No. 2 on the microelectron diffraction pattern); *d* – microelectron diffraction pattern for (*a*).

The analysis of the microelectron diffraction pattern (Fig. 4.39 *b*) obtained from the foil plot shown in Fig. 4.39 *a*, allows us to conclude that the cells are formed by a silver-based solid solution (Fig. 4.39 *c*); interlayers of the second phase separating silver cells are formed by the ZnO phase. The dark-field images shown in Fig. 4.39 *c, d* indicate that ZnO phase particles are present in the cell volume. Particles have a rounded shape, particle sizes vary from 5 nm to 10 nm.

The boundary of the electroexplosive coating with a copper substrate (indicated by the arrow in Fig. 4.23). In the zone of contact of the electroexplosive coating with the volume of the copper electrical contact, the structure of cellular crystallization transforms

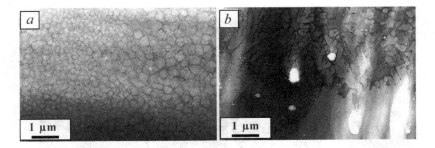

Fig. 4.37. Structure of the electroexplosive coating of the ZnO–Ag system. Images obtained by STEM. *a* – crystallization cells; *b* – the transition region from the layer of electroexplosive coating, not affected by EBT in the volume of the copper electrical contact.

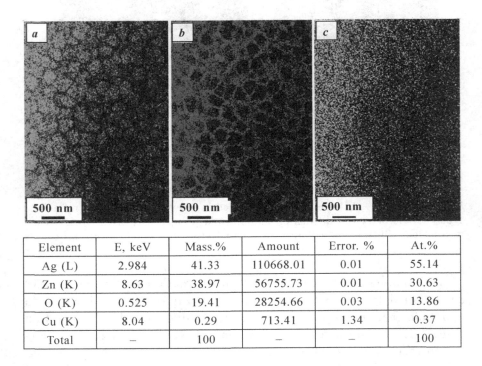

Element	E, keV	Mass.%	Amount	Error. %	At.%
Ag (L)	2.984	41.33	110668.01	0.01	55.14
Zn (K)	8.63	38.97	56755.73	0.01	30.63
O (K)	0.525	19.41	28254.66	0.03	13.86
Cu (K)	8.04	0.29	713.41	1.34	0.37
Total	–	100	–	–	100

Fig. 4.38. Images of the structure of the electric explosion coating of the ZnO–Ag system. The table shows the elemental composition of this portion of the sample. *a* – *c* – images obtained in the characteristic X-ray emissions of silver, zinc and oxygen atoms, respectively

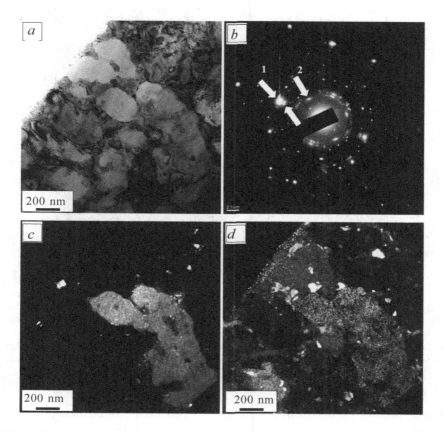

Fig. 4.39. Electron microscopic image of the structure of ZnO–Ag electroexplosive coating layer not affected by EBT. a – bright field image; b – microelectron diffraction pattern; c, d – dark-field images obtained in reflexes of [022] Ag (reflex №1 on the microelectron diffraction pattern) and [111] ZnO (reflex No. 2 on the microelectron diffraction pattern).

into a dendritic structure (Fig. 4.39 b). The relative content of zinc atoms averages 5.3 at.%; oxygen atoms 2.9 at.%

An electron microscopic image of the structure of the material located on the boundary of the electric explosion coating with the copper substrate is shown in Fig. 4.40.

Analyzing the results presented in Fig. 4.40 a, it can be noted that two morphologically distinguishable types of particles of the second phase are present in the grains of a solid solution based on copper. Firstly, lamellar (globular) particles that form lines. The sizes of such particles are (80 × 100) nm. Secondly, round-shaped particles located randomly in the volume of copper grain (Fig. 4.40, d).

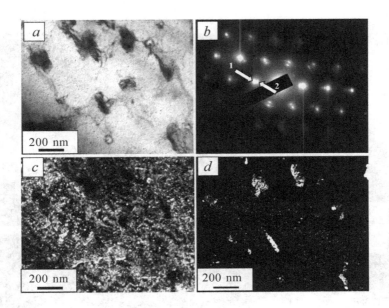

Fig, 4.40. Electron-microscopic image of the structure of the material located on the border of the electroexplosive coating with a copper substrate. *a* – bright field image; *b* – microelectron diffraction pattern; *c, d* – dark-field images obtained in the reflections of [111] Cu (*c*) and [111] Ag (*d*); on (*c*) the arrows indicate reflexes in which dark-field images 1 – (*c*) were obtained; 2 – (*d*).

Particle sizes vary within (5–10) nm. It can be assumed that lamellar (globular) particles are Ag_5Zn_8, and round particles are silver.

Investigations of electroexplosive coatings of the ZnO–Ag system after EBT are confirmed by the results of X-ray diffraction analysis (Fig. 4.41).

4.3. Properties of electroerosion-resistant coatings of CuO–Ag and ZnO–Ag systems

Tests for wear resistance showed that the EES of the copper coating of the CuO–Ag system is accompanied by an increase in the wear resistance of the modified layer by ≈3.3 times; the friction coefficient increases by ≈1.4 times. The mechanical properties of the modified copper layer were characterized by nanohardness and Young's modulus. They were determined on transverse sections, indenting along a straight line parallel to the surface of the modification at a distance of ≈15 μm from the surface of the treatment. The test

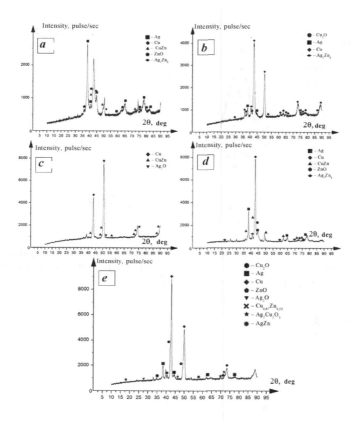

Fig. 4.41. Areas of X-ray diffraction patterns of the electrical contact after electroexplosive spraying of the ZnO–Ag system coating and electron-beam processing in various modes. *a–e* – the conditions EBT in the modes 1–5 respectively.

results presented in Fig. 4.42 show that the nanohardness of the coating layer varies from 280 MPa to 2290 MPa with an average hardness of 866.5 MPa (Fig. 4.42, curve 1), which is more than 2 times the microhardness of annealed copper [162]. Young's modulus varies from 24.3 GPa to 71.7 GPa with an average modulus of 49.6 GPa (Fig. 4.42, curve 2). Note that the Young's modulus of annealed copper varies in the range (110–130) GPa [162].

Let us analyze the dependence of the contact resistance (R) on the number of on/off cycles (N) when testing the coatings of the CuO–Ag system for electrical erosion resistance under conditions of arc erosion (Fig. 4.43). At the beginning of the experiment, the value of R contacts is 11, 7.5, and 9.5 μOhm for phases L_1, L_2, and L_3, respectively. After the first on/off cycles are completed, R

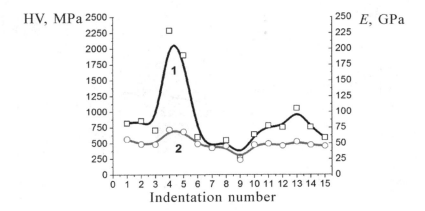

Fig. 4.42. Dependence of nanohardness (curve 1) and Young's modulus (curve 2) of the electric explosive coating of the CuO–Ag system on the indenter position on a line located at a depth of ≈15 µm from the surface.

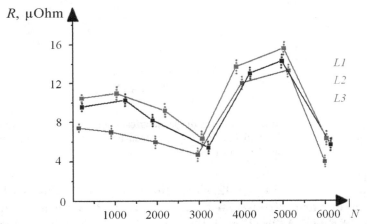

Fig. 4.43. The characteristic dependence of contact resistance (R) on the number of on/off cycles (N) when testing electric explosive coatings of the CuO–Ag system for electrical discharge resistance under conditions of arc erosion.

begins to decrease from the initial values in a linear relationship to the following values: for phase L_1 the value of R is 6.3 µOhm at $N = 3059$; for phase L_2 the value of R is 4.7 µOhm at $N = 2956$ and is the smallest among all phases; for phase L_3 the value of R is 5.4 µOhm at $N = 3211$. A gradual decrease in R with a change in N from 0 to 3211 indicates that the contacts are gradually burned in at this test site, as a result of which a stable surface roughness is created. In the next section of the curve, with an increase in N, R increases

Fig. 4.44. Test results of electric explosion coatings of the system CuO–Ag after electron beam treatment for electroerosoion stability in conditions of arc erosion. Surface images, obtained by scanning electron microscopy. *a* – characteristic dependence of contact resistance (*R*) on the number of on/off cycles (*N*); *b* – a characteristic image of the surface after *N* = 100; *c* – a characteristic image of the surface after *N* = 1500; *d* is a characteristic image of the surface after N = 2500; *e* – a characteristic image of the surface after N = 3000

to the maximum values: for phase L_1 the value of R = 15.6 µOhm at N = 5015; for phase L_2 the value of R = 13.3 µOhm at N = 5123 and is the smallest; for phase L_3 the value R = 14.3 µOhm at N = 4967. This indicates that at the present stage of the experiment, intense evaporation of the low-melting silver matrix begins under the influence of an electric arc. The contact surface is enriched with particles of CuO powder, which has a lower electrical conductivity (10⁻⁸ S/m) compared to silver (62.5 MS/m) [156]. For this reason, the contact resistance in this section of the graph increases. When the maximum values of R are reached in all three phases with a further increase in N, the electrical resistance decreases again. This is due to the fact that at $N \approx 5000$, due to the evaporation of silver, the contact surface is enriched to the maximum with refractory CuO particles with low electrical conductivity. Upon reaching $N \approx 5000$, the mechanical accumulation of CuO particles on the contact surface occurs. As a result of this, the electrical resistance decreases again, namely, for phases L_1 and L_2, the values of R are 6.2 µOhm at $N =$ 6023 and 4 µOhm at $N = 5983$, respectively. For L_3, the value of $R = 5.7$ µOhm at $N = 6122$. The tests performed showed that the formed coatings of the CuO–Ag system satisfy the starter testing for switching wear resistance [139].

Thus, the increase in electrical resistance during tests of the electric explosion coatings of the CuO–Ag system for switching wear resistance is caused by the evaporation of the low-melting silver matrix under the influence of an electric arc and the enrichment of the coating surface with CuO particles. The electrical contacts hardened by electric explosion coatings of the CuO–Ag system are capable of mechanically cleaning the surface of CuO particles. The formed coatings of the CuO–Ag system satisfy the starter testing for switching wear resistance. Tests for electrical discharge resistance (Fig. 4.44) of coatings of the CuO–Ag system after EBT showed that the destruction of the coating occurs after 3000 cycles of on/off. This is 2 times less in comparison with the electric explosive coatings of the CuO–Ag system obtained in [140]. However, for low-current electrical contacts, these values are acceptable [139]. Electrical resistance (Fig. 4.44 a) during accelerated tests for electrical discharge resistance is in the range from 5.8 to 14.8 µOhm, which is also acceptable for low-current electrical contacts.

In the process of testing the coatings, the influence of high temperatures leads to the melting of their surface and the formation of a relief on it with a rough morphology (Fig. 4.44 b–d). With increasing N, the number and size of craters resulting from the action of an electric arc on the coating surface increases. Moreover, silver, having a lower melting point, evaporates and copper oxides with a high melting point remain the main ones in the coating. The refractory component (copper oxides) forms a continuous matrix with silver particles measuring about a few micrometers. In local areas, degradation of the coating is observed up to the material of the copper substrate (Fig. 4.44 e). Probably, the refractory component plays the role of reducing the evaporation of low-melting silver during the test process.

The results of the tests showed that the hardness of the electroexplosive coating of the ZnO–Ag system varies from 750 MPa to 2250 MPa with an average hardness of 1600 MPa, which is 3.8 times higher than the microhardness of annealed copper [162].

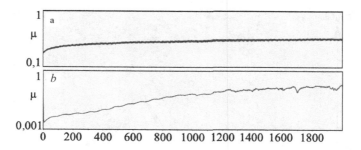

Fig. 4.45. Dependences of the coefficient of friction of the electroexplosive coating of the ZnO–Ag system on the time of tribological tests. *a* – sample without coating; *b* – coated sample.

The Young's modulus of electroexplosive coating varies from 56.1 GPa to 89.0 GPa with an average modulus of 75.1 GPa. Note that the Young's modulus of annealed copper varies in the range of (110–130) GPa; the Young's modulus of silver is 80 GPa [162].

The EES of the copper coating of the ZnO–Ag system is accompanied by a slight ($\approx$1.1 times) increase in the wear resistance of the modified layer; the friction coefficient increases by $\approx$1.3 times. Noteworthy is the change in the friction coefficient in the process of tribological testing (Fig. 4.45). Namely, at the initial stage of testing, the friction coefficient of the modified surface (Fig. 4.45 *b*) is significantly lower than the friction coefficient of the initial copper (Fig. 4.45 *a*). The latter may indicate that the hardened layer is thin and quickly loses its wear-resistant properties.

Let us analyze the dependence of contact resistance (R) on the number of on/off cycles (N) when testing the coatings of the ZnO-Ag system for electrical discharge resistance under conditions of arc erosion (Fig. 4.46). The initial resistance values for phases L_1, L_2, L_3 are 5.6, 3.2, 4.5 µOhm with the number of on/off cycles of 134, 152, 213, respectively. Subsequently, the resistance function increases. For phase L_1, the resistance increases from 5.6 µOhm to 9.2 µΩ with the number of on/off cycles from 134 to 2178. For phase L_2, the resistance increases from 3.2 µOhm to 6 µOhm with the number of on/off cycles from 152 to 2134. For phase L_3, the resistance increases from 4.5 µOhm to 8.2 µOhm with the number of on/off cycles from 213 to 1883. After that, the resistance decreases. For phase L_1, the resistance decreases to 6.3 µOhm with the number of cycles 3002 times. For phase L_2, the resistance decreases to 5.4 µOhm with the

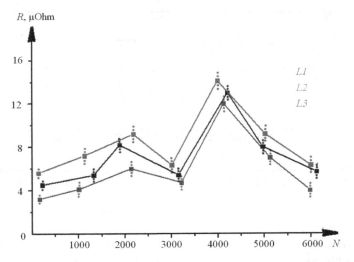

Fig. 4.46. The characteristic dependence of contact resistance (R) on the number of on/off cycles (N) when testing electric explosive coatings of the ZnO–Ag system for electrical discharge resistance under conditions of arc erosion.

number of cycles 3145 times. For phase L_3, the resistance decreases to 4.7 $\mu\Omega$ with the number of cycles 3211 times. Then the resistance index rises again and reaches its maximum value. For phase L_1, the resistance increases to 14.1 μOhm with the number of cycles 3990 times. For phase L_2, the resistance increases to 12 $\mu\Omega$ with the number of cycles 4123 times. For phase L_3, the resistance increases to 13 μOhm with the number of cycles 4207 times. This indicates that at the present stage of the experiment, intensive evaporation of the fusible silver matrix begins under the influence of an electric arc. The contact surface is enriched with particles of ZnO powder, which has a lower electrical conductivity (10^{-8} S/m) compared to silver (62.5 MS/m) [156]. For this reason, the contact resistance in this section of the graph increases. At the end of the test, the resistance decreases again. For phase L_1, the resistance decreases to 6.3 μOhm with the number of cycles 5997 times. For phase L_2, the resistance decreases to 4 μOhm with the number of cycles 5983 times. For phase L_3, the resistance decreases to 5.7 μOhm with the number of cycles 6123 times. At the end of the test, the resistance values for phases L_1, L_2, L_3 are 6.3, 4, 5.7 with the number of on/off cycles 5997, 5983, 6123, respectively. The tests showed that the formed coatings of the ZnO–Ag system satisfy the testing of starters for switching wear resistance [139].

The contacts of the CJ20 grade must ensure not only long-term operation without unacceptable overheating under normal conditions, but also the required thermal and electrodynamic resistance in the short circuit mode. Movable breakable contacts should also not be destroyed by the high temperature of the electric arc, which is formed when they open, and reliably close without welding and fusion when turned on for a short circuit. The operation of these electrical contacts consists of 4 stages – open state, short circuit, closed state and open, each of which affects the reliability of contacting. In the open state, the external medium acts on the electrical contact and, as a result, films form on their surface. In the closed state, when the contacts are pressed against each other and current flows through them, they heat up and deform; under some conditions, if the contacts overheat, welding may occur. When the contacts are closed and opened, bridging or discharge phenomena occur, accompanied by evaporation and transfer of the contact metal, which changes its surface. In addition, mechanical wear of the contacts as a result of impacts and sliding against each other is possible.

Thus, the increase in electrical resistance during testing of ZnO-Ag system electroexplosive coatings for switching wear resistance is caused by evaporation of a low-melting silver matrix under the influence of an electric arc and enrichment of the coating surface with ZnO particles. Electrical contacts hardened by ZnO–Ag electroexplosive coatings are capable of mechanically cleaning the surface of ZnO particles. The formed coatings of the ZnO–Ag system satisfy the starter testing for switching wear resistance.

Tests for electroerosive resistance (Fig. 4.47) of ZnO–Ag system coatings after EBT showed that the destruction of the EBT coating layer occurs after 3000 on/off cycles. This is 2 times less in comparison with the electric explosive coatings of the CuO–Ag system obtained in [140]. However, for low-current electrical contacts, these values are acceptable [139]. Electrical resistance (Fig. 4.47) during accelerated electroerosion tests is in the range from 6.2 to 14.7 µOhm, which is also acceptable for low-current electrical contacts. Contacts of any type should ensure not only long-term operation without unacceptable overheating under normal conditions, but also the required thermal and electrodynamic resistance in the short circuit mode. Movable breakable contacts should also not be destroyed by the high temperature of the electric arc, which is formed when they open, and reliably close without welding and fusion when turned on for a short circuit. The operation of these electrical

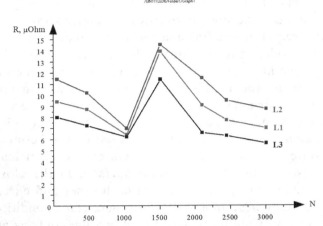

Fig. 4.47. Test results of electric explosion coatings of ZnO – Ag system after electron beam machining for electroerosion resistance in the conditions of arc erosion.

contacts consists of 4 stages – open state, short circuit, closed state and open, each of which affects the reliability of contacting. In the open state, the external medium acts on the electrical contact and, as a result, films form on their surface. In the closed state, when the contacts are pressed against each other and current flows through them, they heat up and deform; under some conditions, if the contacts overheat, welding may occur. When the contacts are closed and opened, bridging or discharge phenomena occur, accompanied by evaporation and transfer of the contact metal, which changes its surface. In addition, mechanical wear of the contacts as a result of impacts and sliding against each other is possible. All of the above requirements are met when testing the obtained coatings of the ZnO–Ag system (Fig. 4.47).

The test results presented in Fig. 4.48 (curve 1) show that the nanohardness of the coating layer varies from 750 to 2250 MPa with an average hardness of 1600 MPa, which is more than 3.8 times the microhardness of annealed copper [162]. Young's modulus varies from 56.1 to 89.0 GPa with an average modulus of 75.1 GPa (Fig. 4.48, curve 2). Note that the Young's modulus of annealed copper varies in the range of (110–130) GPa, while the silver Young's modulus is 80 GPa [162].

After combined treatment, a slight ($\approx$1.1 times) increase in the wear resistance of the modified layer occurs, and the friction coefficient increases by $\approx$1.3 times.

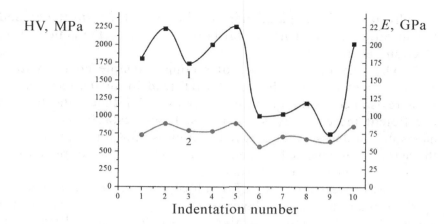

Fig. 4.48. Dependence of nanohardness (curve 1) and Young's modulus (curve 2) of the modified layer on the position of the indenter on the line located at a depth of ≈15 μm from the surface of the coating of the ZnO–Ag system.

4.4. Conclusions

1. The EES of the surface of a copper sample coated with a CuO–Ag system and subsequent EBT lead to an increase in the wear resistance of the modified layer by ≈ 3.3 times; the friction coefficient increases by ≈1.4 times. It was found that the microhardness of the formed coating is more than 2 times greater than the microhardness of annealed copper.

2. Combined processing is accompanied by the formation of a multilayer structure up to 40 microns thick. It was found that in the surface layer with a thickness of ≈30 μm, a high-speed cellular crystallization structure is formed, regardless of the distance to the surface of the modification. The cell size varies from 150 nm to 300 nm. The cells are separated by interlayers of the second phase, the thickness of which varies from 10 nm to 70 nm. Using X-ray microspectral analysis, it was found that the volume of the cells is formed by copper atoms, silver atoms are located mainly in the interlayers along the cell boundaries.

3. The impact of the electron beam leads to the decomposition of copper monoxide CuO, which leads to the formation of oxides Cu_2O, $Cu_{64}O$. Copper oxides with sizes from 0.1 to 0.2 microns are located in the silver matrix of the electroexplosive coating. Changes in the parameters of the crystal lattice and coherent scattering regions of the phases formed in the coating depend on changes in

the physicochemical parameters of the crystalline substance and the specific energy of its crystal lattice caused by the action of an electron beam.

3. The EES of the surface of a copper sample coated with a ZnO–Ag system and subsequent EBT lead to an increase in the wear resistance of the modified layer by ≈ 1.1 times; the friction coefficient increases by ≈ 1.3 times. It was established that the nanosolid hardness of the sprayed coating is ≈3.8 times greater than the hardness of annealed copper. The Young's modulus of the coating is 75.1 MPa, and the nanohardness is 1600 MPa.

4. It was revealed that the EES of a copper sample is accompanied by the formation of a multilayer structure up to 60 μm thick. In the surface layer, a structure of high-speed cellular crystallization is formed, regardless of the distance to the surface of the modification. Cell size ranges from 150 nm to 400 nm. The cells are separated by interlayers of the second phase, the thickness of which varies from 15 nm to 50 nm. It is shown that the transition layer has a dendritic crystallization structure on the surface layer side and a plate type structure on the side of the thermal influence layer. Using X-ray microspectral analysis, it was found that the volume of the cells of the surface layer structure is enriched with silver atoms, zinc and oxygen atoms are located mainly in the interlayers along the cell boundaries.

5. The combined treatment, including electroexplosive deposition of the coating of the ZnO–Ag system and its subsequent electron-beam treatment, leads to the formation of a multilayer coating consisting of four layers. These are the following layers: 1) a surface layer obtained by two-stage processing of EES + EBT; 2) the boundary between the surface layer of EES + EBT and the layer of EES not affected by EBT; 3) a layer of electroexplosive coating not affected by EBT; 4) the boundary of the electroexplosive coating with a copper substrate.

6. High-speed crystallization of the surface layer obtained by two-stage processing of EES + EBT is accompanied by the formation of a submicron net structure. The cell volume is formed by a silver-based solid solution. The ZnO phase is detected in the form of thin (35–73 nm) layers separating silver cells, as well as in the form of nanoscale (5–10 nm) particles located in the volume of silver cells. This layer has a high-speed cellular crystallization structure with a mesh size of (250–380) nm. The cell volume is enriched with silver atoms, zinc atoms are located mainly in the interlayers separating crystallization

cells, oxygen atoms are distributed almost uniformly in the volume of the studied layer. Reflections of silver and ZnO and Ag_5Zn_8 compounds were revealed. It was established that crystallization cells formed by a silver-based solid solution contain nanosized ($\approx$20 nm) particles of the second phases. The cells are separated by extended interlayers, which also have a nanostructured structure and are formed by phases based on silver and zinc. By X-ray diffraction analysis it was revealed that the phase composition of this layer is formed by the phases Ag, ZnO, Cu, CuZn, Ag_5Zn_8, Cu_2O, Ag_2O, $Cu_{0.67}Zn_{0.33}$, AgZn. The percentage of phases varies depending on the processing regime of the electron beam.

7. In the region of the interface between the surface layer of EES + EBT and the EES layer not affected by EBT, a plate-like structure is formed, particles of zinc monoxide in which are located mainly along the boundaries of silver plates.

8. The layer of electroexplosive coating, not affected by EBT, is formed by layers of zinc monoxide separating silver cells, which were formed as a result of high-speed crystallization of the melt by eutectic reaction; zinc monoxide particles located in the volume of silver cells formed as a result of decomposition of a solid solution of zinc monoxide in silver upon cooling of the material from the eutectic transformation temperature to room temperature.

7. The boundary of the electroexplosive coating with a copper substrate is formed by grains of a solid solution based on copper. Silver particles and Ag_5Zn_8 compounds were detected in the volume of grains.

8. Typical sizes of the first and second hierarchical levels of the structure were established, which under the used spraying conditions ranged from 2 to 5 nm and from 10 to 15 nm, respectively. A mechanism is proposed for the formation of hierarchical levels of the structure of electric explosive coatings of the CuO–Ag and ZnO–Ag systems. At the coating/substrate interface, surface periodic structures with a wavelength of 3 nm on average were detected. They represent the residual surface nanorelief that arose after the end of the action of a pulsed plasma jet of electrical explosion products of conductors on the substrate and cooling of the surface.

9. The formed electroexplosive coatings of the CuO–Ag and ZnO-Ag systems after EBT satisfy the requirements for testing starters for switching wear resistance of high-current and low-current electrical contacts. The use of such coatings can double the life of copper electrical contacts.

5

Structure and properties of electroexplosive wear and electroerosion resistant coatings

5.1. Surface roughness of the surface of pseudoalloys of coatings of the Mo–Cu system

This chapter presents the results of studies of the structure and properties of electroexplosive coatings of Mo–C–Cu, W–C–Cu, Mo–Cu, W–Cu, Ti–B–Cu, TiB_2–Cu, and TiB_2–Al systems. The results presented in this chapter are published in scientific articles [163–180], are protected by patents for inventions [181–195], and are summarized in monographs [196, 197].

The following dislocation substructures are formed in the electroexplosive coatings of Mo–C–Cu, WC–Cu, Mo–Cu, W–Cu, Ti–B–Cu, TiB_2–Cu, and TiB_2–Al systems (Table 5.1): cellular, strip, fragmented, subgrain, dislocation chaos or mesh. The predominant type of dislocation substructure for all coatings is a strip substructure, except for coatings of the W–C–Cu system. For this system, the preferred type of dislocation substructure is the subgrain substructure.

Figure 5.1 shows the normal probability distributions of the Ra value for the base surface of the electric-explosive composite coatings of the Mo–Cu system obtained using various conductors for EESs. The roughness parameter Ra for the base surface of the samples prepared for EES was 1.5 μm.

For the layered coatings made using molybdenum and copper foils, the most probable Ra value for the base surface is 2.60 μm (Fig. 5.1 a), and coincides with the average Ra value, the standard deviation is 0.33 μm. For the coatings with a filled structure obtained

Table 5.1. - Substructures (δ,%) formed in electric explosive coatings

Coating	Cellular	Strip	Fragmented	Subgrain	Dislocation chaos or net-like
W-Cu	6	30	6	4	54
Mo-Cu	1	22	1	3	55
Mo-C-Cu	6	42	11	6	35
W-C-Cu	14	20	24	36	6
Ti-B-Cu	6	53	17	5	19
TiB2-Cu	6	55	11	7	16

using molybdenum and copper foils, the most probable Ra value for the base surface is 3.69 µm (Fig. 5.1 *b*), and coincides with the average Ra value, the standard deviation in this case is 0.41 µm. For layered coatings obtained using copper foil and molybdenum powder, the most probable Ra value for the base surface is 2.68 µm (Fig. 5.1, *c*), and coincides with the average Ra value, the standard deviation in this case is 0.30 µm. For coatings with a filled structure, obtained using copper foil and molybdenum powder, the most probable Ra value for the base surface is 3.45 µm (Fig. 5.1 *d*), and coincides with the average Ra value, the standard deviation is 0.27 µm. For coatings with a filled structure, obtained using a CEEM, the most probable value of Ra for the base surface is 2.48 µm (Figure 5.1, d), and coincides with the average value of Ra, the standard deviation in this case is 0.30 µm.

The low values of the roughness parameter of layered coatings are due to the fact that they were obtained during EES, when the most characteristic is the deposition of explosion products from the rear of a pulsed jet onto the surface of liquid particles and subsequent self-quenching [198]. The low values of the roughness parameter Ra for coatings with a filled structure obtained using a CEEM are due to the processing mode close to the spraying of layered coatings.

The increase in the Ra parameter for coatings with a filled structure obtained using powders and foils compared with sprayed layered coatings is caused by the fact that they were formed during EES in the regimes that caused surface melting, mixing of the melt by convection, deposition of condensed particles on the coating surface explosion products from the rear of the jet and subsequent

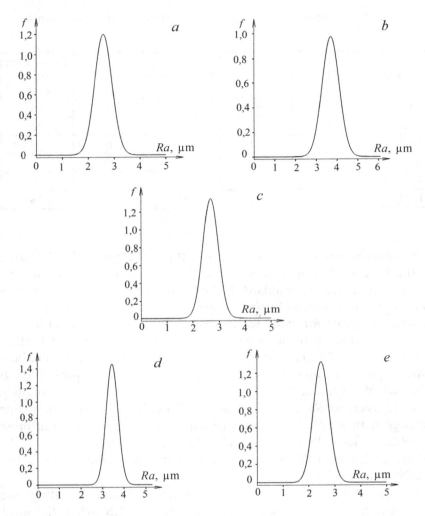

Fig. 5.1 - Normal probability distributions of Ra for the base surface of electro-explosive composite coatings of the Mo-Cu system obtained using various conductors for EES. *a* – layered coatings obtained using molybdenum foils and copper; *b* – coatings with a filled structure, obtained using molybdenum and copper foils; *c* – layered coatings, obtained using copper foil and molybdenum powder; *d* – coatings with a filled structure obtained using copper foil and molybdenum powder; *e* – coatings with filled structure obtained using CEEM.

high-speed self-quenching [198]. Nevertheless, in either case, the obtained roughness parameters do not impede the practical use of coatings, because it is known that during operation of heavy and medium-loaded circuit breakers under constant operating conditions, contact break-in occurs and a stable surface roughness is created.

5.2. Features of surface structure and transverse sections of pseudo-alloy coatings of the Mo-Cu system

Coatings of the Mo–Cu system with a composite layered structure sprayed using molybdenum and copper foils. Figure 5.2 shows typical surface images of such coatings. It can be seen that it has a developed microrelief and a low level of roughness. Relatively smooth irregular regions are formed on the surface. They are located

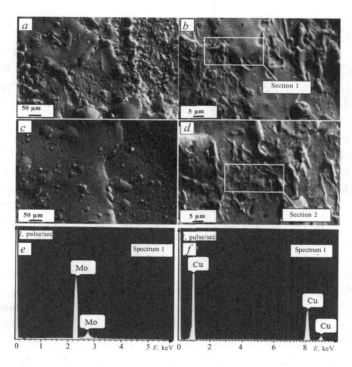

Fig. 5.2. Characteristic image and X-ray spectra of the surface of the coatings of the Mo-Cu system with a layered structure, sprayed using molybdenum and copper foils. Scanning electron microscopy. *a* is a general view of the surface of a single molybdenum layer (q = 4.1 GW/m²), *b* – surface for X-ray spectral analysis, *c* – general view of the surface of a single copper layer (q = 3.7 GW/m²), *d* – surface for x-ray spectral analysis, *d, e* – X-ray spectra (the locations of the set of X-ray spectra are indicated on (*b, d*) by frames).

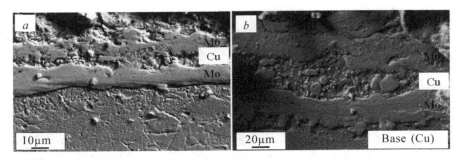

Fig. 5.3. A characteristic image of the cross-sectional structure, coatings of the Mo–Cu system with a layered structure, sprayed using molybdenum and copper foils. Scanning electron microscopy. a – m(Mo) = 170 mg, m(Cu) = 150 mg; b – m(Mo) = 350 mg, m(Cu) = 300 mg.

randomly on the surface of the coating (Fig. 5.3).

X-ray microanalysis (Fig. 5.2, e, f) allows us to state that the structural regions, depending on the sprayed single layer, are formed by numerous deformed crystallized drops of copper or molybdenum deposited on the surface from the back of the jet. The diameter of the droplets is from 1 to 15 μm.

With electric explosion of foils with a lower mass, the thickness of single layers of copper and molybdenum in the coatings is 13–14 and 14–15 μm, respectively (Fig. 5.3). With electric explosion of foils with a larger mass, the thickness of the layers of copper and molybdenum in the coating is 19–21 and 18–20 μm, respectively.

X-ray microanalysis showed that the layers are formed by molybdenum or copper. This suggests that the thickness of the single layers can be set by changing the mass of the foil. Moreover, it is comparable with the thickness of the coating layers obtained by evaporation and condensation by the electron beam method [72]. At the boundaries of the single layers of molybdenum and copper and molybdenum with the substrate, a wave-like microrelief is formed on the surface heated to the melting temperature as a result of the thermal power impact of a pulsed plasma jet on the surface, which improves adhesion.

With an increase in the intensity of exposure to the surface, the interface between the coating and the substrate and between the individual coating layers is distorted and the layered structure is destroyed.

Coatings of the Mo–Cu system with a composite filled structure sprayed using molybdenum and copper foils. Coatings of this type

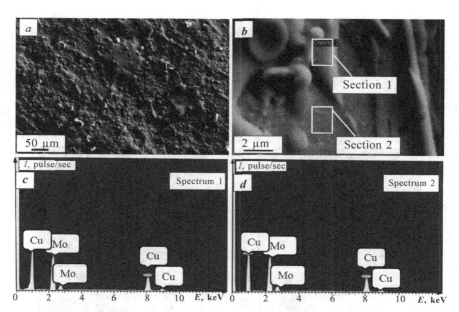

Fig. 5.4. Characteristic image and X-ray spectra of the surface of the coatings of a Mo–Cu system with a filled structure, sprayed using molybdenum and copper foils. Scanning electron microscopy. *a* – general view, *b* – surface for x-ray analysis, *c*, *d* – x-ray spectra (places of their collection are indicated on *b*).

are characterized by developed microrelief and high roughness compared to coatings with a layered structure (Fig. 5.4). Two types of structures are formed on their surface. Relate to the structure of the first kind the relatively smooth regions having an irregular shape. They are located on the surface of the coating chaotic (Fig. 5.4 *a*, *b*). They are deformed crystallized microdrops with diameters from 1 to 15 μm, condensed on the surface from the back of the jet. The structures of the first type occupy a total area of 25%.

X-ray microanalysis allows us to state that the structural components of the first type have a complex chemical composition; the main elements are molybdenum and copper (Fig. 5.4 *c*, *d*). According to these results, it can be stated that these regions were formed as a result of mixing of copper and molybdenum during processing of a single layer of molybdenum by the products of the explosion of copper foil and have a complex phase composition, for example, they contain particles of copper and molybdenum.

The structure of the second type includes globular formations. Their total area on the coating surface is 75% (Fig. 5.4). These structural elements have average sizes, varying over a wide range

Fig. 5.5. Characteristic image and X-ray spectra of the coating surfaces of the Mo-Cu system with filled structure sprayed in low intensity mode using molybdenum and copper foils. Scanning electron microscopy. *a, b* – copper – molybdenum pseudoalloy, *c* – distribution map of Mo for photo *a, d* – distribution map of Cu for photo *a, e* – spectrum x-ray (obtained from 1 to *a*), *f* is the X-ray spectrum (obtained from 2 to *a*).

- from 0.5 to 5 µm. X-ray microanalysis gives the basis to state that the studied formations have a complex elemental composition; the main elements are molybdenum and copper (Figure 5.4 *c, d*). Comparing the X-ray spectra, we can conclude that the relative content of molybdenum is lower in the structure of the second type.

This fact, on the one hand, can indicate the presence of molybdenum and copper coatings in these areas, and, on the other hand, indicates the insufficient thickness of structures of the second type, which leads to the presence of lines from the mixture of molybdenum and copper lying under the inclusion in the X-ray diffraction pattern, and the presence of copper inclusion on the surface.

A study of the cross sections of coatings formed during EES in a low-intensity mode showed (Fig. 5.5) that repeated treatment of copper foil by electric explosion in the molybdenum coating matrix included globule inclusions with sizes from 30 to 200 nm (light areas in Fig. 3.5 *a*).

The largest size of globules reaches 1 μm. Some of them crumble during the preparation of thin sections (Fig. 5.5 *b*). An X-ray microanalysis of such an inclusion (Fig. 5.5 *b*, section 1) showed that the main element in it is copper: its content is 93 and molybdenum is 7 at.% In a section that does not contain individual inclusions (Fig. 5.5 *b*, section 2), the content of molybdenum and copper is 56 and 44 at.%, respectively. An analysis of the distribution maps of elements in the corresponding characteristic x-rays in the region shown in Fig. 5.6 *a*, in which only nanoscale and submicron inclusions of copper are observed, showed (Fig. 5.5 *c, d*) that copper and molybdenum are uniformly distributed in the coating. This is because the resolution of X-ray microanalysis, ranging from 1 to 5 μm, is larger than the size of individual globules in the analyzed region.

An increase in the size of globules in comparison with the low-intensity regime is consistent with the well-known ideas [198], according to which an increase in the intensity of the thermal power action on the irradiated surface during EES is accompanied by an increase in the degree of mixing of the melt formed on it. Figure 5.6 *a* shows a molybdenum solid matrix in which formed isolated copper inclusions with large sizes from 0.1 to 2 μm are distributed.

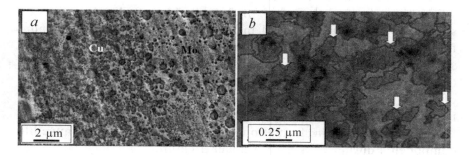

Fig. 5.6. A characteristic image of the cross-sectional structure of an electric explosive coating of the Mo–Cu system with a composite filled structure sprayed in a high-intensity treatment mode using molybdenum and copper foils. Scanning electron microscopy. *a* – pseudoalloy of molybdenum and copper; *b* – region of penetration of molybdenum into copper at the border with the copper substrate. Arrows indicate molybdenum particles.

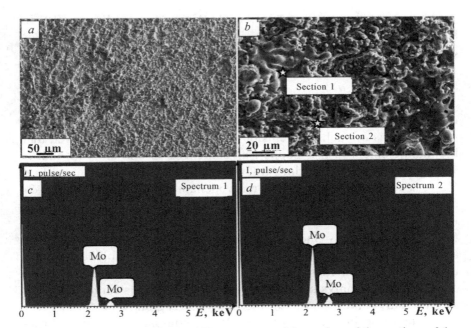

Fig. 5.7. A characteristic image and X-ray spectra of the surface of the coatings of the Mo–Cu system with a layered structure, sprayed using copper foil and molybdenum powder after the EES of a single molybdenum layer at q = 4.1 GW/m². Scanning electron microscopy. a – general view, b – surface for X-ray analysis, c, d – X-ray spectra. Places of the collection of X-ray spectra are indicated in (b).

Moreover, they are firmly held in the matrix, which can help improve the erosion resistance of coatings.

Coatings have a thickness of 25 μm. At their border with the substrate, a region of mutual mixing of copper and molybdenum is formed, in which the formation of isolated submicrocrystalline sizes of molybdenum inclusions in the copper matrix is observed (Fig. 5.6 b). Note that a similar transition region with a thickness of 1 to 3 μm is also formed when the surface of carbon steel 45 is treated by electric explosion of copper foil [199]. This suggests that the mechanism for the formation of pseudo-alloys from immiscible components during EES is of a general nature.

In the case of EES of copper substrates in a high-intensity mode, while mixing the formed melt on the surface, coatings with a filled composite structure based on copper and molybdenum are formed (Fig. 5.6), when the size of copper inclusions is up to 2 μm.

Layered Mo–Cu system coatings sprayed using copper foil and molybdenum powder. After the EES of a single molybdenum layer,

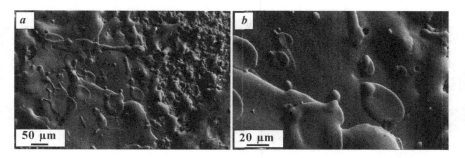

Fig. 5.8. A characteristic image of the surface of layered coatings of the Mo-Cu system, formed using Cu foil and Mo powder, obtained by scanning electron microscopy, after the EES of a single copper layer (q = 3.7 GW/m²). a – radial influx of copper and microdrops, b – copper microdrops/

two types of structures form on the surface of the coating (Figs. 5.7 and 3.8).

The structure of the first type includes relatively smooth areas of irregular shape. They are located randomly on the coating surface (Fig. 5.7 a, b) and are formed by deformed crystallized microdrops with diameters from 6 to 20 µm.

The total area of this structure on the surface of single molybdenum layers is 25%. X-ray microanalysis allows us to conclude that the regions of the structure of the first species are formed by molybdenum (Fig. 5.7 c). It can be assumed that these regions were formed as a result of conglomeration or melting of the largest particles of molybdenum powder in the process of jet formation, their deformation upon impact with the surface and subsequent crystallization.

The structure of the second type is represented by formations of a globular form. They occupy a total area of 75% on the surface of the coating (Fig. 5.7). The average sizes of these structural elements vary over a wide range – from 0.5 to 5 µm. X-ray microanalysis (Fig. 5.7 d) allows us to conclude that the studied formations are formed by molybdenum.

It can be seen that after the EES of a single copper layer, the coating is characterized by a less developed surface topography and lower roughness compared to the EES of a single molybdenum layer. In contrast to the EES of a single molybdenum layer, after the EES of a single copper layer, a structure of the same type is formed on the surface. It is represented by relatively smooth areas of irregular

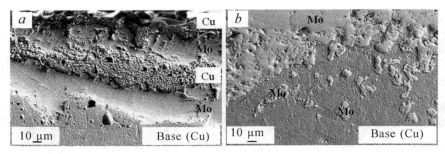

Fig. 5.9. A characteristic image of the cross-sectional structure of coatings of the Mo–Cu system with a layered structure sprayed using molybdenum powder and copper foil. Scanning electron microscopy. *a* – general view, direct section; *b* – molybdenum penetration area in copper on the border with the copper substrate, oblique thin section.

shape, which are located randomly on the surface of the coating (Fig. 5.8).

X-ray microanalysis allows us to conclude that they are formed by copper. Based on these results, we can assume that this structure consists of numerous deformed crystallized drops of copper deposited on the surface from the rear of the jet. The diameter of the droplets varies from 1 to 500 μm.

According to the SEM of the cross sections of coatings, the thickness of single layers of molybdenum and copper in them is 15–30 and 40–45 μm, respectively (Fig. 5.9 *a*). These values are comparable with the thickness of the coating layers obtained by electron-beam evaporation and subsequent vacuum condensation [200]. At the boundaries of single layers of coatings with a copper substrate a small-scale wavy relief is formed (Fig. 5.9 *b*) as a result of the thermal force action of a pulsed plasma jet on a surface heated to the melting temperature.

The presence of relief allows to increase adhesion. If you increase the intensity of exposure to the surface, then there will be a distortion of the interface between the surface layer and the substrate and between single layers and the destruction of the layered structure. A characteristic feature of the EES is the penetration of individual molybdenum particles into the substrate to a depth of several micrometers (Fig. 5.9 *b*).

Coated Mo–Cu system coatings sprayed using copper foil and molybdenum powder. Coatings of this type have a developed relief and a low level of roughness (Fig. 5.10). Two types of structures are formed. The structure of the first type is formed by relatively

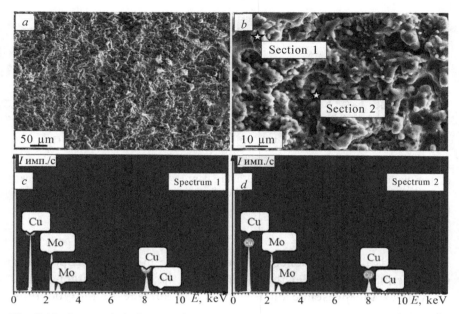

Fig. 5.10 characteristic image of the surface structure of the coatings of a Mo-Cu system with a filled structure, sprayed using copper foil and molybdenum powder. Scanning electron microscopy. *a* – general view, *b* – surface for X-ray microanalysis, *c, d* – X-ray spectra (places of their collection are indicated on *b*).

smooth areas of irregular shape, located in a chaotic manner (Fig. 5.10). Their total area is ≈25%. X-ray microanalysis suggests that, according to the chemical composition, the main elements of these structures are molybdenum and copper (Fig. 5.10 c). Based on these results, we can assume that these areas were formed as a result of mixing copper and molybdenum.

We attribute globular formations to the structure of the second type. In all EES modes, they occupy 75% of the total area on the surface of the coating (Fig. 5.10). These structural elements have average sizes, varying in the range from 0.5 to 10 μm. X-ray microanalysis allows us to state that the studied formations are characterized by complex elemental composition; the main elements are molybdenum and copper (Fig. 5.10 *d*). Comparing the X-ray spectra shown in Fig. 5.10 *c* and *d*, we can conclude that the relative copper content is lower in the structure of the second type. This fact, on the one hand, may indicate the presence of molybdenum particles in these areas of the coating, and on the other hand, indicates the thickness of the structures of the first kind is not large enough,

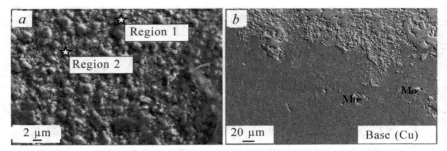

Fig. 5.11. A characteristic image of the cross-section of the coatings of the Mo–Cu system with a filled structure, sprayed using copper foil and molybdenum powder. Scanning electron microscopy. *a* – general view, direct section; *b* – region of penetration of molybdenum into copper on the border with a copper substrate, oblique thin section.

which leads to the presence of lines from the mixture of copper and molybdenum lying under the inclusion on the micro roentgenogram, as well as the presence on the inclusion surface of molybdenum particles.

A study of the cross sections of the coatings showed that their structure is formed by globular inclusions in the matrix (Fig. 5.11). X-ray spectral microanalysis suggests that globular inclusions are mainly formed by molybdenum (Fig. 5.11 *b*). The average sizes of these elements of the structure are structurally in the range from 0.5 to 2.5 µm. Their sizes are comparable with the particle diameter of the molybdenum powder used for spraying. We can assume that these inclusions are formed by particles of molybdenum powder.

X-ray microanalysis of surface areas that do not contain globular inclusions showed that they have a complex chemical composition and are mainly formed by copper (97 at%) and molybdenum.

At the boundary of the coating with the substrate (Fig. 5.11 *b*), as a result of the thermal force action of a pulsed plasma jet on the substrate heated to the melting temperature, a wave-like microrelief appears, which allows increasing adhesion. A characteristic feature of the EES is the penetration of individual molybdenum particles into the copper substrate to a depth of several micrometers.

Coatings of the Mo–Cu system with a composite filled structure formed by an EES using a CEEM. Coatings of this type have a highly developed relief and a low level of roughness (Fig. 5.12).

The surface of the coatings is represented by structures of two types. The first type of structure includes relatively smooth areas of irregular shape. They are located randomly on the surface of the

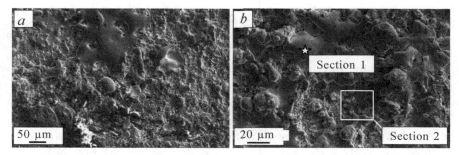

Fig. 5.12. A characteristic image of the surface of the coatings of the Mo–Cu systems with a filled composite structure formed using a composite electrically exploded material (CEEM). Scanning electron microscopy. *a* – general view; *b* – surface for X-ray spectral analysis.

Fig. 5.13. A characteristic image of the structure of sections sprayed with filled composite coatings, detected by scanning electron microscopy after electroexplosive spraying of filled composite coatings of the Mo–Cu system using a CEEM. *a* – general view, direct section; *b* – area of penetration of molybdenum to copper on the border with the copper substrate, oblique thin section.

coating. The total area of these structures is 25%. X-ray microanalysis allows us to state that the regions of the first type of structure have complex chemical compositions; the main elements are molybdenum and copper in amounts of 49 and 51 at.% respectively. Based on these results, it can be argued that these areas were formed due to the mutual mixing of copper and molybdenum during an electric explosion of a CEEM (composite electrically exploded material).

The structure of the second type contains formations of a globular form. They occupy the total area of 75% on the surface of the coating (Fig. 5.12) in all EES modes. The average sizes of these structural elements vary in the range from 0.5 to 12 μm.

X-ray spectral microanalysis suggests that the studied structural formations have complex elemental composition. Their main elements are molybdenum and copper in amounts of 52 and 48 at.% respectively. Note that the relative copper content is lower in the structure of the second type than in the structure of the first. This fact, on the one hand, may indicate the presence of molybdenum particles in these areas of the coating, and on the other hand, talk about the small thickness of the structures of the first type, which leads to the presence of lines from the mixture of copper and molybdenum lying under the inclusion in the X-ray diffraction pattern, as well as the presence of on the surface of the inclusion of molybdenum particles.

At the boundaries of the coating with the substrate (Fig. 5.13 *b*), as a result of the thermal force action of a pulsed plasma jet on the substrate heated to the melting temperature, a wave-like microrelief is formed, which allows to increase adhesion. An important feature of EES is the introduction of individual molybdenum particles into the substrate to a depth of several micrometers.

In conclusion, we note that during the deposition of coatings of all types a pore-free structure is formed, which is a positive property of EES, because the formation of pores inevitably leads to a decrease in the electrical conductivity of the coatings.

5.3. Surface roughness of pseudo-alloy of the W–Cu system coatings

Let us consider the results of a study of the topography of coatings formed on samples of M00 electrotechnical copper in the case of EES of coatings of the W–Cu system.

Figure 5.14 shows the normal probability distributions of the *Ra* value for the base surface of the electroexplosive composite coatings of the W–Cu system, obtained using various conductors for EESs. The roughness parameter *Ra* for the base surface of the samples prepared for EES was 1.5 μm.

For layered coatings obtained using copper foil and tungsten powder, the most probable *Ra* value for the base surface is 2.51 μm (Fig. 5.14 *a*), and coincides with the average *Ra* value, the standard deviation in this case is 0.35 μm. For coatings with a filled structure, obtained using copper foil and tungsten powder, the most probable *Ra* value for the base surface is 3.5 μm (Fig. 5.14, b), and coincides with the average *Ra* value, the standard deviation is 0.36 μm. For coatings with a filled structure, obtained using a CEEM, the most probable value of *Ra* for the base surface is 2.53 μm (Fig. 5.14 *c*),

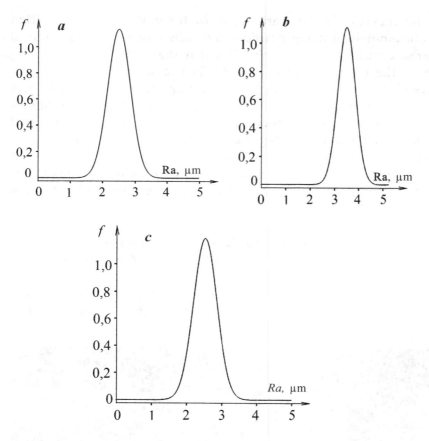

Fig. 5.14. Normal probability distributions of *Ra* for the base surface of electric explosive composite W–Cu system coatings, obtained using various conductors for EES. *a* – layered coatings obtained using copper foil and tungsten powder; *b* – coatings with a filled structure, obtained using copper foil and tungsten powder; *c* – coatings with a filled structure, obtained using CEEM.

and coincides with the average value of *Ra*, the standard deviation in this case is 0.33 μm.

Low values of the roughness parameter of layered coatings are due to the fact that they were formed during electric explosion treatment, which is characterized by the deposition of mainly liquid explosion products from the back of the jet with subsequent self-hardening [198]. The low values of the roughness parameter *Ra* for coatings with a filled structure obtained using a CEEM are due to the processing mode close to the deposition of layered coatings.

The increase in the parameter *Ra* for coatings with a filled structure obtained using powders and foils compared with sprayed layered coatings is due to the fact that they were formed during EES in the regimes that caused surface melting, melt mixing by convection, deposition of condensed coatings on the surface particles of explosion products from the back of the jet and subsequent self-quenching [198]. Nevertheless, in either case, the obtained roughness parameters do not create obstacles for the practical use of electroexplosive coatings, since it is known [201] that during operation of heavy and medium-loaded electrical switches under constant operating conditions, running-in occurs and creates a constant surface roughness.

5.4. Features of surface structure and transverse sections of pseudo-alloy coatings of the W–Cu system

Explosive coatings of the W–Cu system with a layered structure. Figures 5.15 and 3.16 show typical images of the surface structures

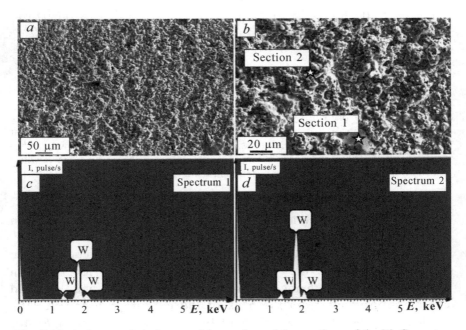

Fig. 5.15. A characteristic image of the surface of the coatings of the W–Cu system with a layered structure after the EES of a single tungsten layer at $q = 4.1$ GW/m². Scanning electron microscopy. a – general view, b – surface for x-ray analysis, c, d – X-ray spectra (places of their collection are indicated on b).

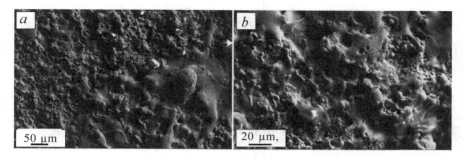

Fig. 5.16. A characteristic image of the surface of the coating system W–Cu with a layered structure after the EES of a single copper layer at $q = 7.6$ GW/m². Scanning electron microscopy. a - microdrops of crystallized copper, b – radial influx of copper.

of the coating formed upon EES of single tungsten and copper layers, respectively.

The surface of the the coatings is represented by structures of two types. The structure of the first type includes relatively smooth areas having an irregular shape. They are located randomly on the surface of the coating (Figs 5.15 a, b). It is deformed crystallized droplets with diameters from 6 to 20 µm. The structures of the first type occupy 25% of the total surface area. X-ray microanalysis gives the basis to state that this structure is formed by tungsten (Fig. 5.15 c). Based on these results, we can assume that it was formed as a result of either conglomeration or melting of the largest particles of tungsten powder in the process of jet formation, their deformation upon impact with the surface, and subsequent crystallization.

The structure of the second type is represented by formations of a globular form. They occupy 75% of the total surface area of the coating (Fig. 5.15 a, b). The average sizes of these structural elements vary in the range from 0.5 to 5 µm. X-ray spectral microanalysis allows us to state that the studied formations are formed by tungsten (Fig. 5.15 d).

After the EES of a single copper layer, the coating has a more developed relief and roughness level compared with the EES of a single tungsten layer (Fig. 5.16).

In contrast to the EES of a tungsten single layer, after the EES of a copper single layer, a structure of the same type is formed on the surface. These are relatively smooth irregularly shaped areas. They are located randomly on the surface of the coating. X-ray microanalysis suggests that these areas are formed by copper. Based

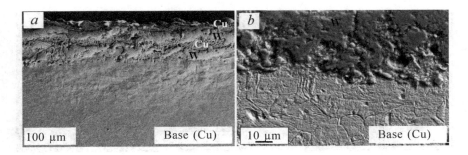

Fig. 5.17 A characteristic image of the cross-sectional structure of the coatings of the W–Cu system with a layered structure. Scanning electron microscopy. *a* – general view, direct section; *b* – zone of penetration of tungsten into copper on the border with a copper base, oblique thin section.

on these results, it can be argued that this structure consists of numerous deformed crystallized drops of copper deposited on the surface from the back of the jet. The diameter of the droplets is in the range from 1 to 400 μm.

According to the SEM of the cross sections of coatings, the thickness of the layers of tungsten and copper in them is 45...50 and 45...50 μm, respectively (Fig. 5.17 *a*). These values are comparable with the thickness of the coating layers obtained by electron beam evaporation and subsequent condensation [72]. At the boundaries of single layers of coatings with a copper substrate, due to the thermal force effect of a pulsed plasma jet on the substrate heated to the melting temperature, a small-sized wavy microrelief is formed (Fig. 5.17 *b*), which allows to increase adhesion.

An increase in the intensity of exposure to the surface leads to a distortion of the interface between the coating and the substrate, as well as between unit coating layers and the destruction of the layered structure. A characteristic feature of the EES is the introduction of individual tungsten and molybdenum particles into the substrate to a depth of several micrometers (Fig. 5.17 *b*).

Electroexplosive coatings of the W–Cu system with a composite filled structure. From Fig. 5.18 it is seen that the coating formed during EES has a developed relief and a low level of roughness. The surface is represented by structures of two types. The structure of the first type is formed by relatively smooth areas of irregular shape, which are located randomly on the surface of the coating. The total area of the first type of structure is 25%. X-ray microanalysis allows us to state that the structural formations of the first type are

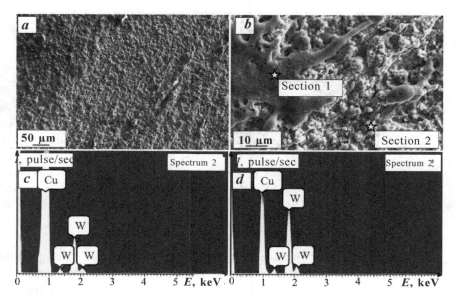

Fig. 5.18. A characteristic image of the surface structure of the coatings of the W–Cu system with a composite filled structure. Scanning electron microscopy. *a* – general view, *b* – surface for x-ray spectral analysis, *c, d* – x-ray spectra (the places for the collection of X-ray spectra are indicated on *b*).

characterized by a complex chemical composition; the main elements of which are tungsten and copper (Fig. 5.17 *c*). Based on these results, it can be argued that these regions were formed as a result of the mixing of copper and tungsten.

The structure of the second type is represented by formations of a globular form. They occupy the total area of 75% on the surface of the coating, regardless of the EES mode (Fig. 5.18). These structural elements have sizes ranging from 0.5 to 10 μm. X-ray microanalysis gives the basis to state that the studied structures are characterized by complex elemental composition; the main elements of which are tungsten and copper (Fig. 5.18 *d*). Comparing the X-ray spectra shown in Fig. 5.18, c and d, we can conclude that the relative copper content is lower in the structure of the second type.

This fact, on the one hand, may indicate the presence of tungsten particles in the present coating areas, and, on the other hand, the small thickness of structures of the first type, which in turn leads to the presence on the X-ray diffraction pattern of lines from a mixture of tungsten and copper lying under the inclusion, as well as the presence of tungsten particles on the inclusion surface.

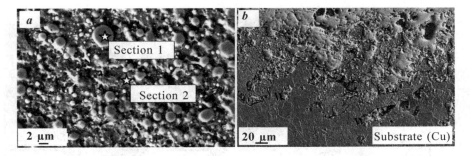

Fig. 5.19. A characteristic image of the structure of the cross sections of coatings of the W–Cu system with a filled structure. Scanning electron microscopy. *a* – general view, direct section; *b* – zone of penetration of tungsten into copper on the border with a copper base, oblique thin section.

The structure of the cross sections of the coatings is the globular inclusions located in the matrix (Fig. 5.19). X-ray microanalysis provides the basis to state that tungsten is the main element of globular inclusions. The inclusions have average sizes, varying in the range from 0.5 to 2.5 μm. It should also be noted that the sizes of globular inclusions are comparable with the particle size of the tungsten powder that was used for spraying. From this it follows that these formations are particles of tungsten powder. An X-ray microanalysis of a surface area that does not contain globular inclusions showed that it has a complex chemical composition, but is mainly formed by copper (98 at.%) and tungsten.

At the boundaries of the coatings with the base (Fig. 5.19 *b*), due to the thermal power action of the plasma jet on the surface heated to the melting temperature, a wave-like relief is formed, which allows to increase adhesion. An important feature of the treatment is the penetration of individual tungsten particles into the base to a depth of several micrometers

Electroexplosive coatings of the W–Cu system with a composite filled structure sprayed using a composite electric explosive material (CEEM). From Fig. 3.20 it is seen that the coating formed during EES is characterized by a developed relief and a low level of roughness. Two types of structures are formed on the surface. Relate to the structure of the first type relatively smooth areas of irregular shape, located on the surface of the coating in a chaotic manner (Fig. 5.20). The total area of the structure of the first type is 25%.

X-ray microanalysis gives the basis to conclude that the regions of the structure of the first type have a complex chemical

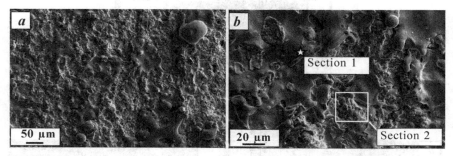

Fig. 5.20. A characteristic image of the surface structure of the coatings of the W–Cu system with a composite filled structure formed using a CEEM. Scanning electron microscopy. *a* – general view, *b* – surface for X-ray analysis.

composition; the main elements are copper and tungsten in the amount of 55 and 45 at. % respectively. Based on these results, we can assume that these regions were formed as a result of mixing of tungsten and copper during the electric explosion of a CEEM.

Comparing the data of X-ray spectral analysis, it can be noted that the relative content of molybdenum is higher in the structure of the second type.

This, on the one hand, can mean the presence of tungsten particles in these coating areas, and on the other hand, indicates the thickness of the structures of the first type is not large enough, which leads to the presence of lines from the mixture of tungsten and copper lying under the inclusion, as well as the presence of tungsten particles on the inclusion surface.

The structure of the second type includes the formation of a globular shape, occupying the total area of 75% on the surface of the coating (Fig. 5.20). The average sizes of these structural elements vary widely – from 0.5 to 15 μm. X-ray microanalysis gives the basis to conclude that the studied formations have a complex elemental composition; the main elements are copper and tungsten in the amount of 44 and 56 at.% respectively.

The cross-sectional structure of the coatings represents globular inclusions of tungsten in a copper matrix (Fig. 5.21).

X-ray microanalysis gives the basis to conclude that tungsten is the main element of globular inclusions. The average sizes of these structural elements vary in the range from 0.5 to 15 μm. Their sizes are comparable to particles of tungsten powder used for spraying. Therefore, these sites are formed by tungsten. This is also confirmed by the analysis of X-ray distribution maps (Fig. 5.21 *b, c*). X-ray

Fig. 5.21. A characteristic image of the structure of the cross-sections of coatings of the W–Cu system with a filled structure, sprayed using a CEEM. Scanning electron Microscopy. *a* – general view, direct section, *b* – copper distribution map for (*a*), *c* – distribution map of tungsten for (*a*), *d* – W–Cu pseudo-alloy, *e* – the zone of penetration of tungsten into copper on the border with copper basis, oblique thin section.

spectral analysis of a surface area that does not contain globular inclusions showed that it has a complex chemical composition, but is mainly formed by copper (97 at.%).

At the boundaries of the coatings with the base (Fig. 5.21 *e*), as a result of the thermal force action of the plasma jet on the surface heated to the melting temperature, a wave-like relief is formed, which allows to increase adhesion. An important feature of the treatment is the penetration of individual tungsten particles into the base to a depth of several micrometers.

At the boundaries of the coatings with the base (Figure 5.21 *e*), as a result of the thermal force action of the plasma jet on the surface heated to the melting temperature, a wave-like relief is formed, which allows to increase adhesion. An important feature of the treatment is the penetration of individual tungsten particles into the base to a depth of several micrometers.

As with the spraying of coatings of the Mo–Cu system, the formed structure of all types of coatings of the W–Cu system is characterized by the absence of pores, which is a positive feature of the spraying method used, since the presence of porosity inevitably leads to a decrease in the electrical conductivity of the coatings.

5.5. Formation of dynamic mesorotations of sprayed coating structures in the electric explosion method

Studies of transverse sections showed that the thickness of the coatings is several tens of micrometers. In the central region of the sample, located under the nozzle of a plasma accelerator with a diameter of 20 mm, the coating thickness changes by no more than 10%, and decreases in the peripheral region. An important feature of electroexplosive coatings is the formation of single randomly located globular areas of mesoscopic size (from several units to 10–30 μm) in them (Fig. 5.22).

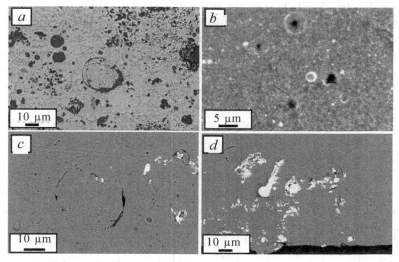

Fig. 5.22. A characteristic image of dynamic mesorotations structures of electroexplosive coatings of various systems. Scanning electron microscopy of oblique sections. *a* – TiB$_2$–Mo system, *b, c* – Cu–W system.

The coating structure of the Mo–TiB$_2$ system is formed by a molybdenum matrix formed from the products of the explosion of a molybdenum foil and particles of titanium diboride powder distributed in it (Fig. 5.22 *a*). Areas of globular shape with a diameter of 10–30 μm, having a clearly distinguishable thin (from 1 to 2–3 μm) border with the surrounding coating material, are noteworthy. The smallest globules in the preparation of thin sections have crumbled out and look in the form of pores in micrographs. Chipping can be associated with a low adhesive bond of the shell of the globule with the matrix. The distances between the globules are 10–50 μm.

The coating of immiscible components of the Cu–W [110] system is formed from the products of the explosion of copper foil with a portion of tungsten powder placed on it (Fig. 5.22 *b, c*). Contoured globules with a diameter of 5–30 μm are also observed in it. The distances between them are 5–30 μm. The thickness of the interface between the inclusions and the matrix in this case is less than 1 μm. The coating matrix is formed by copper. In it are inclusions of tungsten. Globules have the same structure. In some of them, as well as along their boundaries with the matrix, tungsten inclusions are observed. This feature of the coating structure can be attributed to the fact that copper and tungsten do not mix with each other.

Thus, the formation of globular structural features under the influence of shock waves on the surface of a substrate is observed during EES by supersonic multiphase plasma jets of coatings of various systems and, apparently, has the same physical nature. In this regard, we note that the formation of mesoscopic globular structures in dynamically deformable materials under shock loading is known [202]. It can be assumed that the physical nature of the formation of such structures during EES and under conditions of processing the surface of the substrate by shock waves, as in [202], is common. Based on this, we consider a possible mechanism for their formation, following the ideas presented in [203].

The formation of coatings during EES occurs under the conditions of the discharge of a capacitive energy storage device of an electric explosive installation having an oscillatory character and is accompanied by a pulse-periodic thermal force action on a substrate with a coating formed on it. In this case, the coating layer deposited during the first half-period of the discharge is subjected to the shock-wave action of a plasma jet formed during the second half-period. Such an effect is repeated three to four times until the capacitive

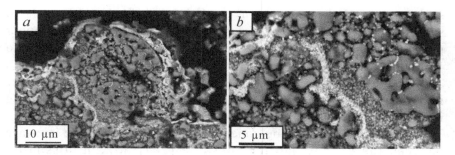

Fig. 5.23. Image of dispersed coating structures of the Cu–TiB$_2$ system. Scanning electron microscopy in the back reflected electrons. a – general view; b – layer of highly dispersed material based on copper and titanium diboride.

storage device is completely discharged. In this case, the propagation front of shock waves that arise in the coating material during their formation is the interface between the dynamically loaded medium and the undeformed material.

Each time with a repeated shock-wave action of a plasma jet on the forming coating, a 'checkerboard' distribution of tensile and compressive normal stresses arises at this boundary [202]. Moreover, in the regions of structural-phase inhomogeneities of the coating, regions of maximum tangential stresses arise, which lead to localized plastic deformation in the form of mesorotations of the material (mesovortices). The location of these regions is random in nature due to the random and locally inhomogeneous nature of the distribution of condensed particles of a pulsed multiphase plasma jet in the coating being formed. The occurrence of mesorotations is facilitated by the fact that the coating material during EES is in a heated and therefore plastic state. In this case, the size of the observed structural features of the coatings in the form of globules corresponds to the size of the rotations. In this connection, we note the influence of the formation of a 'checkerboard' distribution of tensile and compressive normal stresses arising at the interface on the formation of the zone of mutual mixing of materials of electroexplosive coatings and substrate [204].

The formation of electric explosive coatings is accompanied by dispersion of the structure of the sprayed material. This is clearly seen in the image of the coating of the Cu–TiB$_2$ system obtained in back-reflected electrons after electrolytic etching in a solution of HF (5%) + H$_3$PO$_4$ (95%) at a voltage of 10 V for 10 s (Fig. 5.23). In the coating, globular-shaped regions enriched with titanium are observed in the shell enriched with copper (Fig. 5.23 a). The size of such regions reaches 30 μm. Inside the globules, numerous isolated submicron-sized copper particles are observed. Numerous copper particles are also observed in the shell of the globules, crushed to 150 nm (Fig. 5.23 b).

Dispersion of the material of electroexplosive coatings is their important characteristic feature. It also occurs when the coating includes immiscible components, for example, in the Fe–Cu system. The formation of the mixing zone is most pronounced at the interface between the coating and the substrate [204]. Mixing dissimilar materials under the influence of concentrated energy flows is of a general nature. A theoretical analysis of this phenomenon [205, 206] shows that it is based on the following fundamentally important points:

– the effect of the 'checkerboard' in the distribution of stresses and strains at the interface between two dissimilar media in the fields of external influences;

– the appearance of highly excited states and related atom-vacancy configurational excitations near the boundary;

– multilevel vortex mass transfer in a highly excited medium under the conditions of collective atom–vacancy configuration excitations.

Thus, it has been established that during electroexplosive deposition of coatings of various systems, one of their structural elements is globular fragments of a mesoscopic scale. In this case, dispersion and mutual penetration of the components of the sprayed coating are observed. The observed structural features can be explained on the basis of the ideas of physical mesomechanics about the appearance of a 'checkerboard' distribution of compressive and tensile normal stresses, leading to the appearance of mesations of the coating material.

5.6. Features of the surface topography, structure, elemental and phase composition of electric explosive Mo–C–Cu and W–C–Cu systems coatings hardened by synthesized carbides

Consider the surface topography of coatings formed during the EES of coatings of the Mo–C–Cu and W–C–Cu systems. Optical interferometry showed that the roughness of the coatings is characterized by higher parameters compared to the original. The

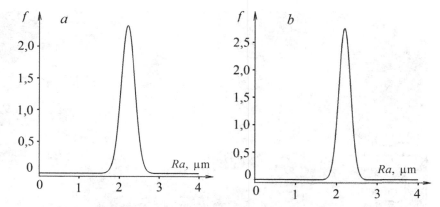

Fig. 5.24. Normal probability distributions of Ra for the base surface of electroexplosive composite coatings, obtained using CEEM. a – Mo–C–Cu system, b – W–C–Cu system.

roughness parameter Ra of the coating surface is 2.0, 2.4, and 2.6 μm for the regimes in which q = 5.5, 6.5, and 7.6 GW/m^2, respectively. An increase in the parameter Ra of the coatings with an increase in the absorbed power density is due to the fact that more intense convective mixing of the melt occurs [198].

Figure 5.24 shows typical normal probability distributions of the Ra value for the base surface of electroexplosive composite coatings of Mo–C–Cu and W–C–Cu systems obtained using various conductors for EESs. The roughness parameter Ra for the base surface of the samples prepared for EES was 1.5 μm.

For coatings with the filled structure of the Mo–C–Cu system (Fig. 5.24 a) obtained using a CEEM, the most probable Ra value for the base surface is 2.22 μm and coincides with the average Ra value; the standard deviation is 0.17 μm. For coatings with the filled structure of the W–C–Cu system (Fig. 5.24 b) obtained using a CEEM, the most probable Ra value for the base surface is 2.2 μm, and coincides with the average Ra value, the standard deviation is 0.14 μm.

The low values of the roughness parameter Ra are caused by the treatment mode close to the spraying of coatings in the premelting deposition mode, which is characterized by the precipitation of predominantly liquid particles of CEEM from the rear of the CEEM from the rear of the jet with subsequent self-hardening.

The indicated roughness parameters do not impede the practical use of EES for hardening contact surfaces, since it is known [205] that the running-in occurs in the service of contact surfaces under

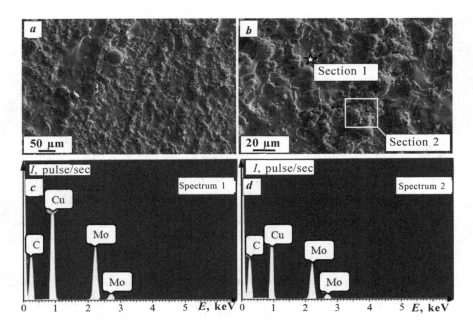

Fig. 5.25. A characteristic image of the surface of composite filled coatings of the Mo–C–Cu system. Scanning electron microscopy. *a* – general view, *b* – surface for x-ray analysis, *c, d* – X-ray spectra (places of collection of X-ray spectra are indicated in the photo *b*).

constant operating conditions and a stable surface roughness is created.

Figure 5.25 shows typical images of the structure of the surface of the coating formed during the EES of composite coatings of the Mo–C–Cu system with a filled structure. It can be seen that two types of structures are formed on the surface.

The structure of the first type includes relatively smooth areas of irregular shape, located on the surface of the coating in a chaotic manner.

The total area of the structure of this type is 25%. X-ray microspectral analysis suggests that these regions of the structure have a complex chemical composition; the main elements are copper, molybdenum and carbon (Fig. 5.25 *c*). Based on these results, we can assume that these areas were formed as a result of mixing of molybdenum, carbon and copper. One can also assume the presence of molybdenum carbides in them.

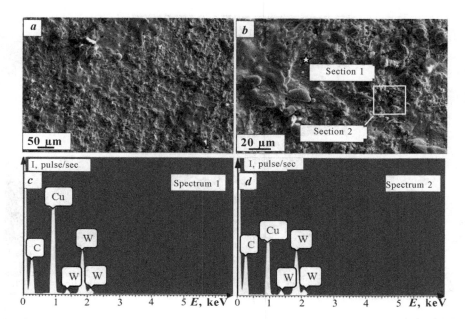

Fig. 5.26. A characteristic image of the surface of composite filled coatings of the W–C–Cu system formed using a CEEM. Scanning electron microscopy. *a* – general view, *b* – surface for X-ray analysis, *c, d* – X-ray spectra (places of a set of X-ray spectra marked on *b*).

The structure of the second type is formed by globular particles, which occupy a total area of 75% on the surface of the coating in all EES modes. (Fig. 5.26 *a, b*). The average sizes of these structural elements vary widely – from 0.5 to 10 µm. X-ray spectral analysis showed that they have a complex elemental composition; the main elements are copper, carbon and molybdenum (Fig. 5.26 *d*). Comparing the X-ray spectra shown in Fig. 5.26 *c* and *d*, it can be noted that the relative content of molybdenum and carbon is higher in the structure of the second type. This may indicate the presence of molybdenum and molybdenum carbides in these coating areas, and, in addition, indicates the insufficient thickness of the structures of the first type. This leads to the presence on the X-ray of the lines from the mixture of molybdenum, carbon and copper lying under the inclusion, as well as the presence of molybdenum particles, carbon and molybdenum carbides on the inclusion surface.

Investigations of the transverse sections of the coatings of the Mo–C–Cu system by the SEM method showed that, as a result of EES, coatings 28...30 µm thick are formed on the surface (Fig. 5.27

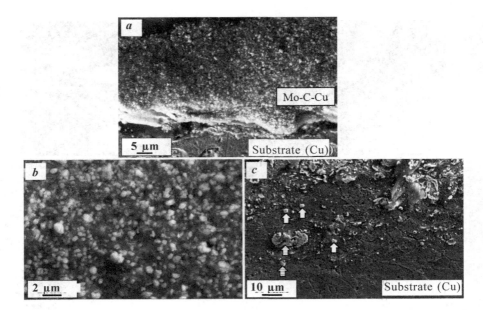

Fig. 5.27. A characteristic image of the structure of cross sections of the composite filled coatings of the Mo–C–Cu system. Scanning electron microscopy. *a* – general view, direct thin section, *b* – finely dispersed nature of the structure (direct thin section); *c* – the zone of mutual mixing of molybdenum, carbides molybdenum and copper at the border with the copper base (oblique thin section).

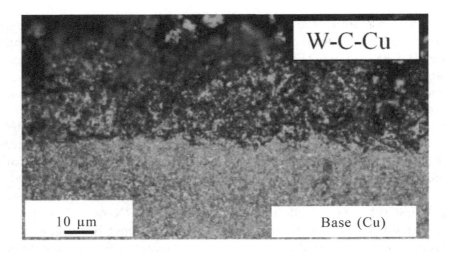

Fig. 5.28. A characteristic image of the cross-sectional structure coatings of the W–C–Cu system formed at $q = 6.5$ GW/m^2. Light microscopy

a). In the copper matrix are inclusions with dimensions of the order of 0.1...1.0 μm (Fig. 5.27 *b*).

At the boundary of the coatings with the base, a mixing zone of molybdenum, molybdenum carbides and copper is formed. In this zone, isolated inclusions of molybdenum and micron-sized molybdenum carbides are observed in the copper matrix (Fig. 5.28 *c*). This is evidenced by the results of nanoscale measurements. In the places of inclusions, it amounts to 900...1100 HV, which corresponds to the nanohardness of molybdenum carbides, at the same time in some areas its values reach 320 HV, which corresponds to the microhardness of molybdenum [207].

The formed structure is characterized by the absence of pores, which is a positive feature of the spraying method used, since the presence of porosity inevitably leads to a decrease in the electrical conductivity of the coatings.

For the W–C–Cu system, the cross-sectional structure has the same features (Fig. 5.28). As a result of processing, layers are formed (Fig. 5.28) with a thickness of 20...25 μm. In the copper matrix are inclusions with dimensions of the order of 0.1...1 μm. The nanohardness at the inclusions is 1100...1200 HV, which corresponds to the nanohardness of tungsten carbides [207]. At the same time, in some regions its value reaches 460 HV, which corresponds to the microhardness of tungsten [207].

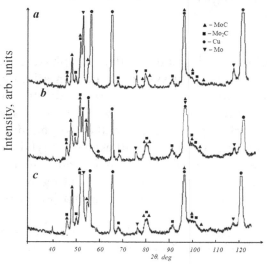

$a - q = 5.5$ GW/m²; $b - q = 6.5$ GW/m²; $c - q = 7.6$ GW/m²

Fig. 5.29. Diffractograms of the surface after electroexplosive spraying of coatings of the Mo–C–Cu system.

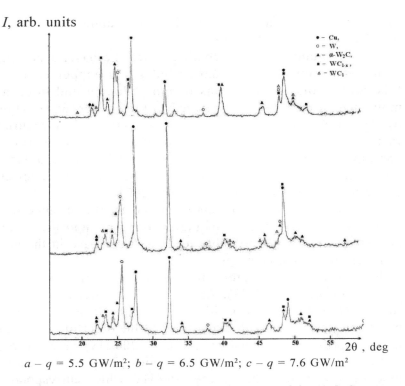

$a - q = 5.5$ GW/m^2; $b - q = 6.5$ GW/m^2; $c - q = 7.6$ GW/m^2

Fig. 5.30. Plots of diffractograms of the surface of coatings of the W–C–Cu systems after electric explosion spraying.

X-ray diffraction studies showed that the phase composition of the coatings of the Mo–C–Cu system formed in all spraying modes is formed by MoC, Mo$_2$C carbides and structurally free molybdenum and copper forming a pseudo-alloy (Fig. 5.29). It is seen that with an increase in absorbed power density, the molybdenum content in the coatings decreases, while the synthesized molybdenum carbides increase. This can be attributed to an increase in the degree of mixing of interacting components in the coating with an increase in the temperature and pressure of the plasma jet on the irradiated surface [198].

X-ray diffraction analysis showed that the coatings of the W–C–Cu system contain highly hard tungsten carbides α-W$_2$C, WC$_{1-x}$, WC, tungsten and copper (Fig. 5.30). The copper content after processing in the mode $q = 6.5$ GW/m^2 is maximum.

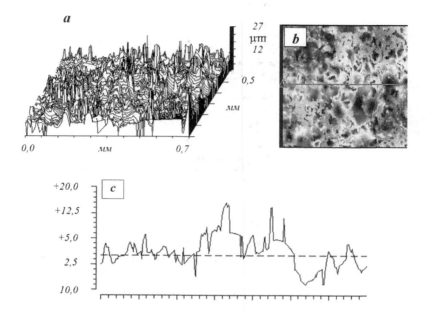

Fig. 5.31. Optical interferometry of the coating surface of the Ti–B–Cu systems with a composite filled structure, *a* – distribution of the unevenness of the relief along the height, *b* – position of the secant (top view), *c* – distribution of the unevenness along the base length

5.7. Features of the surface topography, structure, elemental and phase composition of electric explosive Ti–B–Cu system coatings hardened with synthesized borides

Optical interferometry showed that the roughness parameters are the same over the entire coating area.

The arithmetic mean deviation of the profile for the base surface $Ra = 3.2$ μm and for the base length $Ra = 3.5$ μm (Fig. 5.31).

A single profile protrusion with a height of 26.7 μm and a depression with a depth of 11.8 μm cause high values of the highest profile height for the base surface $R_{max} = 38.5$ μm (Fig. 5.31 *a*) and for the base length $R_{max} = 24.0$ μm (Fig. 5.31 *b*, *c*). The average pitch of irregularities is $Sm = 45$ μm, the average pitch of local protrusions is $Sm = 40$ μm. The obtained roughness parameters are due to the fact that they were obtained by electric explosion treatment, which

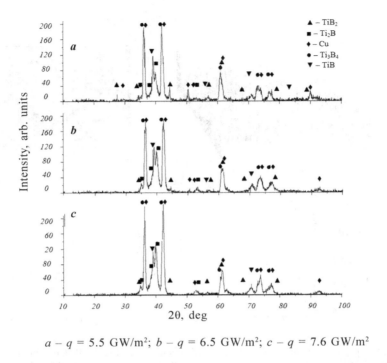

$a - q = 5.5$ GW/m²; $b - q = 6.5$ GW/m²; $c - q = 7.6$ GW/m²

Fig. 5.32. X-ray analysis.of Ti–B–Cu system coating surfaces after electroexplosive spraying in various modes.

causes surface melting, convective mixing of the melt, deposition of explosion products from the rear of the jet on the surface of condensed particles, and subsequent self-quenching [198].

X-ray diffraction analysis showed that using all processing modes, coatings are formed containing titanium borides TiB_2, Ti_2B, Ti_3B_4, TiB and copper (Fig. 5.32). An increase in absorbed power density leads to a decrease in the content of the most refractory phase TiB_2 with a melting point of 3225°C and TiB with a melting point of 2200°C, as well as to a decrease in the copper content.

After using all spraying modes, the content of the refractory Ti_3B_4 phase, having a melting point of 2200°C, does not change. This can be attributed to the fact that the TiB_2 crystals are the first to precipitate under equilibrium crystallization conditions in the region of homogeneity 66...68% B [110]. The formation of the the Ti_2B phase is associated with non-equilibrium high-speed crystallization conditions. An increase in the Ti_2B content is in good agreement with the well-known ideas [202], according to which the crystallization rate increases with an increase in the intensity of exposure. In this

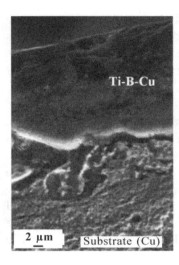

Fig. 5.33. Structural features of the cross section electroexplosive coating system Ti–B–Cu. scanning electron Microscopy.

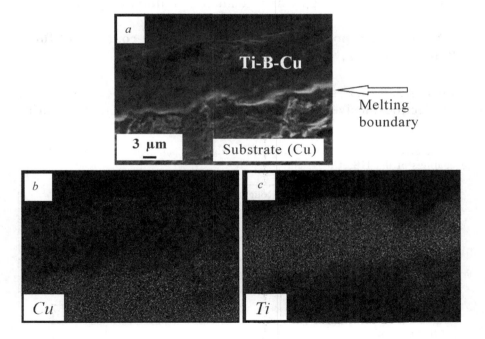

Fig. 5.34. Cross-sectional structure of an electric explosive Ti–B–Cu system coatings formed at $q = 6.5$ GW/m². Scanning electron microscopy. a – general view of the coating; b – copper distribution map in characteristic rays for photo a; c – titanium distribution map in characteristic rays for photo a.

of which the copper is unevenly distributed over the volume of the alloyed layer, and above 7.6 GW/m², a developed surface relief is formed due to the melt flow under the influence of inhomogeneous pressure a jet of explosion products, which impairs the quality of the EES surface [198].

SEM studies of transverse sections showed that after processing the copper contact surface in all the studied modes, the formation of porous coatings uniform in depth with a thickness of 15...16 μm occurs.

At high magnification, it is seen (Fig. 5.33) that the coatings are finely dispersed. The border between them and the base is blurred.

This is also confirmed by X-ray microanalysis of the elemental composition of the coatings (Fig. 5.34 *b, c*) and suggests that the coatings have a cohesive-adhesive bond with the material of the copper contact surface.

At the same time, X-ray microanalysis showed that after processing at $q = 6.5$ GW/m² along the depth of the formed coating, the distribution of copper and titanium is uniform (Fig. 5.34).

5.8. Surface topography of electroexplosive coatings of the TiB$_2$–Cu system

Figures 5.35–5.37 show typical results of profilometry of the surface of electroexplosive coatings of the TiB$_2$–Cu system formed during

Table 5.2. Average values of the surface roughness parameters of electric blasting coatings of the TiB$_2$–Cu system

Investigated sample	Roughness parameters for base			
	Surface		Length	
	Ra, μm	R_{max}, μm	Ra, μm	R_{max}, μm
Initial	1.5	21.5	1.5	13.8
After EES of single layer	2.5	32.4	2.7	18.8
After EES of 2 layers	2.6	35.4	2.6	18.7
After EES of 3 layers	2.7	30.9	2.6	18.8

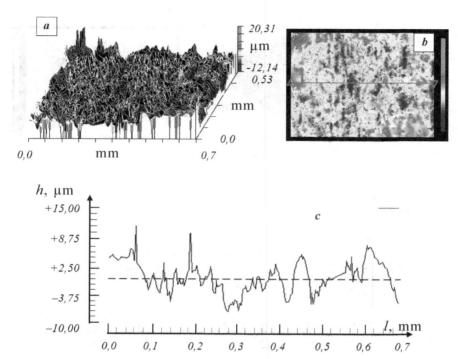

Fig. 5.35. Optical interferometry of the surface of the samples after spraying a single layer of the composite coating of the TiB$_2$–Cu system. *a* – the distribution of unevenness of the relief in height, *b* – the position of the secant (top view), *c* – distribution of roughness along the base length.

single, double, or triple spraying of single layers. It is clearly seen that the surface of the coating is characterized by higher roughness parameters compared to the initial surface of the samples (Table 5.2).

After one, two and three times processing, the roughness parameter Ra is 2.5...2.7 μm for the base surface and 2.6...2.7 μm for the base length.

Below is a detailed description of optical interferometry data for the case of an EES of three unit layers. The arithmetic mean deviation of the profile Ra = 2.7 μm (Fig. 5.37). A single protrusion of the profile with a height of 14.0 μm and a depression with a depth of 16.9 μm cause high values of the highest profile height for the base surface R_{max} = 30.9 μm (Fig. 5.37 *a*) and for the base length R_{max} = 18.8 μm (Fig. 5.37 *b*, *c*).

The average pitch of irregularities is Sm = 50 μm, the average pitch of local protrusions is Sm = 40 μm.

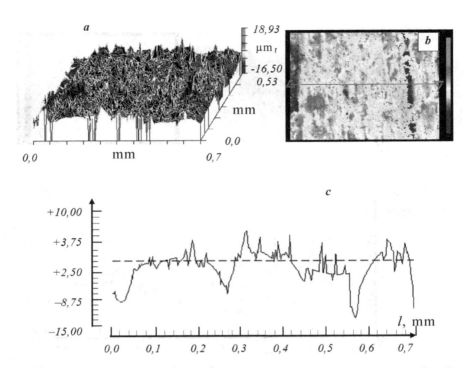

Fig. 5.36. Optical interferometry of the surface of the samples after deposition of two single coating layers of the TiB$_2$–Cu system. a – distribution of the unevenness of the relief along the height, b – position of the secant (top view), c – distribution of the unevenness along the base length.

The obtained roughness parameters are due to the fact that the surface layers were obtained by electric explosive treatment, which is characterized by the predominant deposition of liquid particles of explosion products from the rear of the jet with subsequent self-hardening [198].

5.9. Study of the structure, elemental and phase composition of electroexplosive coatings of TiB$_2$–Cu systems

Consider the results of a study of the structure of the coating formed on samples of electrotechnical copper during EES, depending on the number of spraying of individual layers.

Figures 5.38–5.41 show typical images of the structure of the surface of coatings formed upon EES of one, two, and three unit layers of composite coatings of the TiB$_2$–Cu system, respectively.

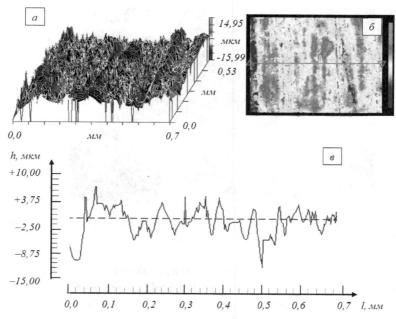

Fig. 5.37. Optical surface interferometry after electroexplosive spraying of three single layers of TiB$_2$–Cu composite coating. a – height distribution of bumps in the relief, b – position of the secant (top view), c – distribution of bumps along the base length.

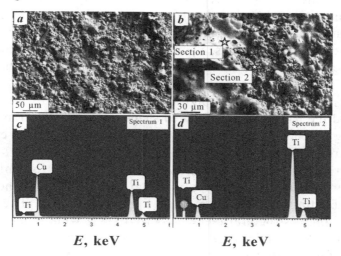

Fig. 5.38. A characteristic image of the surface of the composite coating of the TiB$_2$-Cu system formed by spraying a single layer at q = 4.5 GW/m^2. Scanning electron nicroscopy. a – general view, b – surface for x-ray analysis, c, d – X-ray spectra (places of collection of the X-ray spectrum marked with a star icon).

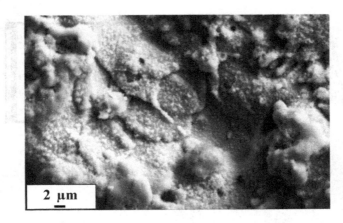

Fig. 5.39. Structure formed during electric explosion spraying a single coating layer of the TiB$_0$–Cu system. SEM.

It can be seen that the coatings formed during EES are characterized by a developed relief and a low level of roughness. Three types of structures stand out on the surface. Relate to the structure of the first type relatively smooth areas of irregular shape, located on the surface of the coating in a chaotic manner (Figs. 5.38 *b*, 5.40 *b*). Their total area is 20%.

X-ray microanalysis gives the basis to conclude that regions of the structure of this type have a complex chemical composition; The main elements are copper and titanium (Figs. 5.38 *c* and 3.40 *c*). Based on these results, we can assume that these regions were formed as a result of mixing of the particles of titanium diboride and copper during an electric explosion of a CEEM. Indeed, a detailed analysis of the surface morphology of these regions of the structure revealed the particles of a rounded shape, located either randomly or forming extended rows (Fig. 5.39). Particle sizes vary over a wide range from 250 to 500 nm.

We refer to the structure of the second type the formations of a globular shape, which occupy the total area of 75% on the surface of the coating in all EES modes (Figs. 5.40, 5.41). The average sizes of these structural elements vary over a wide range – from 1 to 10 μm. X-ray microanalysis gives the basis to conclude that the studied formations have a complex elemental composition; the main elements are copper and titanium (Fig. 5.40 *c, d*). Comparing the X-ray spectra shown in Figs. 5.40 *c* and *d*, it can be noted that the relative titanium content is higher in the structure of the second type.

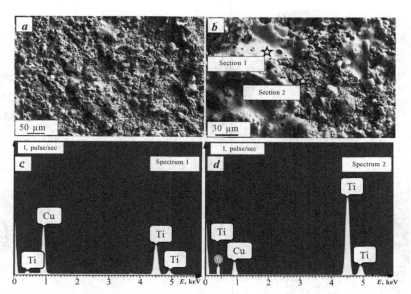

Fig. 5.40. A characteristic image of the surface of the composite coating of the TiB$_2$–Cu system formed by spraying two single layers at q = 4.5 GW/m^2. Scanning electron microscopy. a – general view, b – surface for X-ray analysis,

This leads to the presence on the X-ray of the lines from the mixture of titanium diboride and copper lying under the inclusion, as well as the presence of titanium diboride on the surface of the particles. On the one hand, this may mean the presence of titanium diboride particles in these coating areas. On the other hand, it indicates the insufficiently large thickness of the structures of the first type.

In connection with the use of CEEM for deposition, it was of interest to find out whether particles of titanium diboride powder are present on the surface of the coating. The total area occupied by the structure of the third type on the surface of the coating filling the space between the structures of the first and second type (Fig. 5.41) is 9%. X-ray microspectral analysis suggests that the main element of these formations is titanium (Fig. 5.41 d). The average sizes of these structural elements vary from 500 nm to 2 µm. Their size is comparable to particles of titanium diboride powder. Therefore, these formations are particles of titanium diboride powder used in the electric explosion of a CEEM and transferred to the processing surface without mixing with copper.

Analysis of the transverse sections of the coatings (Fig. 5.42) showed that after the EES, the coating thickness is 58...60, 115...120

Fig. 5.41. A characteristic image of the surface of the composite coating of the TiB$_2$-Cu system formed when spraying three single layers at $q = 4.5$ GW/m^2. Scanning electron microscopy. a – general view, b – surface for x-ray analysis, c, d – x-ray spectra (places of collection the x-ray spectrum is indicated on (b) by the star icon).

and 170 µm with one, two and three times processing, respectively. The border between the sprayed layers is absent. Based on this, it can be concluded that reprocessing leads to a proportional increase in coating thickness.

In all EES modes, the cross-sectional structure is globular inclusions of titanium diboride in a copper matrix (Fig. 5.43). X-ray microspectral analysis suggests that the main element of globular inclusions is titanium (Fig. 5.43 b). The average sizes of these structural elements vary in the range from 0.5 to 2.5 µm. Their sizes are comparable to particles of titanium diboride powder used for spraying.

Therefore, these formations are particles of titanium diboride powder. Analysis of the X-ray spectrum for the region containing no inclusions (Fig. 5.43) showed that these regions have a complex chemical composition; the main elements are copper and titanium (Fig. 5.43 c).

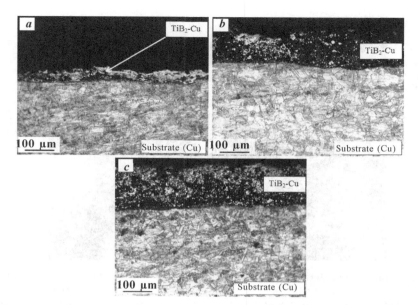

Fig. 5.42. A characteristic image of the cross-sectional structure of the composite coating of the TiB_2–Cu system. Light microscopy. a – EES of a single layer; b – EES of two single layers; c – EES of three single layers.

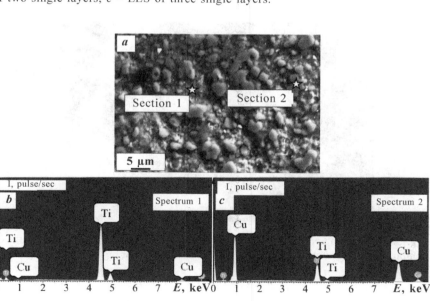

Fig. 5.43. A characteristic image of the cross-sectional structure of a composite coating of a TiB_2–Cu sprayed system at $q = 4.5$ GW/m². Scanning electron microscopy. a – general view, b – X-ray spectrum (place of collection of the X-ray spectrum - plot 1), c – X-ray spectrum (place of collection of the X-ray spectrum – plot 2).

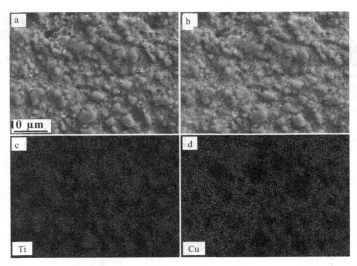

Fig. 5.44. A characteristic image of the cross-sectional structure of the composite coating of a TiB_2–Cu system sprayed at $q = 4.5$ GW/m². Scanning Electron Microscopy. a - general view; b - overlay of distribution maps of titanium and copper in the area shown on *a*, *b* – map of the distribution of titanium, *c* – map of the distribution of copper.

Fig. 5.45. A characteristic image of the structure at the boundary of the TiB_2–Cu composite coating with the substrate, direct section. Scanning electron microscopy.

Based on these results, we can assume that these areas were formed as a result of mixing of titanium diboride and copper during an electric explosion of a composite electrically exploded material.

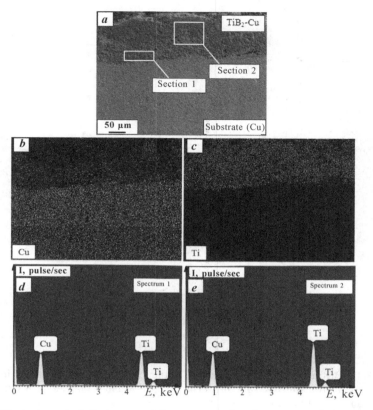

Fig. 5.46. A characteristic image of the cross-sectional structure of the composite coating of the TiB_2–Cu system sprayed at $q = 4.5$ GW/m². Scanning electron microscopy. *a* – general view, *b* – copper distribution map, *c* – distribution map of titanium, *d* – X-ray spectrum (obtained from section 1 on a), *e* – X-ray spectrum (obtained from section 2 on *a*).

This is also evidenced by a comparison of the distribution maps of titanium and copper over the coating (Fig. 5.44).

At the boundaries of the coatings with the base, due to the thermal force effect of the plasma jet on the surface heated to the melting temperature, a wave-like relief is formed, which allows to increase adhesion (Fig. 5.45). An important processing feature is the penetration of individual particles of titanium diboride into the substrate to a depth of several micrometers.

Comparing the X-ray spectra shown in Figs. 5.46 *d* and *e*, it can be noted that the relative titanium content is higher in the structure in section 2. However, a comparison of the distribution maps of copper and titanium (Figs. 5.46 *b*, *c*) shows that in the formed

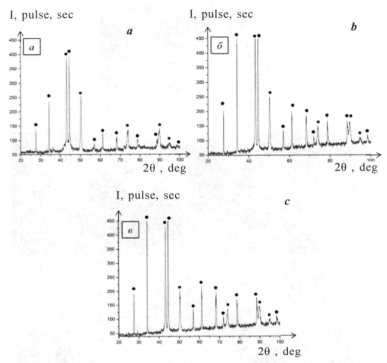

Fig. 5.47. Diffraction pattern of coatings of the TiB$_2$–Cu system, obtained in various modes of electroexplosive spraying. The symbols ■ and ● indicate peaks, belonging to Cu and TiB$_2$ titanium respectively. *a* – EES of a single layer; *b* – EES of two single layers; *c* – EES of three single layers.

coating, titanium diboride and copper is evenly distributed. Boron is not detected by this method.

The formed structure is characterized by the absence of pores, which is a positive feature of the spraying method used, since the presence of porosity inevitably leads to a decrease in the electrical conductivity of the coatings.

X-ray diffraction analysis showed that in all coating modes they contain titanium diboride and copper in approximately equal proportions (Fig. 5.47). Thus, titanium diboride remains stable during EES.

Let us analyze the values of the thickness of the mixing zone at the coating – substrate interface described above in this chapter.

It is seen (Fig. 5.48) that the maximum values of the thickness of the mixing zone at the coating – substrate interface are observed in the W–Cu and W–C–Cu systems.

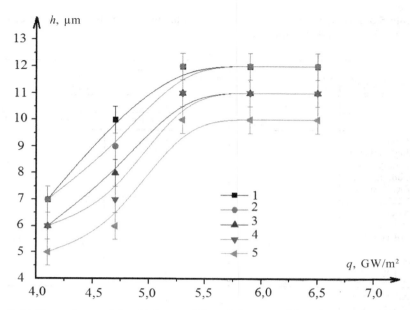

Fig. 5.48. Dependence of the thickness of the mixing zone (h) various systems formed on a copper substrate with the absorbed power density (q). 1 – W–Cu system, 2 – W–C–Cu system, 3 – Mo–Cu system, 4 – Mo–C–Cu system, 5 – TiB$_2$–Cu system.

The minimum values of the thickness of the mixing zone at the coating–substrate interface are characteristic of coating the TiB$_2$– Cu system. The average values of the thickness of the mixing zone at the coating–substrate interface are observed in the Mo–Cu and Mo–C–Cu systems. This is due to the fact that tungsten is a heavier element, that is, it has a greater atomic mass compared to molybdenum and titanium diboride.

For all systems, the graphical dependence of the thickness of the mixing zone at the coating – substrate interface on the absorbed power density can be conditionally divided into 2 sections. The first section of almost linear growth of the thickness of the mixing zone at the coating-substrate interface in the range of absorbed power density from 4.2 to 5.2 GW/m^2 and the second section in which there is a steady-state value of the thickness of the mixing zone in the range of absorbed power density from 5.2 up to 6.5 GW/m^2.

Table 5.3. Average values of the roughness parameters of the surface of coatings of the TiB$_2$–Al systems produced by EES

Investigated sample	Roughness parameter for base					
	Surface			Length		
Initial	1.54	21.52	10.13	1.51	13.80	10.13
After EES of single layer of coating in the mode mTiB2/ mAl = 50/100	2.52	32.41	49.34	2.70	18.82	41.93
After EES of single layer of coating in the mode mTiB$_2$/mAl = 100/100	2.61	35.44	49.52	2.60	18.73	42.22
After EES of single layer of coating in the mode mTiB$_2$/mAl = 150/100	2.71	30.94	50.12	2.63	18.81	40.80

5.10. Study of surface roughness of electroexplosive coatings of the TiB$_2$–Al system

Let us consider the results of studying the surface roughness of a coating obtained on substrates made of technical aluminium of grade A99 at EES, depending on the EES mode of single layers.

Analysis of laser interferometry data showed that the obtained coatings have higher roughness parameters in comparison with the surface of the samples for EES (Table 5.3). After a single spraying of the coating in the m_{TiB2}/m_{Al} = 50/100, 100/100 and 150/100 modes, the arithmetic mean deviation of the Ra profile reaches from 2.52 to 2.71 µm on the base surface and from 2.60 to 2.70 on the base length, the maximum profile height R_{max} is from 30.94 to 35.44 µm on the base surface and from 18.73 to 18.82 µm on the base length. The roughness parameter for Sm profile irregularities is from 49.34 to 50.12 µm, and the roughness parameter for local Sm projections is from 40.80 to 42.22 µm.

Fig. 5.49. - Surface morphology of technically pure aluminium after electric explosion spraying TiB$_2$–Al composite coating system in m_{TiB2}/m_{Al} = 100/100 mode. a – general view, b – flows, c – micropores and microcraters, d – microcracks, e – layering, f – volumes, formed by fine round titanium diboride particles

We give a detailed description of the laser interferometry data for the EES coating of the TiB$_2$–Al system in the m_{TiB2}/m_{Al} = 150/100 mode. The roughness parameter Ra in this case is 2.73 μm. The profile cavity with a depth of 12.2 μm and a single protrusion with a height of 59.9 μm explain the values of the parameter R_{max} = 72.1 μm for the base surface (Fig. 4.16) and R_{max} = 19.3 μm for the base length. The average pitch of irregularities Sm = 45 μm, the average pitch of local protrusions Sm = 38 μm.

Such low values of surface roughness are explained by the fact that the coatings were formed during EES, which is characterized by condensation on the surface of mostly liquid drops of explosion

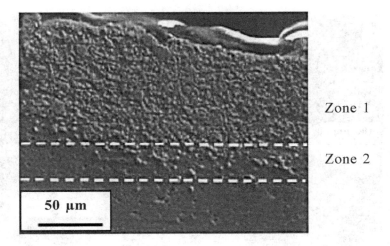

Zone 1

Zone 2

50 μm

Fig. 5.50. A characteristic image of the coating structure of the TiB_2–Al system. Straight cut.

products from the rear of the plasma stream, after which self-quenching occurs [198].

5.11. Structural–phase states of TiB_2–Al system coatings

Let us analyze the effect of the spraying mode of coatings obtained on substrates made of technical aluminium of grade A99 at EES on the coating structure.

Scanning electron microscopy studies of the irradiation surface showed (Fig. 5.49) that the structure formed on the surface of the samples is characterized by a low level of roughness (Fig. 5.49 *a*). A number of relief features can be distinguished on the surface: inflows caused by the radial flow of metal from the centre of the spraying spot to the periphery (Fig. 5.49 *b*), microcraters (Fig. 5.49 *c*), microcracks (Fig. 5.49 *d*), layers formed as a result of condensation of particles explosion products of foil and TiB_2 powder reaching the irradiated surface from the rear of the jet [198] (Fig. 5.49 *e, f*). The arrow in Fig. 5.49 *c* shows a microcrater, the arrow in Fig. 5.49 *d* shows a microcrack.

Analysis of transverse sections showed (Fig. 5.50) that the coatings with a thickness of about 100 μm are relatively uniform in depth and are characterized by the absence of pores. Two zones are distinguished in the structure of coatings. Zone 1 has a composite filled structure.

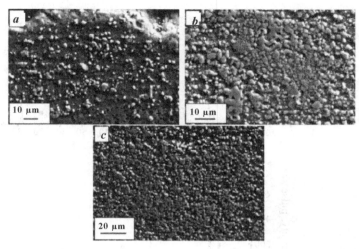

Fig. 5.51. Composite filled structure of TiB$_2$–Al system coatings sprayed in various modes. Straight sections. a – mode $m_{\text{TiB2}}/m_{\text{Al}}$ = 50/100, b – mode $m_{\text{TiB2}}/m_{\text{Al}}$ = 100/100, c – $m_{\text{TiB2}}/m_{\text{Al}}$ = 150/100 mode.

Studies at high magnifications showed (Fig. 5.51) that it is represented by an aluminium matrix with reinforcing inclusions of titanium diboride particles located in it. Depending on the spraying mode, the ratio of the volumes of the matrix and inclusions is 1:3 (Fig 5.51 a), 1:1 (Fig. 5.51 b), and 3:1 (Fig. 5.51 c) for the modes 1, 2, and 3, respectively.

Zone 2 is intermediate between the coating and the substrate. Its characteristic feature is that TiB$_2$ powder particles penetrate the substrate without breaking its continuity.

This can be explained on the basis of the ideas of physical mesomechanics about the appearance of atomic-vacancy configurational excitations during the spraying in the surface layer of the base and the distribution of tensile and compressive stresses and strains at the 'strongly non-equilibrium layer–base' boundary in the form of a 'checkerboard' [198]. The formation of this zone helps to ensure high adhesion of the coatings to the substrate.

X-ray phase analysis of coatings sprayed in various modes showed (Fig. 5.52) that they consist of Al, TiB$_2$ and TiBO$_3$. The presence of the TiBO$_3$ phase can be associated with the oxidation of titanium diboride particles due to the presence of air oxygen in the process chamber.

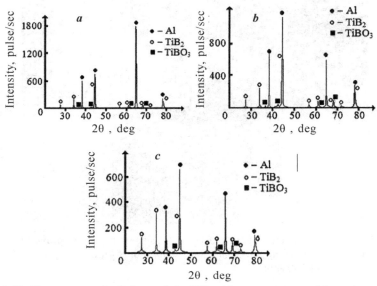

Fig. 5.52. X-ray areas of coatings of the TiB_2–Al system, sprayed in various modes. a – mode m_{TiB2}/m_{Al} = 50/100, b – mode m_{TiB2}/m_{Al} = 100/100, c – m_{TiB2}/m_{Al} = 150/100 mode.

Comparing the intensity of the peaks, we can state that the percentage of hardening inclusions of TiB_2 and $TiBO_3$ and the aluminium matrix is 25 and 75, 50 and 50, 75 and 25% for the modes m_{TiB2}/m_{Al} = 50/100, m_{TiB2}/m_{Al} = 100/100 and m_{TiB2}/m_{Al} = 150/100, respectively, and is consistent with the data of scanning electron microscopy. The absence of titanium aluminides in the coating indicates that there was no dissolution of TiB_2 particles in aluminium.

Summarizing the foregoing, it can be noted that the EES allows the formation of porous, uniform in depth, composite coatings of the Al–TiB_2 system with a thickness of 100 μm. The arithmetic average deviation of the profile Ra surface of the coating is 2.0 μm. The surface morphology is characterized by the presence of inflows, micropores, microcraters, microcracks, and layers formed by fine particles of rounded titanium diboride and drops of explosion products of aluminium foil. The sizes of inclusions of titanium diboride in the aluminium matrix are distributed in the range of 0.5...2.5 μm. At the interface between the coating and the substrate, an EES forms the zone of penetration of titanium diboride particles into the substrate without breaking its continuity.

Table 5.4. Values of tribological characteristics, micro- and nanohardness, elastic modulus of the first kind of electric explosive W–Cu, Mo–Cu, W–C–Cu, Mo–C–Cu, Ti–B–Cu, TiB_2–Cu and TiB_2–Al coatings

Coating	W, 10^{-6}, mm²/N m	W(subst-rate)/ W(coating)	µ	Microhard-ness, HV	Nanohardness HN, GPa	E, GPa
Cu (subst-rate)	301.8		0.627	150	1.6	110
W-Cu	197.8	1.5	0.411	150…460	4.7	260
Mo-Cu	117.0	2.6	0.243	150…320	3.5	355
Mo-C-Cu	181.5	1.7	0.377	900…1100	11.2	396
W-C-Cu	164.1	1.8	0.341	1100…1750	18.1	470
TiB2-Cu	139.1	2.2	0.289	500…3500	26.4	450
TiB2-Al	183.5	1.9	0.306	45…3000	27.9	233
Al	351.2		0.501	25	0.3	70

5.12. Properties of electroexplosive wear and tear and electroerosion resistant coatings

A summary Table 5.4 of the values of tribological characteristics, micro- and nanohardness, modulus of elasticity of the first kind of electroexplosive electroerosion-resistant coatings with a filled structure is given below.

Consider the results of wear resistance tests in dry friction-slip conditions without lubricating the coatings of the W–Cu, Mo–Cu, WC–Cu, Mo–C–Cu, Ti–B–Cu, TiB_2–Cu and TiB_2–Al systems with a composite filled structure. The coatings formed during EES have greater wear resistance compared to the initial surface of M00 grade copper (A99 grade aluminium for the TiB_2–Al system). It is seen (Table 5.4) that the composite coating of the TiB_2–Cu system has the best wear resistance. This is explained by the fact that, when applied, the hardest of the titanium borides TiB_2 is formed [207].

A study of the surface structure of the wear holes (Fig. 5.53 a) reveals submicron boride particles in the copper matrix. Obviously, during the wear process, solid borides are held in a ductile copper matrix. The coatings of the W–C–Cu system have a similar surface structure of the wear holes (Fig. 5.53 b). The wear values for the

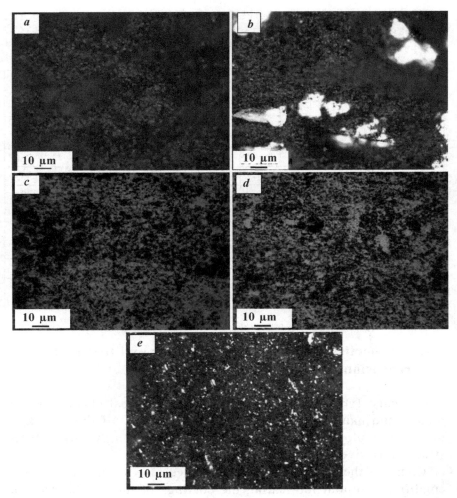

Fig. 5.53. The structure of the wear surface of composite filled coatings. *a –* Ti–B–Cu system, *b –* W–C–Cu system, *c –* Mo–Cu system, *d –* system W–Cu, *e –* system Cu–Mo.

WC–Cu and W–Cu systems are the same, since in the ternary system, in addition to α-W_2C, WC_{1-x} and WC carbides, the copper matrix also contains unreacted carbon W. Higher wear resistance of the coatings of the Mo-Cu system with a filled structure 'molybdenum matrix–copper inclusions' compared to a coating with a filled structure of the copper matrix–molybdenum inclusions is due to the fact that in the first case, a rigid molybdenum matrix holds plastic copper inclusions.

The surface structure of the wear holes of the coating with the filled structure 'copper matrix–tungsten inclusions' (Fig. 5.53 *c*) represents submicron and microcrystalline Mo particles in the copper matrix in approximately equal proportions, of coating samples with the filled structure 'copper matrix–tungsten inclusions' (Fig. 5.53 *d*) – submicron and microcrystalline tungsten particles in a copper matrix, coating samples with a filled structure 'molybdenum matrix–copper inclusions' (Fig. 5.53 *e*) – submicron and microcrystalline particles of copper in a molybdenum matrix.

According to the test results, it can be stated that the electrocontact composite surface layers of the W–Cu, Mo–Cu, Ti–B–Cu, WC–Cu systems formed by the electric explosion treatment show an increase in wear resistance in the conditions of dry sliding friction without lubrication compared to electrical grade copper M00 1.5...2.2 times, and systems TiB_2–Al–1.9 times compared with aluminium grade A99.

Electroerosive resistance in conditions of arc erosion. Let us consider the test results of coatings of the W–Cu, Mo–Cu, W–C–Cu, Mo–C–Cu, Ti–B–Cu, TiB_2–Cu and TiB_2–Al systems with a composite filled structure for electrical erosion resistance under conditions of arc erosion.

As shown in this chapter, in the initial state, the coating structure of all systems is a copper matrix with globular inclusions of hardening phases. Coatings of the Ti–B–Cu system contain titanium borides TiB_2, Ti_2B, Ti_3B_4, TiB, and copper synthesized during EES.

It is known [208, 209] that the rate of destruction of the contact surface depends on the power density in the region of the supporting spots of the arc, the method of arc excitation and the duration of its impact on the electrodes, geometry and material of the contacts.

In this regard, the change in the morphology of coatings can be explained on the basis that copper is evaporated during the test cycles, the surface of the coatings is enriched with a refractory component, their temperature is increased due to a decrease in electrical conductivity and, as a consequence, an increase in the fracture rate with respect to the initial value [209]. For several milliseconds, the arc on open contacts remains motionless and erodes them. In this case, the arc discharge is a short contracted arc burning in the vapours of metal contacts.

Under the influence of discrete energy fluxes, microbubbles arise on the surface of the arc reference spot, the internal pressure of which causes them to explode, the outflow of plasma microstructures conducting current, and the formation of craters, accompanied by the expansion of drops of liquid metal and solid particles. Several craters function simultaneously on the supporting spot. The current in plasma

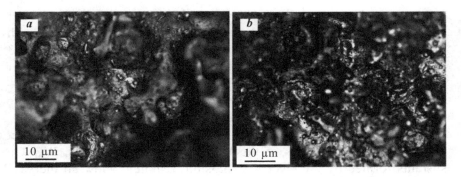

Fig. 5.54. Typical surface structure of coatings after tests for electrical discharge resistance in conditions of arc erosion, a – system W–Cu, b – system Mo–Cu.

microjets can be of the order of ~100 A, the current density is ~100 A/cm², and the pressure in the plasma microjet can be ~10^7 Pa [209].

Under the influence of high temperatures during the testing of coatings of all systems, their surface is melted and a rough relief forms on it (Fig. 5.54).

In this case, low-melting copper evaporates and the refractory component becomes the main coating element, which form a continuous matrix with copper inclusions with sizes of the order of several micrometers (Fig. 3.54). In certain areas, the coating breaks down to the substrate material.

Common to all systems is that a composite filled structure formed by a refractory filler and a matrix helps to maintain a flat contact surface. Apparently, the role of the refractory component is reduced to a decrease in the evaporation of the matrix during operation.

During testing, the resistance of the coatings of all systems is in the range of 4.2...14 μOhm. At the same time, the coatings withstand 6000 on/off cycles. According to the results of the tests of composite coatings of all systems for electroerosion resistance according to the AC-3 mode, it can be stated that the coatings obtained in the work satisfy the GOST State Standart [139] for testing electromagnetic starters for switching wear resistance.

Electroerosive resistance in the conditions of spark erosion. Consider the results of tests of coatings with a composite filled structure for electrical erosion resistance under conditions of spark erosion. The coatings formed during EES have a higher electrical erosion resistance in the conditions of spark discharge in comparison

Table 5.5. The relative wear resistance of the coatings with composite filled structure

System	W-Cu	W-C-Cu	TiB$_2$-Cu	Mo-Cu	Mo-C-Cu	Ti-B-Cu	TiB$_2$-Al
m_e/m (EES)	9.6	10.0	10.4	10.0	9.9	9.0	9.0

Note. m_e – mass loss of copper or aluminium (TiB$_2$-Al system), adopted as a standard at 10,000 test cycles, m – coating mass loss. The measurement error is not more than 1%.

From Table 5.5 it can be seen that the composite coating of the TiB$_2$–Cu system has the best electroerosion stability in the conditions of a spark discharge. This can be explained by the fact that, when applied, titanium diboride TiB$_2$ is used, which has better characteristics in comparison with other titanium borides [207]. In general, it can be noted that all coatings show an increase in electrical erosion resistance under conditions of spark discharge by ~10 times. Features of the destruction of the surface of the coatings are similar to those in tests for electrical discharge resistance in conditions of arc erosion.

The resulting electroexplosive coatings have an electrical conductivity in the range of 22 to 29 nS.

5.13. Conclusions

1. For the first time, nanocomposite coatings of the W–Cu, Mo–Cu, W–C–Cu, Mo–C–Cu, Ti–B–Cu, TiB$_2$–Cu, and TiB$_2$–Al systems were obtained by the method of electric explosion spraying.

2. Layered coatings are formed during surface treatment without melting it. Moreover, an increase in the mass of exploding conductors leads to an increase in the thickness of the layers of molybdenum (tungsten) and copper in the range from 15 to 50 μm. Surface melting treatment leads to the destruction of the layered structure of the coating and the mixing of molybdenum (tungsten) and copper.

After electroexplosive spraying using foils, the surface morphology is represented by deformed drops of copper or molybdenum, and after spraying using powders, by deformed drops.

3. Coatings 'molybdenum matrix–copper inclusions' are characterized by a relatively uniform distribution of molybdenum and copper throughout the volume. They have a submicrocrystalline and nanoscale composite filled structure. The application of the electroexplosive copper plating mode, when the absorbed power density is 10.0 GW/m^2, leads to an increase in the thermal force effect of a multiphase plasma jet of explosion products of copper foil

on the irradiated surface and the formation of surface layers with a thickness of 25 μm with larger (up to 2 μm) copper inclusions. Two characteristic morphological constituent structures are identified on the surface, which form the microrelief of the coating with a uniform distribution of molybdenum and copper: relatively smooth regions and conglomerates of particles of globular morphology.

4. Coatings 'copper matrix–molybdenum (tungsten) inclusions', with a relatively uniform distribution throughout the volume of tungsten or molybdenum and copper, have a thickness of up to 250 μm. The sizes of tungsten or molybdenum inclusions in the copper matrix vary from 1 to 10 μm. Two characteristic morphological constituent structures are formed on the surface that form the microrelief of the coating: relatively smooth areas based on molybdenum (tungsten); conglomerates of particles of molybdenum (tungsten) and copper of globular morphology.

5. All studied coatings have a finely dispersed non-porous structure. At the boundary of the coating with the base during spraying, both tungsten and molybdenum form a mutual mixing zone, which forms a metallurgical cohesion-adhesive bond with the substrate.

6. Using optical interferometry methods, a set of characteristics of the surface topography of coatings has been determined. After electroexplosive spraying, an increase in surface roughness occurs compared to the initial value of the surface roughness of the sprayed copper samples. It is shown that the lowest arithmetic mean deviation of the profile $Ra = 2.1...3.2$ μm is possessed by layered coatings and coatings with a filled structure, sprayed using a composite electrically explosive material, since they were obtained by electric explosion treatment, which is characterized mainly by liquid deposition on the surface particles of explosion products from the rear of the jet, followed by self-hardening. The increased value $Ra = 2.2...4.7$ μm of coatings with a filled structure is due to the fact that they were obtained by electric explosion treatment, which causes surface melting, convective mixing of the melt, deposition of explosion products from the rear of the jet on the surface of condensed particles, and subsequent self-hardening.

7. It has been established that during the electroexplosive spraying of coatings of various systems, one of their structural elements is globular fragments of a mesoscopic scale. In this case, dispersion and mutual penetration of the components of the sprayed coating are observed. The observed structural features can be explained on the

basis of the ideas of physical mesomechanics about the appearance of a 'checkerboard' distribution of compressive and tensile normal stresses, leading to the appearance of mesations of the coating material.

8. By the method of electroexplosive spraying on a copper contact surface, composite coatings of the Mo–C–Cu system with a thickness of 28...30 μm having a microcrystalline composite filled structure are formed. Their phase composition is formed by the pseudo-alloy of molybdenum and copper and inclusions of the carbides MoC and Mo_2C synthesized during spraying. An increase in the parameters of the thermal power action on the irradiated surface leads to an increase in the carbide content in the coating. Coatings are characterized by a non-uniform surface topography, the absence of pores and metallurgical bond with the base. The surface roughness parameter $Ra = 2.0...2.6$ μm.

9. By the method of electric explosive spraying on a copper contact surface, composite coatings of the W–C–Cu system with a thickness of 28...30 μm are formed, having a microcrystalline composite filled structure. Their phase composition is formed by a pseudo-alloy of tungsten and copper and inclusions of carbides $\alpha\text{-}W_2C$, WC_{1-x}, and WC synthesized during spraying. An increase in the parameters of the thermal force action on the irradiated surface leads to an increase in the carbide content in the coating. Coatings are characterized by a non-uniform surface topography, the absence of pores and metallurgical bond with the base. The surface roughness parameter $Ra = 2.0...2.6$ μm.

10. An electric explosion method yields composite coatings containing titanium borides TiB_2, Ti_2B, Ti_3B_4, TiB and copper. The roughness parameter of their surface Ra varies between 3.2...3.5 μm. The formed structure is characterized by the absence of pores. The optimal from the point of view of the formation of the most refractory TiB_2 phase should be considered the mode of coating formation at an exposure intensity of 5.5 GW/m^2. The thickness of the composite titanium–boron–copper coatings formed in the optimal mode is 15...16 μm.

11. It was established that the surface roughness of the TiB_2–Cu system coatings is higher than that of the initial samples. After one, two and three times the treatment, the roughness parameter Ra is 2.5...2.7 μm. The obtained roughness parameters do not interfere with the practical use of electroexplosive surface layers, since during the operation of medium and heavy-loaded circuit breakers under

constant operating conditions, running-in occurs and a stable surface roughness is created.

12. After the EES of the composite coatings of the TiB_2–Cu system, three characteristic morphological components of the structure that form the microrelief of the coating are distinguished on the surface: submicrocrystalline particles of titanium diboride powder used for the EES; relatively smooth regions based on titanium and copper diboride containing submicrocrystalline inclusions of titanium diboride; conglomerates of particles of titanium diboride and copper of globular morphology.

13. The structure of the cross sections of the coatings does not contain pores and is a copper matrix with inclusions of titanium diboride, the sizes of which vary from 0.5 to 2.5 µm. Titanium diboride and copper are distributed over the coating volume in an approximately equal ratio. In the process of EES, recrystallization of titanium diboride with the formation of other compounds does not occur. At the boundary of the coating with the base during spraying, a mutual mixing zone is formed, which helps to ensure high adhesion of the coatings to the base.

14. Electroexplosive spraying allows the formation of non-porous and uniform in depth composite coatings of the Al–TiB_2 system with a thickness of 100 µm. The arithmetic average deviation of the profile Ra surface of the coating is 2.0 µm. The surface morphology is characterized by the presence of inflows, micropores, microcraters, microcracks, and layers, formed by fine particles of rounded titanium diboride and drops of explosion products of aluminium foil. The sizes of inclusions of titanium diboride in the aluminium matrix are in the range of 0.5...2.5 µm. At the interface between the coating and the substrate during spraying, a zone of penetration of titanium diboride particles into the base is formed without braking its continuity.

15. It has been established that EES leads to a simultaneous increase in several times of various operational properties of a copper substrate – nano- and microhardness, first-type elastic modulus, wear resistance under conditions of dry sliding friction, electrical discharge resistance under conditions of arc and spark erosion. Electroexplosive coatings have electrical conductivity in the range from 22 to 29 nS.

6

Structure and properties of electric explosive wear and electroerosion resistant coatings processed by an electron beam

The results presented in this chapter are published in scientific articles [210–217] and are protected by patents for inventions [218–223] and utility models [224, 224].

6.1. Surface topography and structural phase states of coatings of Mo–Cu and W–Cu systems of immiscible components

Let us analyze the results of a study of changes in the structure of electroexplosive coatings of Mo–Cu and W–Cu systems from immiscible components obtained at copper electrical contacts during EES, formed after EBT (electron beam treatment) in various modes.

Electroexplosive coatings of the Mo–Cu system after EBT. Figures 6.1 and 6.2 show typical microimages of structural components on the coating surface of the Mo–Cu system formed after EBT.

SEM studies of the irradiation surface showed that exposure to samples by an electron beam under all treatment conditions leads to significant transformations of the sample surface. In the central part of the zone of influence of the electron beam (the region whose sizes increase from 10 mm² at an electron beam energy density of 45 J/cm² to 18 mm at 60 J/cm²), microdrops, microcraters, and microcracks

172

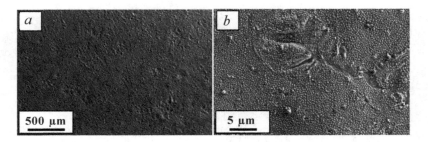

Fig. 6.1. Typical SEM images of the surface of the electroexplosive composite coating of the Mo–Cu system after EBT. Images obtained in secondary electrons. *a* – general view of the surface topography; *b* – cellular structure of the surface.

described earlier in [198] disappear. The surface topography is smoothed out (Fig. 6.1). Outside the central zone of EBT, the surface topography of the electroexplosive coating is also smoothed and is characterized by varying degrees of homogeneity.

A polycrystalline structure is revealed on the surface of coatings after EBT, the average grain size of which increases with increasing electron beam energy density from 10 μm at 45 J/cm^2 to 22 μm at 50 J/cm^2. A cellular structure characteristic of high-speed crystallization is revealed in grains [135, 136]. The average transverse cell size is 1.3 μm (Fig. 6.2).

According to the evolution of the morphology of the irradiation surface, the distribution of elements in the structure of the surface layer also changes. In the central zone, a composite coating with a uniform distribution of molybdenum and copper in the amount of 70 and 30 at.% respectively. Larger regions of structurally free molybdenum or copper are observed at the boundary of the central zone and beyond. Thus, all the EBT modes used make it possible to form homogeneous and smooth surface layers with a microcrystalline two-phase structure.

After EES, the coating thickness varies from 100 to 125 μm. After EBT, three layers are distinguished in the coating structure (Fig. 6.2): I – surface coating layer remelted during EBT; II – an intermediate layer, in which structural changes occurred in the solid state; III – a layer of thermal influence of the base, in which by chemical etching grain boundaries are detected worse than in depth.

Electron-beam processing of the coating surface is accompanied not only by smoothing the surface relief, but also leads to equalization of the thickness of the modified layer I (Fig. 6.2). The

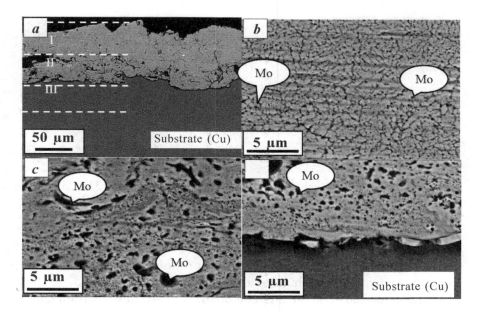

Fig. 6.2. Representative cross-sectional SEM images of the electroexplosive composite coating of the Mo-Cu system after EBT. Images obtained in backward reflected electrons. *a* – cross-sectional structure; *b* – coating layer after subsequent EBT; *c* – a coating layer not affected by EBT; *d* – the boundary of the electro- explosion coating with the substrate; I – coating layer after EBT; II – coating layer unaffected by EBT; III – a layer of thermal influence.

thickness of the modified layers after EBT varies from 30 to 50 μm and slightly decreases with increasing electron beam energy density.

Electron-beam processing, accompanied by the remelting of layer I of an electroexplosive coating, leads to the formation of a composite dispersion-hardened [130] structure over the entire section of the layer (Fig. 6.2 *b*, layer I in Fig. 6.2 *a*).

Defects in the form of micropores and microcracks are not observed in it. The sizes of copper inclusions in the molybdenum matrix vary from 0.1 to 0.2 μm, while the sizes of copper inclusions in layer II vary from 0.1 to 2.0 μm (layer II in Fig. 6.2 *a*, Fig. 6.2 *c*). Thus, pulse-periodic remelting of surface layer I leads to the formation of a more dispersed and uniform structure in it.

The phase composition of the coatings treated with an electron beam was studied by analyzing microelectron diffraction patterns obtained from thin foils. According to data from previous studies, the solubility of molybdenum or tungsten in copper is practically zero

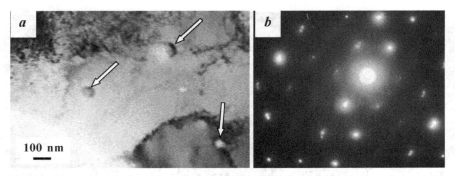

Fig. 6.3. Electron microscopic image of the coating structure of the Mo–Cu system. Arrows indicate molybdenum particles. *a –* image obtained in a bright field; *b –* microelectron diffraction pattern.

[110, 226]. . Consequently, the presence of molybdenum particles can be expected in the coatings of the Mo–Cu system. Indeed, studies have revealed particles of this composition. Particles are rounded in size and can be divided into two classes. Firstly, these are particles whose sizes vary within 80...150 nm (Fig. 6.3). Most likely, these are particles of the originally used powder that did not dissolve during the irradiation process. Secondly, particles whose sizes vary within 10...15 nm (Fig. 6.3). Obviously, particles of this size range precipitated during crystallization of the melt.

Electroexplosive coatings of the W–Cu system after EBT. SEM studies of the irradiation surface showed that the processing of a sample by an electron beam in all modes leads to cardinal transformations of the sample surface. Two areas are distinguished in it: central and peripheral. In the central region of the electron beam exposure (the region whose sizes increase from 10 to 18 mm with an increase in the energy density from 45 to 60 J/cm², respectively), the microdroplets, microcraters and microcracks described earlier in [198] disappear, the surface relief is smoothed (Fig. 6.4 *a*). A structure is formed that includes areas *A* with a smooth relief of irregular shape, placed on the surface of the coating in an arbitrary way, and rough areas *B* (Fig. 6.4 *a*).

The X-ray microanalysis of section 1 in Fig. 6.4 *b* allows us to conclude that the regions of the structure with a smooth relief are formed by copper and tungsten in the amount of 95 and 5 at. % respectively. Smooth regions have a polycrystalline structure (Fig. 6.4 *b*), the average grain size of which increases from 10 to 30 μm with an increase in energy density from 45 to 50 J/cm²,

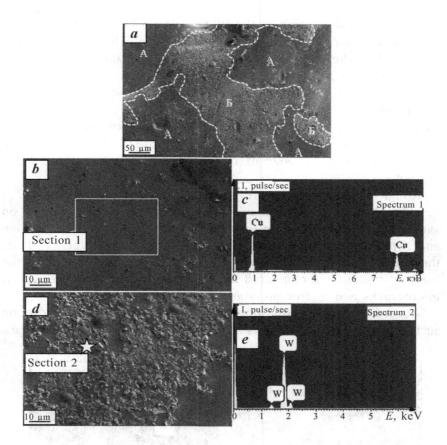

Fig. 6.4. Typical SEM images of the surface of an electroexplosive composite coating of the W–Cu system after EBT. Images obtained in secondary electrons. *a* – general view of the surface topography; *a* – surface for x-ray analysis with a smooth relief; *d* – surface for x-ray analysis with a rough relief; *c, e* – X-ray spectra (the places of collection of which are indicated in the photographs (*b, d*)); *A* - areas with a smooth relief, *B* – rough areas. The border between areas *A* and *B* is indicated by a dotted line.

respectively. An increase in the electron beam energy density to 60 J /cm² (pulse exposure time 100 μs) is accompanied by the formation of a polycrystalline structure with grain sizes that vary from 3 to 40 μm.

Small grains are grouped in the area. It can be assumed that during EBT in this mode, the conditions conducive to the dynamic recrystallization process [135, 136] are realized in the surface layer of the composite coating of the W–Cu system [135, 136], in which small grains locally combine into large ones. This assumption is supported by the fact that in $E_S = 60$ J/cm², $t = 200$ μs, and $N = 20$ pulses. (Section 2), in which the beam power density was the lowest, a more even-grained structure was formed, the grain size of which is in the range of 3...20 μm. In the volume of grains, regardless of the energy density of the electron beam, a cellular structure is revealed (Fig. 6.4 *b*), which is characteristic of high-speed crystallization [224]. The transverse size of the cells in it varies between 0.5... 1.0 μm.

Rough regions are formed by particles with sizes from 0.5 to 5.0 μm. The X-ray microanalysis of section 1 in Fig. 6.4 *d*, selected on such a particle, gives reason to conclude that it is formed by tungsten and copper in the amount of 93 and 7 at. %, respectively. Outside the central zone of the specimen, a structure is observed in which the surface is smoothed compared to the specimen after EES, however, microcracks and microcraters are still present in it.

According to the evolution of the morphology of the irradiation surface, the elemental composition of the surface layer also changes.

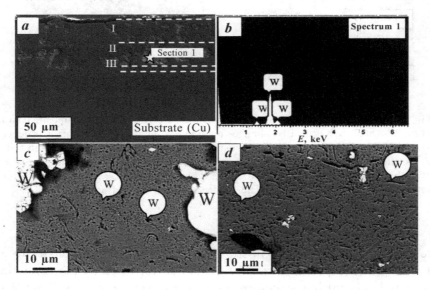

Fig. 6.5. Typical SEM images of the cross section of the electroexplosive composite coating of the W–Cu system after EBT. Images obtained in secondary electrons. *a* – cross-sectional structure; *b* – X-ray spectrum (the location of the X-ray spectrum is indicated on (*a*)); *c* – a coating layer and subsequent EBT; *d* – coating layer not affected by EBT; I – coating layer after EBT; II – coating layer unaffected by EBT; III – thermal influence layer.

On the border of the central zone and beyond, the regions enriched in tungsten or copper are preserved.

Smoothing the surface by EBT leads to equalization of the thickness of the modified layer (Fig. 6.5). As follows from the analysis of the image of the structure of the transverse section, the thickness of the modified layer after EBT in various modes varies from 30 to 50 µm and slightly decreases with increasing energy density of the electron beam. Moreover, the total coating thickness is 60–80 µm. The boundary between the coating and the substrate has a wave-like relief, which indicates a high adhesion of the coating to the substrate.

Processing leads to the elimination of defects caused by the ingress of tungsten powder particles into the melt: micropores and microcracks are practically not detected in the modified electron beam electroexplosive coating (Fig. 6.5 *a, b*). Three layers are distinguished in the coating structure (Fig. 6.9): I – coating layer after EBT; II – coating layer not affected by EBT; III – a layer of thermal influence, in which by chemical etching the grain boundaries are detected worse than at the base.

Smoothing the surface of the coating during EBT results in equalization of the thickness of layer I, in which the composite filled layer structure is formed (Fig. 6.5 *b*). The sizes of tungsten inclusions in the copper matrix are in the range from 0.5 to 2.0 µm. In layer II, the sizes of tungsten inclusions vary from 0.5 to 5.0 µm (Fig. 7.5 *c*). The layers I and II contain large isolated tungsten inclusions with sizes from 2 to 30 µm (Fig. 6.5). These inclusions are not uniformly distributed over the coating volume.

Thus, the performed studies show that the EBT of the surface layer of the electric explosive coating of copper electrical contacts, carried out in the melting mode, leads to the formation of a structurally and concentrationally uniform surface layer.

The phase composition of the coatings treated with an electron beam was studied by analyzing microelectron diffraction patterns obtained from thin foils. According to numerous studies, the solubility of molybdenum or tungsten in copper is practically zero [135, 136]. Consequently, the presence of tungsten particles can be expected in the coatings of the W–Cu system. Indeed, studies have revealed particles of this composition. Particles are rounded in size and can be divided into two classes. Firstly, these are particles whose sizes vary within 80...150 nm. It is likely that these are particles of

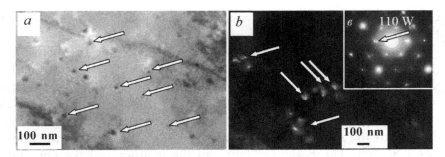

Fig. 6.6. Electron microscopic image of the coating structure of the W–Cu system. The arrows on *a, b* indicate tungsten particles: *a* – image obtained in a bright field; *b* – the dark field obtained in the reflex [110] W (the reflex is indicated on (*c*) by the arrow), *c* – microelectron diffraction pattern.

the originally used powder that did not dissolve during irradiation. Secondly, particles whose sizes vary within 10...15 nm (Figure 6.6). Obviously, particles of this size range precipitated during crystallization of the melt.

6.2. Surface relief, structure, phase and elemental composition of coatings of Mo–C–Cu and W–C–Cu systems, hardened by synthesized carbide phases of molybdenum or tungsten

Let us analyze the results of a change in the structure of pseudo-alloy coatings of the Mo–C–Cu and W–C–Cu systems obtained on copper substrates during EES formed after EBT.

Electroexplosive coatings of the Mo–C–Cu system after EBT. SEM studies of the irradiation surface showed that the processing of a sample by an electron beam in all modes leads to cardinal transformations of the sample surface. Two areas are distinguished in it – central and peripheral. In the central region of the electron beam exposure (the region whose sizes increase from 10 to 18 mm with an increase in the energy density from 45 to 60 J/cm², respectively), the microdroplets, microcraters and microcracks described earlier in [198] disappear, the surface relief is smoothed (Fig. 6.7 *a*). A structure is formed that includes relatively smooth areas *A* of irregular shape, located on the surface of the coating in an arbitrary way, and rough areas (Fig. 6.7 *a*).

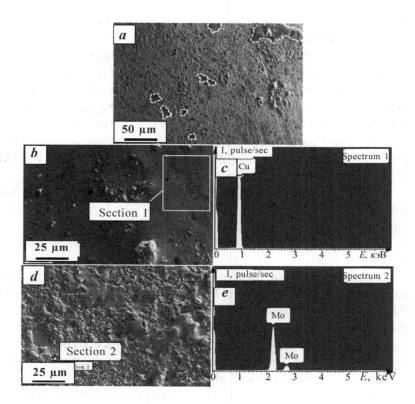

Fig. 6.7. Typical SEM images of the surface of an electric explosive composite coating of the Mo–C–Cu system after EBT. Images obtained in secondary electrons. a – general view of the surface topography; b – surface for X-ray analysis with a smooth relief; d – surface for x-ray spectral analysis with a rough relief; c, e – X-ray spectra (the places of collection of which are indicated on (b, d)); A – areas with smooth relief. The border of areas A is indicated by a dotted line.

The X-ray microanalysis of section 1 in Figure 6.7, b allows us to conclude that regions of the structure with a smooth relief are formed by copper and molybdenum in an amount of 94 and 6 at. %, respectively. Smooth regions have a polycrystalline structure, the average grain size of which increases from 5 to 15 μm with an increase in energy density from 45 to 50 J/cm². respectively.

An increase in the electron beam energy density to 60 J/cm² (pulse exposure time 100 μs) is accompanied by the formation of a polycrystalline structure with a characteristic grain size varying from 5 to 30 μm. Small grains are grouped in the area. It can be assumed that during EBT in this mode, the conditions conducive to the dynamic recrystallization process [135, 136] are realized in the surface layer of the composite coating of the Mo–C–Cu system [135, 136], at which small grains are formed.

This assumption is supported by the fact that in the mode $E_S = 60$ J/cm^2, $t = 200$ μs, and $N = 20$ pulses (Section 2), in which the beam power density was the lowest, a more even-grained structure was formed, the grain size of which was in the range from 5 to 10 μm. In the volume of grains, regardless of the energy density of the electron beam, a cellular structure characteristic of high-speed crystallization is revealed [227]. The transverse size of the cells in it varies between 0.5...1.0 μm.

Rough regions are formed by particles with sizes from 0.5 to 5.0 μm. The X-ray microanalysis of section 1 in Fig. 6.7 *d*, containing such a particle, suggests that it is formed by molybdenum and copper in an amount of 95 and 5 at.%, respectively. Carbon is not detected by this method.

Outside the central zone of the specimen, a structure is observed in which the surface is smoothed compared to the specimen after EES, however, microcracks and microcraters are still present in it. According to the evolution of the morphology of the irradiation surface, the elemental composition of the surface layer also changes. On the border of the central zone and beyond, areas enriched in molybdenum or copper are preserved.

Using the method of x-ray phase analysis of the central zone (Fig. 6.8), it was found that the main phases in it are molybdenum and copper in a ratio of approximately 1: 1. Diffraction lines belonging to molybdenum carbide of the composition Mo$_2$C, the volume fraction of which is 5..10%, were revealed.

Smoothing the surface of EBT leads to equalization of the thickness of the modified layer (Fig. 6.9 *a*). As follows from the analysis of the image of the structure of the transverse section, the thickness of the modified layer after EBT in various modes varies from 30 to 50 μm and slightly decreases with increasing energy density of the electron beam. Moreover, the total coating thickness is 60–80 μm. The boundary between the coating and the substrate has a wave-like relief, which indicates a high adhesion of the coating to the substrate.

EBT eliminates defects caused by the ingress of particles of molybdenum and carbon powders into the melt: micropores and microcracks in the modified electroexplosive coating are practically not detected (Fig. 6.9 *a, b*). Three layers are distinguished by coating thickness (Fig. 6.9 *a*): I – coating layer after EBT; II – coating layer

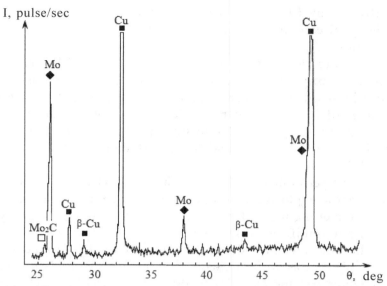

Fig. 6.8. Diffraction patterns of the electric explosion coating of the Mo–C–Cu system after EBT.

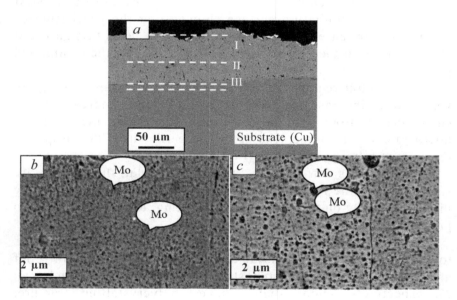

Fig. 6.9. Representative cross-sectional SEM images of electroexplosive composite coating system Mo–C–Cu after EBT. Images obtained in secondary electrons. *a* – cross-sectional structure; *b* – coating layer after subsequent EBT; *c* – a coating layer not affected by EBT; I – coating layer after EBT; II – coating layer unaffected by EBT; III – thermal influence layer.

not affected by EBT; III – a layer of thermal influence, in which by chemical etching the grain boundaries are detected worse than in the substrate.

Smoothing the surface of the coating during EBT results in equalization of the thickness of layer I, in which a composite filled (dispersion-hardened) layer structure [227] is formed (Fig. 6.9 b). The sizes of inclusions of molybdenum and Mo_2C carbide in the copper matrix vary from 0.1 to 0.5 µm. In layer II, the sizes of inclusions of molybdenum and Mo_2C carbide are in the range from 0.5 to 1.5 µm (Fig. 6.9 c).

Thus, the performed studies show that the EBT of the surface layer of the electric explosive coating of copper electrical contacts, carried out in the melting mode, leads to the formation of a structurally and concentration-uniform surface layer.

In the coatings of the Mo–C–Cu system, the formation of a carbide phase was to be expected. Indeed, TEM studies revealed molybdenum carbide particles of the composition Mo_2C (Fig. 6.10) with particle sizes of the carbide phase from 10 to 30 nm.

Electroexplosive coatings of the W–C–Cu system after EBT. SEM studies of the irradiation surface showed that the processing of the material by an electron beam in all modes leads to significant changes in its surface: two areas are distinguished - the central and peripheral.

In the central region of the electron beam exposure (the region whose sizes increase from 10 to 18 mm with an increase in the energy density from 45 to 60 J/cm^2, respectively), the microdroplets, microcraters and microcracks described earlier in [198] disappear, the surface relief is smoothed (Fig. 6.10).

A structure is formed that includes irregular shapes that are smoother than the rest of the surface of region *A*. These areas are placed randomly on the surface of the coating. Rough areas are also present on the surface (Fig, 6.11 a).

The X-ray microanalysis of section 1 in Fig. 6.11 b allows us to conclude that the regions of the structure with a smooth relief are formed by copper and tungsten in the amount of 94 and 6 at. %, respectively. Smooth regions have a polycrystalline structure, the average grain size of which increases from 5 to 15 µm with an increase in energy density from 45 to 50 J/cm^2, respectively. An increase in the electron beam energy density to 60 J/cm^2 at a pulse exposure time of 100 µs leads to the formation of a polycrystalline structure with grain sizes varying in the range from 5 to 30 µm. Small grains are grouped in the area. It can be assumed that during EBT in this mode, the conditions conducive to the dynamic recrystallization process [135, 136] are realized in the surface layer of the composite coating of the W–C–Cu system [135, 136], at which small grains are formed. This assumption is supported by the fact that in the mode $E_S = 60$ J/cm^2, $t = 200$ µs, $N = 20$ pulses. (Chapter 1) at which the beam power density was the lowest, a more even-grained structure was formed, the grain size of which is in the range from 5 to 10 µm. In the volume of grains, regardless of the energy density of the electron beam, a cellular structure characteristic of high-speed crystallization is revealed [227]. The transverse size of the cells in it varies between 0.5...1.0 µm.

Rough regions are formed by particles with sizes from 0.5 to 5.0 µm. The X-ray microanalysis of section 1 in Fig. 6.11 d, containing such a particle, makes it possible to conclude that it is formed by tungsten and copper in an amount of 93 and 7 at.%, respectively.

Outside the central zone of the specimen, a structure is observed in which the surface is smoothed compared to the specimen after EES, however, microcracks and microcraters are still present in it.

According to the evolution of the morphology of the irradiation surface, the elemental composition of the surface layer also changes. On the border of the central zone and beyond, the regions enriched in tungsten or copper are preserved.

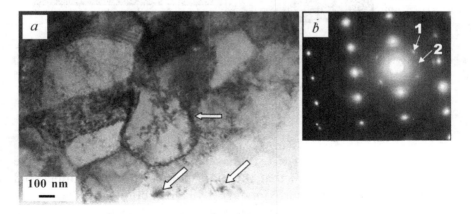

Fig. 6.10. Electron microscopic image of the structure of the electroexplosive coating system Mo–C–Cu, processed by the high-intensity pulsed electron beam. The arrows indicate (a) – Mo$_2$C carbide particles; on (b) reflexes of the carbide Mo$_2$C: 1 – [011], 2 – [001]. a – image obtained in a bright field; b – microelectron diffraction pattern.

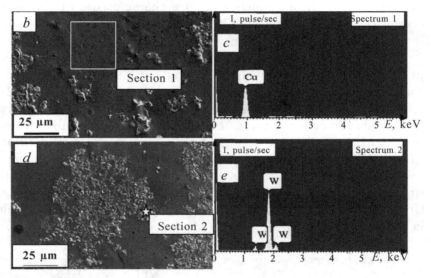

Fig. 6.11 Typical SEM images of the surface of the electroexplosive composite coating system W–C–Cu after EBT. Images obtained in secondary electrons. *a* - general view of the surface topography; *b* – surface for X-ray spectral analysis with a smooth relief; *d* – surface for X-ray spectral analysis with a rough relief; *c, e* – X-ray spectra (the areas of collection of which are indicated on (*b, d*)); *A* – areas with a smooth relief. The border of areas *A* is indicated by a dotted line.

Using the method of x-ray phase analysis of the central zone (Fig. 6.12), it was found that the main phases in it are copper and tungsten in a ratio of approximately 3:1. Diffraction lines belonging to tungsten carbide of composition W_2C were detected, the volume fraction of which is 5..10%.

Smoothing the surface by EBT leads to equalization of the thickness of the modified layer (Fig. 6.13). As follows from the analysis of the image of the structure of the transverse section, the thickness of the modified layer after EBT in various modes varies from 30 to 50 µm and slightly decreases with increasing energy density of the electron beam. Moreover, the total coating thickness is 80–100 µm. The boundary between the coating and the substrate has a wave-like relief, which indicates a high adhesion of the coating to the substrate.

EBT eliminates defects caused by tungsten and carbon powders entering the melt: micropores and microcracks in the modified electroexplosive coating are practically not detected (Fig. 6.13 a, b). Three layers are distinguished by coating thickness (Fig. 5.13): I – coating layer after EBT; II – coating layer not affected by EBT; III – a layer of thermal influence, in which by chemical etching of the grain boundaries is detected worse than in the substrate.

Smoothing the surface of the coating during EBT leads to an equalization of the thickness of layer I, in which a composite filled (dispersion-hardened) layer structure [130] is formed (Fig. 6.13 b). The sizes of tungsten and W_2C carbide inclusions in the copper matrix vary from 0.2 to 1.0 µm. In layer II, the sizes of inclusions of tungsten and W_2C carbide vary from 0.5 to 3.5 µm (Fig. 6.13 c).

In the coatings of the W–C–Cu system, the formation of a carbide phase was to be expected. Indeed, TEM studies revealed WC molybdenum carbide particles (Fig. 6.14) with carbide phase particles ranging in size from 10 to 30 nm.

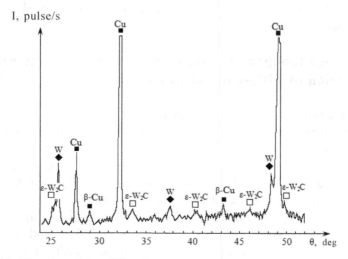

Fig. 6.12. The plot of the diffraction patterns of the electric explosion coating of the W–C–Cu system after EBT.

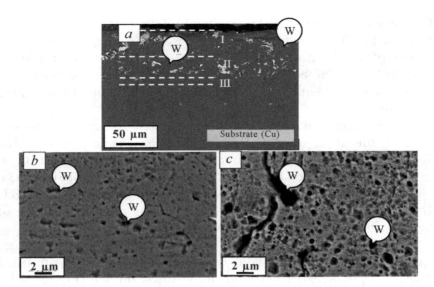

Fig. 6.13. Representative cross-sectional SEM images of the electroexplosive composite coating system W–C–Cu after EBT. Images obtained in secondary electrons. *a* – cross-sectional structure; *b* – coating layer after subsequent EBT; *c* – a coating layer not affected by EBT; I – coating layer after EBT; II – coating layer unaffected by EBT; III – thermal influence layer.

Thus, the performed studies show that the EBT of the surface layer of the electric explosive coating of copper electrical contacts, carried out in the melting mode, leads to the formation of a layer structurally homogeneous with particles uniformly distributed throughout the volume.

6.3. Surface topography, structure, phase and elemental composition of TiB_2–Cu system coatings

Let us analyze the results of a change in the structure of pseudo-alloy coatings of the TiB_2–Cu system obtained on copper substrates during EES formed after EBT.

As in Section 6.2, it was found that surface treatment with an electron beam in all modes leads to its cardinal transformations. In the central area of the electron beam, microdrops, microcraters and microcracks disappear, the surface relief is smoothed out (Fig. 6.15 *a*). A polycrystalline structure is formed (Fig. 6.15 *b*) and its average grain size which increases from 10 to 30 μm with an increase in energy density from 45 to 50 J/cm², respectively.

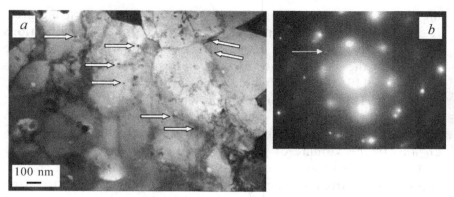

Fig. 6.14. Electron-microscopic image of the structure of the electric explosive coating of the W–C–Cu system treated with a high-intensity pulsed electron beam. Arrows indicate: on (*a*) WC carbide particles; on (*b*) WC carbide reflex [001]. *a* – image obtained in a bright field; *b* – microelectron diffraction pattern,

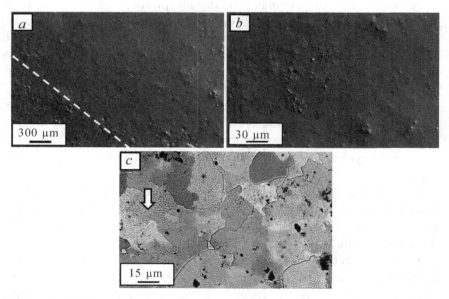

Fig. 6.15 SEM image of the surface of an electric explosion composite coating of the TiB$_2$–Cu system after EBT. The arrow on *c* shows the cellular structure. Images received in secondary electrons (*a, b*); and backward reflected (*c*) electrons. *a* – surface structure at the border (shown by a dotted line) of the central and peripheral areas after EBT; *b, c* – heterogeneous polycrystalline structure in the central region of EBT.

An increase in the electron beam energy density to 60 J/cm^2 at a pulse exposure time of 100 μs is accompanied by the formation of a polycrystalline structure (Fig. 6.15 *c*) whose grain size is in the range from 3 to 40 μm. Small grains are grouped in the area. It can be assumed that during EBT in this regime, the conditions conducive to the dynamic recrystallization process [135, 136] are realized in the surface layer of the composite coating of the TiB_2–Cu system [135, 136], in which small grains locally combine into large ones. This assumption is supported by the fact that in mode 5, in which the beam power density was the lowest, a more uniform structure was formed, the grain size of which varies from 3 to 20 μm. In the volume of grains, regardless of the energy density of the electron beam, a cellular structure is revealed (Fig. 6.15 *c* shown by an arrow), characteristic of high-speed crystallization [227]. The transverse size of the cells in it varies between 0.5...1.0 μm. Outside the central zone, a structure is observed in which the surface is smoothed compared to the material after the EES, however, microcracks and microcraters are still present in it.

As a result of the evolution of the morphology of the irradiation surface, the elemental composition of the surface layer also changes. In the central zone, a homogeneous composite coating is fixed containing titanium and copper in amounts of 35 and 65 at.% respectively. On the border of the central zone and beyond, areas enriched in titanium or copper are preserved.

By the method of X-ray phase analysis of the central zone (Fig. 6.16) it was found that the coating contains titanium diboride and copper in a ratio of approximately 1:1. At the boundary of the central zone and beyond, areas enriched in titanium diboride or copper are preserved.

Smoothing the surface of EBT leads to equalization of the thickness of the modified layer (Fig. 6.17). As follows from the analysis of the image of the structure of the transverse section, the thickness of the modified layer after EBT varies from 30 to 50 μm and slightly decreases with increasing energy density of the electron beam. Moreover, the total coating thickness is 250–300 μm. The boundary between the coating and the substrate has a wave-like relief, which indicates a high adhesion of the coating to the substrate.

Processing leads to the elimination of defects caused by the ingress of particles of titanium diboride powder into the melt: micropores and microcracks are practically not detected in the modified electron beam electroexplosive coating (Fig. 6.5 *a* and *b*). Three layers are distinguished in the coating structure (Fig. 6.5): I – coating layer after EBT; II – coating layer not affected by EBT;

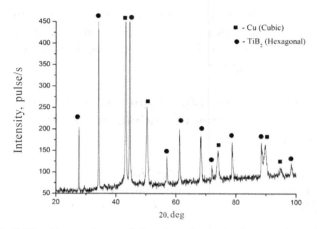

Fig. 6.16. Diffraction pattern of the electric explosion coating of the TiB_2–Cu systems after EBT.

Fig. 6.17. Cross section of a copper electrical contact with electroexplosive coating of the TiB_2–Cu system after EBT. Images obtained in secondary electrons. I – coating layer, remelted during EBT; II – zone of thermal influence in the coating after EBT; III – zone of thermal influence in the substrate after EBT.

III – a layer of thermal influence, in which by chemical etching grain boundaries are detected worse than in the substrate.

Smoothing the surface of the coating during EBT results in equalization of the thickness of layer I, in which a composite filled (dispersion-hardened) layer structure [130] is formed (Fig. 6.5 *b*). The particle size of titanium diboride in the copper matrix is in the range from 0.5 to 2.0 µm. In layer II, the sizes of inclusions of titanium diboride vary from 0.5 to 5.0 µm (Fig. 6.18 *b*).

Thus, the performed studies show that the EBT of the surface layer of the electric explosive coating of copper electrical contacts, carried out in the melting mode, leads to the formation of a surface layer that is uniform in structure and concentration.

Using the TEM method, in the coatings of this system, along with TiB_2 particles, particles of the composition Ti_2B_5 were revealed, which may indicate partial dissolution of the TiB_2 powder and its re-isolation in the composition of Ti_2B_5.

6.4. The study of surface topography, structure, phase and elemental composition of coatings of W–Ni–Cu and Mo–Ni–Cu systems

Electroexplosive coatings of the Mo–Ni–Cu system after EBT. Molybdenum, having a larger atomic mass (95.96 a.m.u) with respect to nickel (58.7 a.m.u) and copper (63.8 a.m.u), reflects the probe electrons to a greater extent. Therefore, in electron-microscopic images of the material in the back-reflected electrons, the regions enriched in molybdenum atoms will have a lighter contrast. The presence of such areas on the surface of the coating follows from an analysis of the results presented in Fig. 6.24 (areas indicated by arrows). Indeed, X-ray microanalysis of the surface of samples

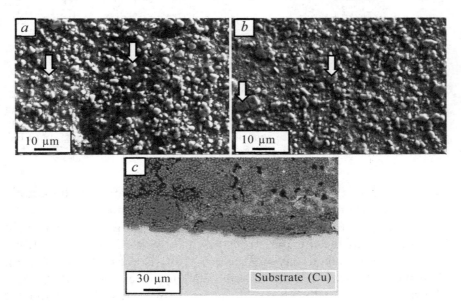

Fig. 6.18. SEM image of the cross-sectional structure of the composite coating of the TiB_2–Cu system after EBT. The arrows in *a, b* indicate the inclusion of titanium diboride. Images obtained in secondary electrons (*a, b*) and backward reflected (*c*) electrons. *a* is the structure of layer I; *b* – the structure of layer II; *c* – relief features of the border of the coating with the substrate.

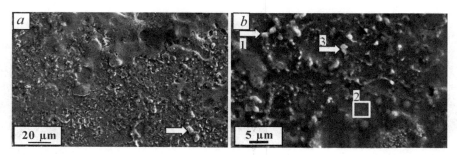

Fig. 6.19. Electron microscopic image of the structure of the plasma modified copper contact surfaces, formed when electrically composite electrically exploding Mo–Ni–Cu conductor (in (*b*) areas are highlighted X-ray spectral analysis). *a* – microglobules, *b* – compositional structure of microglobules

subjected to EHV coatings of the Mo-Ni-Cu system without EBT revealed mainly molybdenum atoms in them (Table 6.1). In addition to this, the micro X-ray spectral analysis of this coating revealed the presence of oxygen and carbon atoms (Table 6.1), which may be due to the EES of the coatings under conditions of not sufficiently high vacuum. The detected coating elements are distributed very nonuniformly over the surface layer of the material being modified, which follows from an analysis of the results given in Table 6.1.

The most heterogeneous in the surface volume of the material is molybdenum, the concentration of which from region to region varies from 97.0 at.% to 5.0 at.%, i.e. may vary 5–19 times.

Irradiation of the surface of electric explosive spraying by a high-intensity electron beam leads to melting of the surface layer and, as a result, smoothing of the surface relief. Therefore, the samples that underwent additional processing with a high-intensity electron beam were subjected to preliminary analysis by optical microscopy and detailed analysis by scanning electron microscopy.

Table 6.1. The results of X-ray microspectral analysis of the surface areas highlighted in Fig. 6.24 *b*.

No. of regions of determination of elemental composition	Concentration of element, at.%				
	Mo	Ni	Cu	O	C
1	95.0	2.0	2.0	0.5	0.5
2	5.0	45.0	50.0	1.0	1.0
3	97.0	1.0	1.0	0.5	0.5

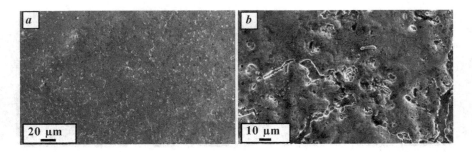

Fig. 6.20. The structure of the surface layer of copper contact after electroexplosive spraying of the composite coating Mo–Ni–Cu and EBT systems in mode 1.

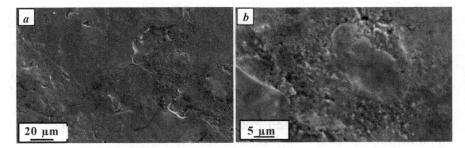

Fig. 6.21. The structure of the surface layer of copper contact after electroexplosive spraying of the composite coating Mo–Ni–Cu and EBT systems in mode 2.

Fig. 6.22. Fragmented structure of the surface layer of a copper contact after electroexplosive spraying of a composite coatings M))o–Ni–Cu and EBT coatings in mode 2.)

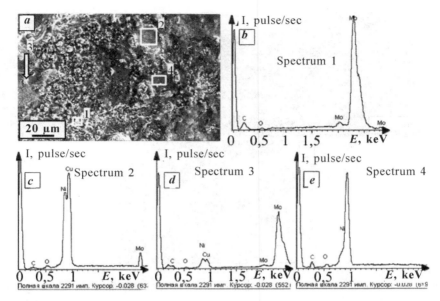

Fig. 6.23. The surface structure of the copper contact, subjected to EES and subsequent EBT. *a* – the choice of areas for X-ray microanalysis, *b – e* – energy spectra selected in photo *a*.

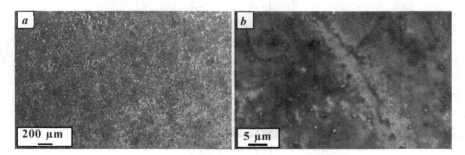

Fig. 6.24. Surface structure of an electric explosion coating Mo–Ni–Cu system and subsequent EBT in mode 4.

It is clearly seen that the morphology of the surface structure of the modification substantially depends on the irradiation regime (in our case, on the energy density of the electron beam). Electron beam irradiation in mode 1 is accompanied by the formation of a fragmented structure in the surface layer (Fig. 6.20).

The sizes of the fragments vary from 150 to 400 μm. Fragments are separated by interlayers, the thickness of which is from 5 to 15 μm. Judging by the contrast of the image, the fragments and layers separating them have different elemental composition (Fig. 6.21

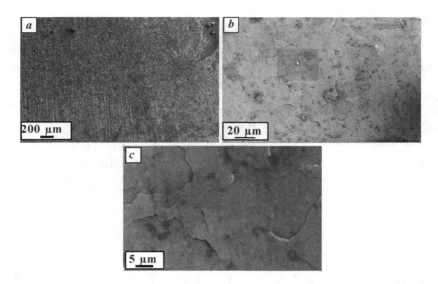

Fig. 6.25. The surface structure of an electric explosion coating Mo–Ni–Cu system and subsequent EBT in mode 5.

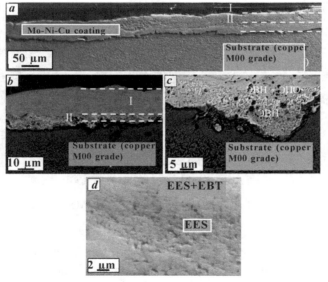

Fig. 6.26. A characteristic cross-sectional structure of a sample of M00 copper specimen subjected to an EES composite electric explosive coatings of the Mo-Ni–Cu system after electron-beam processing. Scanning electron microscopy in secondary (*a, d*) and backward reflected (*b, c*) electrons. *a* – cross section of the central part of the coating after EBT in mode 4; *b* – cross sectional peripheral parts of the coating after EBT in mode 1; *c* - compositional contrast coatings, *d* - features of the boundary between layers I and II, I – coating layer, remelted with EBT; II – heat affected zone

b). Fragments are structured (Fig. 6.21 a). The sizes of structural components vary from 1.5 to 2.0 μm.

Globular inclusions on the surface of the coating are particles of molybdenum powder that are formed as a result of reaching the surface of the coating last during electroexplosive spraying and condensed after plasma melting of the copper surface, i.e. particles of the original molybdenum powder.

The morphology of the structure and the elemental composition of its microregions were studied in detail by scanning electron microscopy. A typical morphology of the surface of electric explosive spraying, after additional irradiation with a high-intensity pulsed electron beam in mode 2, obtained by scanning electron microscopy, is shown in Fig. 6.21. Analyzing the images presented in Fig, 6.21, it can be noted that the additional irradiation of copper samples, after EES of the composite coating of the Mo–Ni–Cu system and irradiation with a high-intensity pulsed electron beam, leads, as noted above, to the formation of a fragmented structure (Fig. 6.26 a). A study of the structure in backward-reflected electrons shows that the fragments differ in contrast (the so-called compositional contrast). Following the above arguments, it can be assumed that dark fragments are enriched in nickel and copper atoms, lighter fragments are enriched in molybdenum atoms. The ratio of the areas occupied by light and dark fragments is 60:40. Thus, upon irradiation of the surface of an electric explosive spraying with a high-intensity pulsed electron beam in mode 1, a surface layer enriched in molybdenum atoms is formed.

A detailed analysis of the structure of light-contrast islands (islands enriched in molybdenum atoms) revealed their division into regions (hereinafter referred to as 'molybdenum particles'), the sizes of which vary from 0.5 μm to 2 μm (Fig. 6.26 b).

Molybdenum particles are often separated by thin (micrometer fractions) interlayers with dark contrast, i.e. layers enriched with nickel and copper atoms. Areas enriched with nickel and copper are also detected as islands in the structure of molybdenum (Fig. 6.26 b). Taken together, these facts indicate a phase separation process occurring during crystallization that occurs even at cooling rates of the material up to 10^8 K/s, which are realized upon irradiation with an electron beam. The islands enriched with nickel and copper, which have a dark contrast when examining the material in back-reflected electrons, contain inclusions of light contrast (inclusions enriched in molybdenum) (Fig. 6.26 b and Fig. 6.27). The inclusions have a rounded shape, their sizes vary from 0.1 µm to 1.0 µm (Fig. 6.28). The molybdenum inclusions are located either randomly or by chains contouring certain volumes (grains) of nickel and copper.

Elemental composition studies performed by X-ray spectral analysis confirmed the above results. It was established that the main volume of the surface layer of the copper electrical contact after the EES of the composite coating of the Mo–Ni–Cu system and irradiated with an electron beam in mode 1 (regions of material having a bright contrast when shooting in back-reflected electrons) is enriched in molybdenum (Fig. 6.28, spectrum 1). The islands, which have a dark contrast when shooting in backward-reflected electrons, are enriched with nickel and copper (Fig. 6.28, spectrum 2). The bright contrast inclusions detected in the islands of nickel and copper are also enriched in molybdenum atoms (Fig, 6.28, spectrum 3). In quantitative terms, the results of X-ray microspectral analysis of the material section, presented in Fig. 6.28 a, are shown in Table 6.2.

Thus, using X-ray microspectral analysis, it was found that as a result of high-speed crystallization and subsequent quenching of the electric explosive coating of the Mo–Ni–Cu system, initiated by irradiating the material with a high-intensity pulsed electron beam, regions with significantly different atomic concentrations of molybdenum, nickel, and copper are formed in the surface layer of the coating samples.

An increase in the energy density of the electron beam in modes 2–4 (with other parameters of the beam unchanged) leads to a gradual decrease in the relative content of the regions enriched in molybdenum. The typical structure formed as a result of irradiation of the surface of an electric explosion with an electron beam in mode 4 is shown in Fig. 6.29.

Table 6.2. X-ray microspectral analysis of surface areas highlighted in Figure 6.28

No. of region of dtermination of element composition	Concentration of element, at.%				
	Mo	Ni	Cu	O	C
1	96.8			1.0	2.2
2	4.0	47.5	45.5	1.2	1.8
3	82.0	7.0	8.0	1.5	1.5
4		30.0	63.0	2.0	4.0

Irradiation of the surface of the Mo–Ni–Cu electroexplosive coating with a high-intensity pulsed electron beam in mode 5 led to the formation of a grain-type structure in the surface layer with grain sizes ranging from 5 μm to 35 μm (Fig. 6.30). An analysis of the structure in the back-reflected electrons revealed areas with different types of contrast. A structure of a globular type is fixed in the volume of grains (Fig. 6.31 c). The size of the globules varies from 0.5 μm to 1 μm. Judging by the contrast, they are formed by molybdenum particles. The study of elemental composition, performed by X-ray spectral analysis, confirmed this fact.

From the analysis of the image of the structure of transverse sections (Fig. 6.31), it follows that the thickness of the modified layer after EBT varies from 15 to 30 μm and slightly increases with increasing energy density of the electron beam (Fig. 6.31).

The coating thickness after EES is 50...52 μm in the central part and 25...27 μm in the peripheral. The peripheral part of the coating occupies 3% of the total coating area. The melting of the modified layer by an electron beam leads to the complete elimination of defects in the form of craters caused by the ingress of particles of a powder sample of molybdenum and nickel into the melt. Electron-beam processing is accompanied by melting of the electric explosive coating and leads to the formation of a layered structure. Regardless of the treatment regime after EBT, a predominantly composite filled structure forms in the coating, which differs in the degree of dispersion of molybdenum particles (Fig. 6.31 b) 0.1...2 μm, with large inclusions of 0.5...2 μm in size accounting for 5...7% of all inclusions.

Thus, the molybdenum particles in the electroexplosive coating after EBT are more dispersed than in the layer not affected by EBT. In the characteristic radiation of molybdenum, nickel, and copper (violet, red, and green in Fig. 6.32), the combined image of the structure of the layer of the electric explosive coating without EBT with the distribution maps of the corresponding elements confirms that the matrix consists of nickel and copper, and the inclusion consists of molybdenum. The volume ratio of nickel and copper to particles of molybdenum powder in a layer not affected by EBT corresponds to their ratio in a composite electrically exploded conductor used for spraying. Along with this, in the coating layer not subjected to EBT, traces of the melt flow in the form of globules 5...15 μm in size are locally observed (Fig. 6.32 c). They represent various 'twists'. The boundary between the coating and the substrate has a wave-like relief [228], which indicates a high adhesion of the coating to the substrate.

Electroexplosive coatings of the W–Ni–Cu system after EBT. Coatings formed by the method of electric explosion of conductive material, as a rule, are characterized by highly developed relief (sagging, drops, micropores) [198]. Subsequent irradiation of such coatings with a high-intensity pulsed electron beam in the melting mode of the surface layer leads, under the action of surface tension forces, to smoothing the irradiation surface (Fig. 6.33 *a*).

The forming coating is multilayer (Fig. 6.33 *b*).

The performed studies show that the revealed layers differ not only in structure, but also in elemental composition, as evidenced by the results of X-ray microanalysis of the elemental composition of the coating, presented in Fig. 6.34 and Table 6.3

Analyzing the results presented in Figure 6.34 and Table 6.3, it can be noted that the elements of the sprayed coating are distributed nonuniformly over the thickness of the modified layer. In addition to sprayed elements, chromium, titanium, carbon, and oxygen atoms are identified in the coating. The presence of carbon atoms indicates the fundamental possibility of the formation of tungsten carbides in the coating. The presence of chromium and oxygen atoms in the coating is due to the ingress of chromium oxide powder into the tungsten particles crumbled from the copper–nickel matrix, which was used to polish the thin sections.

The distribution of elements in the coating is more clearly revealed by the mapping method [229]. A typical image of the distribution maps of the main elements in the coating of the W–Ni–Cu system is shown in Fig. 6.30.

The maps presented in Figure 6.30 (*b–f*) clearly demonstrate the heterogeneous distribution of alloying elements and, above all, tungsten atoms (Fig. 6.30, c). Namely, the coating region directly adjacent to the substrate is enriched in tungsten atoms.

In addition, chaotically enriched tungsten-rich regions are detected in the coating volume. It can be assumed that the inhomogeneous distribution of tungsten atoms (the formation of a layer along the boundary of the coating with the matrix) is due to the action of gravitational forces, since the atomic weight of tungsten is significantly greater than the atomic weight of the remaining elements of the coating.

The phase composition and defective substructure of the coating were analyzed by transmission electron diffraction microscopy of thin foils. The coating layer was analyzed at a depth of 15–20 μm.

A typical electron microscopic image of the coating is shown in Fig. 6.31. Two characteristic elements of the coating structure are clearly revealed – inclusions of various shapes and sizes and the matrix in which they are located.

Microdiffraction analysis of the foil section, shown in Fig. 6.31 a, indicates that the coating is formed by a solid solution based on Cu–Ni, hereinafter referred to as the 'matrix'. It is known [110] that in the Cu–Ni system the formation of a continuous series of solid solutions is observed. These metals have the same type of crystal lattice (space group Fm3m) and close interatomic distances. The sizes of the inclusions of the second phase, randomly located in the matrix volume, vary from 50 to 150 nm. Inclusions are fragmented, i.e. divided into weakly oriented areas with sizes from 20 to 50 nm (Fig. 6.31 b). An analysis of the microelectron diffraction pattern obtained from such particles (Fig. 6.31 c) indicates that they are tungsten. The absence of bending extinction contours near the tungsten particle-matrix interface indicates that the coating is a mechanical mixture of two phases – a matrix based on a solid solution of the Cu–Ni system and tungsten particles that were present in the powder mixture (state before EES) and did not evaporate (not turned into a stream of ions) during an electric explosion of a powder mixture.

The matrix has a polycrystalline structure, the grain size of which varies in a very wide range (Fig. 6.32). The basis of the coating is grains, the dimensions of which are tens of micrometers (Fig. 6.32 a). In the volume of such grains, a dislocation substructure in the form of chaos or networks is revealed; the scalar dislocation density is $3 \cdot 10^{10}$ cm^{-2}. As a rule, chaotically located inclusions of tungsten of submicron sizes are observed in such grains.

Less common are the coating regions with grain sizes ranging from 20 to 40 nm (Fig. 6.32 b). Microelectron diffraction patterns obtained from such areas of the coating have a ring structure, which also indicates a small (nanoscale) grain size. A characteristic feature of such regions is the presence of nanosized inclusions of the second phase. The analysis of microelectron diffraction patterns (Fig. 6.32 c) indicates that these particles are tungsten. The particle size of tungsten is from 5 to 20 nm. These particles are a source of internal stress fields, as evidenced by the bending extinction contours located around the particles (Fig. 6.32 b, particles with contours indicated by

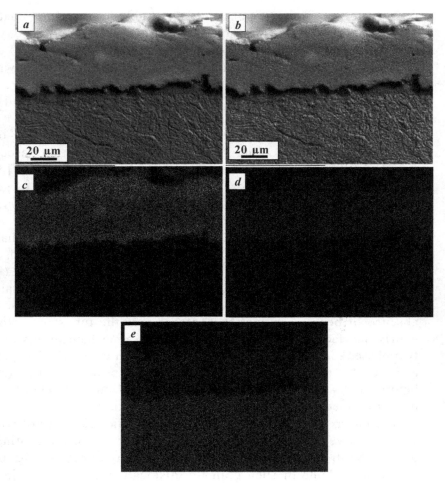

Fig. 6.27. The characteristic structure of the cross-section of a sample of copper grade M00 subjected to EES of composite electric explosive Mo–Ni–Cu system coatings after electron-beam processing. Scanning electron microscopy in secondary electrons. *a* – cross section, *b* – combined image structures with images obtained in characteristic studies of molybdenum, nickel and copper shown in purple, red and green colors respectively *c, d, e* – images of the transverse beam in the characteristic rays of molybdenum, nickel and copper, respectively

arrows). Taking into account the small particle size and the presence of a bond between the matrix and particles (the presence of bending extinction loops), it can be assumed that they precipitated from the solid solution during crystallization and cooling of the coating.

6.5. Study of the surface topography, structure, phase and elemental composition of the coatings of the Cr–C–Cu system

Coatings formed by the method of electric explosion of conductive material, as a rule, are characterized by highly developed relief (sagging, drops, micropores) [198].

Subsequent irradiation of such coatings with a high-intensity pulsed electron beam in the melting mode of the surface layer leads, under the influence of surface tension forces, to smoothing the irradiation surface (Fig. 6.33). As the electron beam energy density increases, the level of surface roughness decreases.

The forming coating is multilayer (Fig. 6.34). Analysis of the structure of transverse sections by scanning electron microscopy revealed 4 layers. The performed studies show that the identified layers differ not only in structure, but also in elemental composition. The results of X-ray microanalysis of the elemental composition of each of the identified coating layers are presented in Table 6.4. Analyzing the results presented in Table 6.4, it can be noted that the main element of layer No. 1, regardless of the mode of irradiation of the coating with an electron beam, is carbon, the concentration of which depends on the irradiation mode with the electron beam and changes from 66 at.% to 40 at.%. With increasing distance from the irradiation surface, the concentration of carbon atoms decreases and in the layer No. 4 (the layer located at the interface between the coating and the substrate) varies from 7 at.% up to 52 at.% Therefore, carbon, being a carbide-forming element, is sufficiently

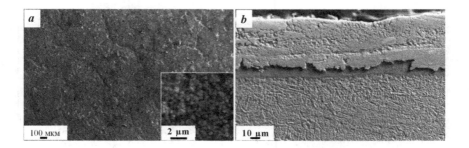

Fig. 6.28. Electroexplosive coating system W–Ni–Cu, formed on a copper sample and irradiated with high-intensity pulsed electron beam. *a* – surface structure, *b* – cross-sectional structure.

present in the formed coating, which indicates the fundamental possibility of the formation of chromium carbides in the coating.

The chromium concentration in the coating varies nonlinearly, reaching a maximum value, regardless of the irradiation mode, in layer No. 2 and No. 3. In addition to chromium atoms in the coating under study, concomitant carbide-forming elements were revealed, namely, Ti and Mo, the concentration of which is ambiguously dependent on both the irradiation mode and the layer number. Iron and nickel atoms are present as an impurity in the coating. The presence of oxygen atoms was detected in all samples. Regardless of the irradiation regime, oxygen is detected mainly in the layer located at the interface between the coating and the substrate.

It can be assumed that the cause of the appearance of oxygen atoms in the coating is the oxide film present on the surface of copper samples before the coating is sprayed.

As noted above, the presence of chromium and carbon atoms in the coating indicates the possibility of the formation of a carbide phase. Indeed, studies performed by X-ray diffraction methods revealed the presence of carbides of the composition Cr_3C_2, Cr_7C_3 and $Cr_{23}C_6$ (Fig. 6.35).

Thus, an analysis of the results obtained in the study of the structure, elemental, and phase composition allows us to state that, using the combined method combining electroexplosive sputtering and subsequent irradiation with a high-intensity pulsed electron beam, it is possible to form multilayer multiphase coatings on the surface of copper based on the Cr–C–Cu system containing, along with copper and chromium, chromium carbides.

The performed studies show that the identified layers differ not only in structure, but also in elemental composition. The results of

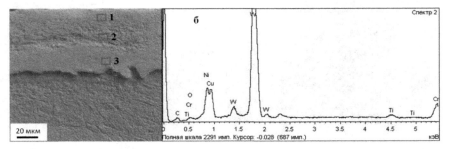

Fig. 6.29. Cross-sectional structure of the irradiated coating by the high-intensity pulsed electron beam. Scanning electron microscopy. a – selection of places for a set of energy spectra; b – energy spectrum obtained from region 2 (a).

X-ray microanalysis of the elemental composition of each of the identified coating layers are presented in Fig. 6.36.

Analyzing the results presented in Fig. 6.41, it can be noted that the main element of layer No. 1, regardless of the mode of irradiation of the coating with an electron beam, is carbon, the concentration of which monotonously decreases when changing from mode No. 1 to mode No. 5, varying from 71 at.% to 42 at.%. With increasing distance from the irradiation surface, the concentration of carbon

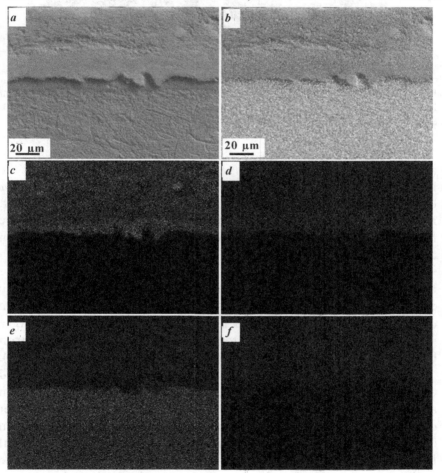

Fig. 6.30. Electron microscopic image of a section of a transverse section of the coating of the W–Ni–Cu system, additionally processed by electron beam mode 55 J/cm²; 100 µs, 10 pulses, 0.3 s. a – general view, b – image obtained by superposition of spectra radiation of copper (green), tungsten (red) and nickel purple color), $(c - f)$ – images obtained by the method of mapping in characteristic X-ray cure W $Ma1$ (c), Ni $Ka1$ (d), Cu $Ka1$ (e), Cr $Ka1$ (f).

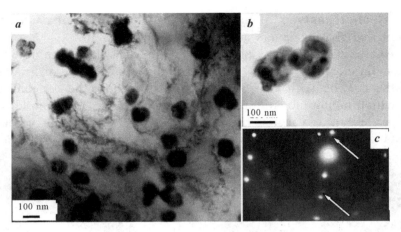

Fig. 6.31. Electron microscopy image of the coating structure of a W–Ni–Cu system formed on copper. *a, b* – bright field; *c* – microelectron diffraction pattern for (*b*); arrows indicate reflexes of the type [110] W and [220] W.

atoms decreases and in the layer No. 4 (the layer located at the interface between the coating and the substrate) varies from 8 at. % up to 61 at. % Therefore, carbon, being a carbide-forming element, is sufficiently present in the formed coating, which indicates the fundamental possibility of the formation of chromium carbides in the coating.

Indeed, studies performed by X-ray diffraction methods have revealed the presence of particles of the carbide phase; the main carbide is carbide of the composition Cr_7C_3. The volume fraction of Cr_7C_3 carbide changes in a nonmonotonic manner, reaching a maximum value when the material is irradiated with an electron beam with parameters 45 and 60 J/cm^2; 100 μs, 10 pulses (Fig. 6.37).

The results of the analysis of the lattice parameter of copper and chromium depending on the energy density of the electron beam are presented in Fig. 6.38. It can be seen that the lattice parameter of copper varies non-monotonously (Fig. 6.38 *a*). At an electron beam power density of 0.3 • 10^6 W/cm^2, the parameter of the crystal lattice of copper in the coating is close to the parameter of the lattice of copper used as a substrate (copper in the initial state). At high values of the electron beam power density, the copper crystal lattice parameter approaches the tabular value of the copper crystal lattice parameter [110]. Therefore, the processing of the coating by an electron beam is accompanied by the purification of copper from various kinds of impurities.

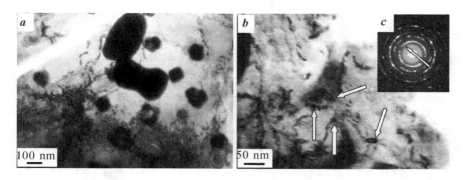

Fig. 6.32. Electron microscopic image of the coating structure of the W–Ni–Cu system formed on copper. *a, b* – bright field; *c* – microelectron diffraction pattern for (*b*); arrows on (*b*) indicate tungsten particles; na (*c*) – reflex of the type [110]W.

The chromium crystal lattice parameter also changes non-monotonously and does not show dependence on the power density of the electron beam, oscillating near the tabular value of the chromium lattice parameter (Fig. 6.38 *b*). In the solid state, two phases coexist in the Cu–Cr system: an α-solid solution of chromium in copper and a β-solid solution of copper in chromium [110]. Due to the very low solubility of copper in chromium in the solid state (at 1150°C, 0.06% and decreases to almost zero at lower temperatures [110]), the second solid phase is almost pure chromium.

Thus, an analysis of the results obtained in the study of the structure, elemental, and phase composition allows us to state that, using the combined method combining electroexplosive sputtering and subsequent irradiation with a high-intensity pulsed electron beam, it is possible to form multilayer multiphase coatings based on the Cu–Cr system on the copper surface containing, along with copper and chromium, chromium carbides.

6.6. Investigation of the dislocation substructure formed in electroerosion-resistant coatings after electron-beam treatment

In the electric blasting coatings of the Mo–Cu, W–Cu, Mo–C–Cu, WC–Cu, W–Ni–Cu, Mo–Ni–Cu, Cr–C–Cu and TiB$_2$–Cu systems, the following dislocation substructures are formed after EBT (Table 6.5): cellular, strip, fragmented, subgrain, dislocation chaos, or mesh. The preferred type of dislocation substructure for all coatings is the

Table 6.3. The elemental composition of the modified layer, presented in Fig. 6.34 *a*

Section No.	Element, at.%						
	W	Ni	Cu	Ti	Cr	C	O
1	28.2	22.9	19.9	1.5	8.0	14.6	4.9
2	23.5	16.9	14.2	2.4	13.3	19.6	10.1
3	37.7	31.3	18.5	1.2	2.7	8.6	0.0

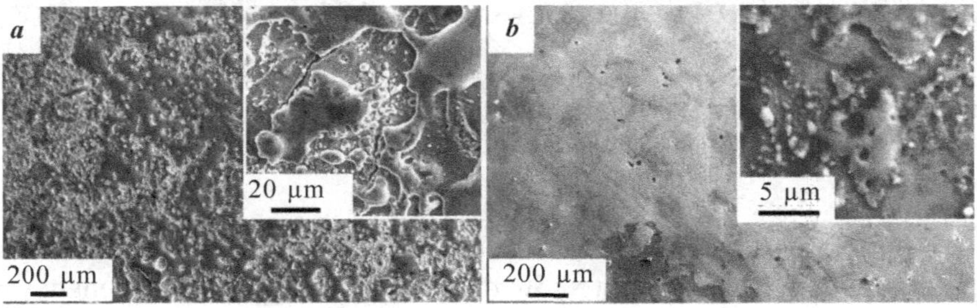

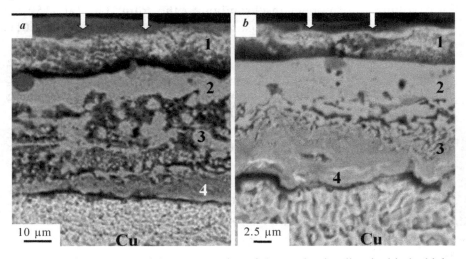

Fig. 6.33. The surface structure of the coating based on Cu-Cr, irradiated by a high-intensity pulsed electron beam with parameters. *a* – 45 J/cm², 10 pulses; *b* – 60 J/cm², 20 pulses.

Fig. 6.34. The structure of the cross section of the coating irradiated with the high-intensity pulsed electron beam. Arrows indicate the irradiation surface. *a* – according to the mode of 55 J/cm², 100 μs, 10 pulses, *b* – according to the mode of 60 J / cm², 200 μs, 20 pulses.

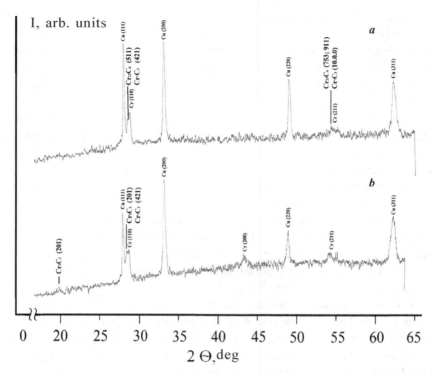

Fig. 6.35. Plots of radiographs obtained from the coating of the Cr–C–Cu system treated with EBT in the modes. a – 45 J/cm², 100 μs, 10 pulses, b –50 J/cm², 100 μs, 10 pulses.

strip substructure, except for coatings of the W–C–Cu and Cr–C–Cu systems. For these systems, the predominant type is a subgrain dislocation substructure. The following is a detailed description of dislocation substructures formed in coatings.

Electron microscopic studies of the coatings of Mo–Cu, W–Cu, TiB$_2$–Cu systems treated with a high-intensity pulsed electron beam revealed a wide variety of substructures: cellular, strip, fragmented, in the analyzed material layer, regardless of the phase composition of the coating and the electron beam irradiation mode subgrain, as well as grains with randomly distributed dislocations and dislocations that form networks (Fig. 6.39). The randomly distributed dislocations and dislocations that form the grids are also detected in all the substructures indicated above. A quantitative characteristic of the network substructure and substructure of dislocation chaos is the scalar density of dislocations.

The performed studies showed that the scalar density of randomly distributed dislocations $(2.6...3.3) \cdot 10^{10}$ cm^{-2}, of the mesh substructure $- (4.6...5.2) \cdot 10^{10}$ cm^{-2} and within the measurement error (~20 % of the measured value) does not depend on the type of sprayed coating and the mode of its irradiation with an electron beam.

Cellular, strip, fragmented, subgrain structures are disoriented. Analyzing microelectron diffraction patterns obtained from grains containing a cellular substructure, azimuthal strands on reflexes were detected, indicating continuous cell misorientation [230]. The maximum azimuthal component of the total angle of disorientation of the cellular structure is ~2.7 deg.

The misorientation of the strip, fragmented, and subgrain structure is discrete – microelectron diffraction patterns obtained from these structures show a splitting of the reflex into several separately spaced reflexes. The value of the discrete disorientation of these substructures varies from 3.7 to 4.7 degrees.

It should be noted that an increase in the pulse duration of the beam (from 100 to 200 μs) and the number of pulses (from 10 to 20 pulses), which occurs when the TiB$_2$–Cu coating is irradiated, contributed, firstly, to the formation of a dislocation substructure with better boundaries (Fig. 6.40 *a*) and, secondly, the course of the initial stage of recrystallization (Fig. 6.40 *b*, the section is indicated by the 'P' icon).

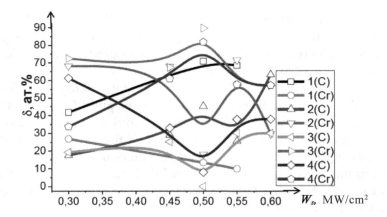

Fig. 6.36. Dependence of the concentration of carbon atoms and chromium atoms on the power density of the electron beam; numbers in the designations indicated layer numbers, electron microscopic the image of which is shown in Fig. 6.39.

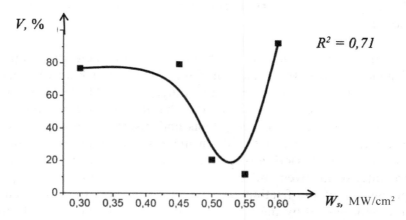

Fig. 6.37. Dependence of the volume fraction of carbide Cr_7C_3 on the electron beam power density.

Table 6.4. Elemental composition of the modified layer (at.%; Cu rest)

	EBT mode																			
	No. 1				No 2				No.3				No. 4				No.5			
	Sublayer number																			
	1	2	3	4	1	2	3	4	1	2	3	4	1	2	3	4	1	2	3	4
C	65.0	26.2	22.9	26.5	64.0	43.5	0	72	62.7	24.6	29.8	32.4	65	45	25.7	21	40	15.7	18	52
Cr	12.3	61.6	61.3	49.1	0.5	17.4	75	73.1	12.6	68.9	56.9	49.5	12	21	27.5	24.0	26	60.9	68	28
Ti	0.5	2.8	5.3	4.3	0	0.7	1.9	1.4	0.4	1.9	1.3	1.6	0.5	0.5	0.5	1.8	0.9	4.4	1.7	2.1
Mo	0	3.0	2.3	3.6	0	0.8	9.7	5.3	0	1.8	0	2.6	0	17	28.6	25.6	0.8	4.3	2.6	2.3
Ni	0.8	1.8	1.5	1.5	0.8	2.5	5.3	3.5	0.5	0.5	0	1	0.8	9.7	12.8	11.5	1.8	2.0	1.6	1.0
Fe	0	0.4	0	0.4	0	0	0	0	0	0	0	0	0	0.4	0	0.4	0	0	0	0.2
O	0	0	0	9.8	0	0	0	0	3.2	0	0	10	0	0	0	10.5	0	0	0	9.4

As a rule, a high-speed heat treatment method, which is realized by irradiating a material with a pulsed electron beam, is accompanied by the formation of internal stress fields. When studying the structure of a material by the method of thin foils, stress fields are detected by the presence of bending extinction contours in the images (Fig. 6.42). Sources of stress fields in the coatings under study are interfaces: interphase (grain, subgrain, strip substructure) and interphase (particle / matrix interfaces).

The performed studies showed that the contours formed at the interfacial boundaries are significantly thinner. This indicates a higher level of internal stress fields formed at these boundaries [231].

6.7. Properties of electroexplosive coatings, electron beam treated

A summary table of the values of tribological characteristics, micro- and nanohardness, the elastic modulus of the first kind of electric explosive electroerosion-resistant coatings after EBT is given below.

Below are detailed studies of the characteristics given for some systems. Common to all the systems under study is that an increase in the wear rate correlates with an increase in the average value of the coefficient of friction: the higher the coefficient of friction, the more intense the wear of the material. Figure 6.43 shows typical dependences of the friction coefficient on the test time (the length of the path passed by the counterbody or the number of revolutions of the sample relative to the counterbody of VK8 hard alloy) for the coatings under study.

Analyzing the results presented in Fig. 6.43, it can be noted that the change in the coefficient of friction of the coatings during the test depends on its elemental composition. Namely, for coatings of the Mo–Cu systems (Fig. 6.48 a) and W–Cu systems (Fig. 6.48 c), a two-stage change in the friction coefficient is characteristic: the first stage of an almost linear increase in the friction coefficient with relatively small fluctuations $\delta(\mu)$ (for Mo coating–Cu $\delta(\mu) = 0.015$; for W–Cu $\delta(\mu) = 0.07$), increasing as one approaches the second stage. The second stage is characterized by a steady state behaviour of the coefficient of friction, the values of which (μ) are shown in Table 6.6.

For coatings of Mo–C–Cu systems (Fig. 6.43 b) and WC–Cu (Fig. 6.48 d), the friction coefficient increases with increasing test time, varying with fluctuations within 0.126...0.499 (Mo–C–Cu

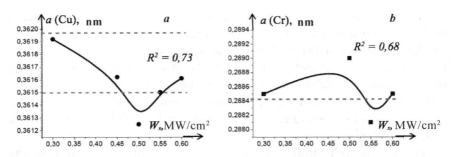

Fig. 6.38. Dependences of the parameters of the crystal lattice on the electron beam power density.

system coating) and 0.102...0.48 (coating system WC–Cu), reaching a maximum value at the end of the test.

The value of fluctuations of the friction coefficient $\delta(\mu)$ for the Mo–C–Cu coating increases with increasing test time in the range of 0.023...0.095, for the W–C–Cu coating in the range of 0.037...0.054.

The evolution of the coefficient of friction of a coating of TiB_2-Cu composition differs from the coatings considered above (Fig. 6.43 e). The initial stage of testing is characterized by a high level of fluctuation of the friction coefficient ($\delta(\mu) \sim 0.16$), then the stage with a relatively low fluctuation level of $\delta(\mu) \sim 0.05$, which increases

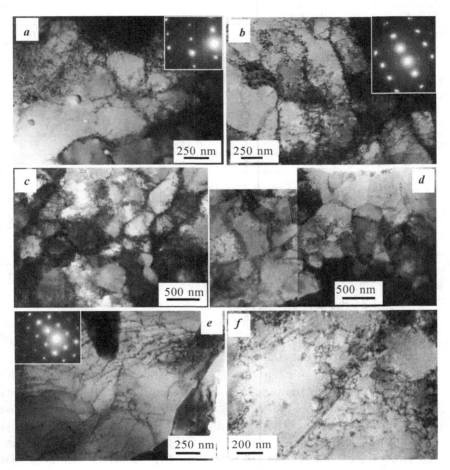

Fig. 6.39. Electron microscopic image of the dislocation substructure formed in an electric explosion coating synthesized on copper after EBT. a is a cellular substructure, b is a strip substructure, c – fragmented substructure, d – subgrain structure, e is the substructure of the dislocation chaos, f – mesh dislocation substructure.

Table 6.5. Substructures (δ, %) formed in electroexplosion coatings

Coating	Cell	Strip	Fragmented	Subgrain	Dislocation chaos or mesh
W-Cu	5	32	5	4	54
Mo-Cu	9	20	9	3	59
Mo-C-Cu	5	40	10	6	39
W-C-Cu	10	25	23	36	6
TiB2-Cu	5	57	15	7	16
Mo-Ni-Cu	15	35	10	4	36
W-Ni -Cu	10	28	12	3	47
Cr-C-Cu	9	23	20	38	10
Comment. Colour indicates preferred type of dislocation substructure.					

Table 6.6. Values of tribological characteristics, micro- and nanohardness, elastic modulus of the first kind of electric explosive coatings after EBT

Coating	W, 10^{-6}, mm³/Nm	W(sustrate)/ (coating)	μ	HV	HV, GPa	E, GPa
W-Cu	197.8	1.5	0.411	150...460	4.7	260
Mo-Cu	117.0	2.6	0.243	150...320	3.5	355
Mo-C-Cu	181.5	1.7	0.377	900...1100	11.2	396
W-C-Cu	164.1	1.8	0.341	1100...1750	18.1	470
TiB2-Cu	139.1	2.2	0.289	500...3500	26.4	450
Mo-Ni-Cu	45.2	6.7	0.452	150...325	2.4	302
W-Ni-Cu	37.3	8.1	0.485	170...470	3.6	298
Cr-C-Cu	76.7	3.9	0.332	170...1555	4	125

to the end of the test to δ(μ) ~ 0.11, is fixed. At the same time, the friction coefficient varies with fluctuations within 0.094...0.415 and reaches its maximum value by the end of the test (average value of the friction coefficient 0.289).

The data array was processed and the information on the dependences of the nanoscale hardness and the elastic modulus of the first kind on load was systematized. We present the most characteristic ranges of dependences of the values of nanohardness and Young's modulus for the Cr–C–Cu system and analyze them. An analysis of the results presented in Fig. 6.44 *a*, indicates that the graph of the hardness *HV* versus load *P* can be conditionally divided into two sections. At small values of the load ($P \leq 100$ mN), the hardness substantially depends on the value of *P*; at

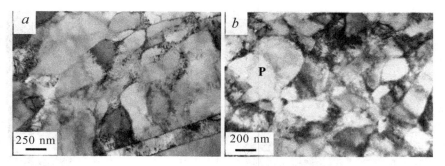

Fig. 6.40. Electron microscopic image of a dislocation substructure formed in a coating of TiB$_2$-Cu composition synthesized on the surface of copper by the electric explosion method and processed by a pulsed electron beam. *a* – increasing the degree of perfection of borders of the dislocation substructure; *b* – local formation of the initial stage of recrystallization.

$P \geq 100$ mN, the hardness of the coating is practically independent of the load on the indenter.

It is obvious that the value of hardness at low loads ($P \leq 100$ mN) is due not so much to the properties of the coating as to the features of the interaction of the diamond tip with the material [232]. Given this assumption, the hardness of the coating should be considered as $HV \approx 3.5$ GPa, which corresponds to the average hardness of section 2 of the graph shown in Fig. 6.44 *a*. Note that the hardness of the Cu-Cr alloy is ≈ 0.6 GPa. After annealing by dispersion hardening, the hardness can increase to 1.4 GPa. The microhardness of bronze samples in the delivery state is 1.2 GPa [233]. Therefore, the hardness of the coating formed on copper by the combined method exceeds the hardness of the Cu-Cr alloy subjected to additional hardening heat treatment by 2.5 times.

In a similar way, depends on the load on the indenter and the magnitude of the Young's modulus of the coating (Fig. 6.44 *b*). At $P \geq 100$ mN, the Young's modulus of the coating is practically independent of the load on the indenter and is ≈ 125 GPa. Young's modulus of copper is 110 GPa, bronze 100 GPa [233]. Therefore, the Young's modulus of the coating exceeds the Young's modulus of copper by ≈ 1.15 times.

Electroerosive resistance in conditions of arc erosion. Consider the results of tests of electroexplosive coatings of W–Cu, WC–Cu, W–Ni–Cu, TiB$_2$–Cu, Mo–Cu, Mo–C–Cu, Mo–Ni–Cu, Ti–B–Cu and Cr–C–Cu systems treated by a high-intensity electron beam for electrical discharge resistance under the conditions of an electric arc.

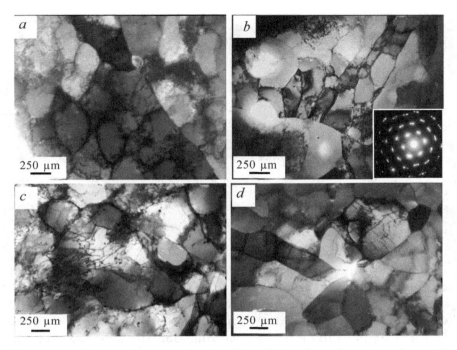

Fig. 6.41. Electron microscopy image of the dislocation substructure formed in electroexplosive coatings of Mo–C–Cu (*a*) and W–C–Cu (*b–d*) systems, after EBT.

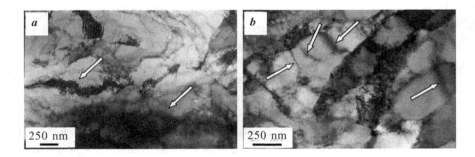

Fig. 6.42. Bending extinction contours (indicated by the arrows) that are present on electron microscopic images of the structure of electroexplosive coatings, formed on the surface of copper after EBT. *a* – coating system Mo–Cu, *b* – coating system TiB_2–Cu.

As established in this chapter, after EBT, the structure of electroexplosive coatings of the W–Cu, WC–Cu, W–Ni–Cu, TiB_2-Cu, Mo–Cu, Mo–C–Cu, Mo–Ni–Cu, Ti–B–Cu and Cr–C–Cu system is a copper matrix with globular inclusions of hardening phases. Prior

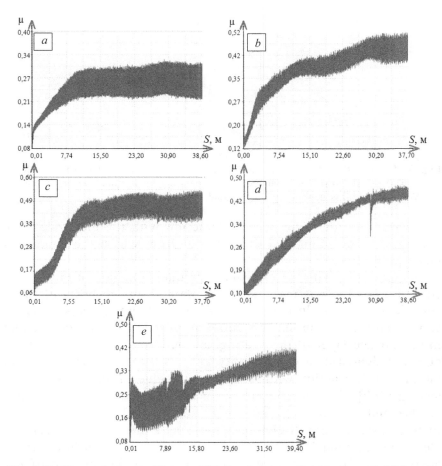

Fig. 6.43. Change in the coefficient of friction (μ) depending on the path (S) travelled by the counterbody for coatings treated with a pulsed electron beam. Counter-body: VK8 carbide. a – Mo–Cu system, b – Mo–C–Cu system, c – W–Cu system, d – system W–C–Cu, e – system TiB$_2$–Cu.

to the tests for electroerosion resistance, the surface relief of the coatings, irrespective of the elemental composition and irradiation mode, is a surface with a specular gloss. After completion of the tests for electrical discharge resistance under the conditions of an electric arc, the surface of the coatings of all systems changes. On it, the formation of craters is observed that arise as a result of the processes of electric arc erosion (Fig 6.45).

It is known that during electrical erosion, the rate of degradation of the surface of electrical contacts depends on the power density in the area of the supporting spots of the arc, the method of arc

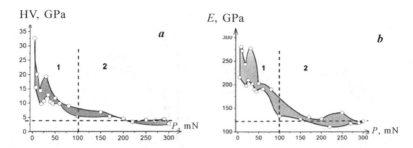

Fig. 6.44. Strength characteristics of the coating system Cr–C–Cu. EBT mode 45 J/cm², 100 μs, 10 pulses. *a* – nanosolidity depending on the load on the indenter, *b* – Young's modulus depending on the load on the indenter.

generation and the time of its interaction with the electrodes, the geometric dimensions and the material from which the contact is made [208, 209].

In connection with the foregoing, the transformation of the surface structures of the coatings can be explained on the basis of those considerations that during the on/off cycles there is evaporation of copper, an increase in the concentration of the refractory component in the surface layer of the coating, an increase in their temperature due to a decrease in conductivity and, as a result, an increase in the rate of destruction with respect to its values at the beginning of testing [209]. The electric arc when the contacts open for several milliseconds remains in a stationary state, which leads to erosion. In this case, the arc discharge appears as a short arc between the electrodes burning in pairs of contact materials. When intermittent energy flows occur, microbubbles appear on the surface of the reference arc spot. An increase in the internal pressure in the microbubbles leads them to explode, the flow of plasma microjets capable of conducting current, and the formation of craters, which is accompanied by spraying of liquid metal droplets and particles in the solid state. On the reference arc spot, several craters act together. The current values in plasma microjets reach ~100 A, the current density ~100 A/cm², and the pressure in the plasma microjet ~10⁷ Pa.

In the process of testing coatings, the influence of high temperatures leads to the melting of their surface and the formation of a relief on it with a rough morphology (Fig. 6.45). Moreover, copper, having a lower melting point, evaporates and the component with a high melting point remains the main component in the coating. The refractory component forms a continuous matrix with copper particles measuring about a few micrometers.

In local areas, degradation of the coating is observed up to the base material. Probably, the refractory component plays the role of reducing the evaporation of low-melting copper during the test process. During the tests, the resistance of the coatings of all systems is in the range 4.2...14 μOhm (Fig. 6.46). Moreover, in the range from 0 to 4000 on/off cycles, the value of the resistance of the coatings varies in the range of 4.2...8 μOhm. At 5000 cycles, the resistance increases to 11...14 μOhm and decreases to 8...12 μOhm to 6000 on/off cycles.

The increase in resistance at the end of the test (at N = 5000 ... 6000) can be explained on the basis that, due to a change in the surface topography, a decrease in the contact area of the contacts occurs.

According to the results of the tests of composite coatings of all systems for electroerosion resistance according to the AC-3 mode, it can be stated that the coatings obtained in the work satisfy GOST [139] for testing electromagnetic starters for switching wear resistance.

Electroerosive resistance in the conditions of spark erosion. Consider the results of tests of electroexplosive coatings of W–Cu, WC–Cu, W–Ni–Cu, TiB$_2$–Cu, Mo–Cu, Mo–C–Cu, Mo–Ni–Cu, Ti–B–Cu and Cr–C–Cu systems treated by a high-intensity electron beam for electrical discharge resistance under conditions of spark erosion.

The electrical conductivity of electroexplosive coatings after EBT is in the range from 22 to 29 nS.

Electroexplosive coatings after EBT show greater electrical discharge resistance during spark erosion compared to M00 grade copper used for the manufacture of electrical contacts (Table 6.7). It is obvious that the composite coating of the TiB$_2$–Cu system has a high electrical discharge erosion resistance during spark erosion. This fact is due to the fact that TiB$_2$ titanium diboride, which has better performance in comparison with other titanium borides, is used for the deposition of this coating [206]. In general, it can be said that all coatings demonstrate an increase in electroerosion resistance during spark erosion to values of ~10 times. The specificity of coating degradation is similar to that in the case of tests for electrical discharge resistance under the conditions of an electric arc. Comparing the test data of electroexplosive coatings after EBT with the case of EES of these coatings without EBT [198], it can be noted that the EES under conditions of a spark discharge increases by ~10%.

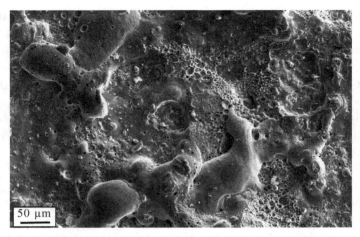

Fig. 6.45. A characteristic image of the surface of composite coatings after tests for electrical discharge resistance under the conditions of an electric arc.

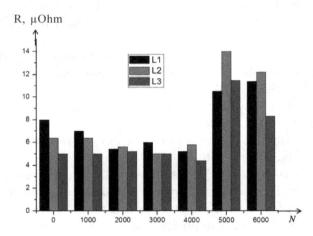

Fig. 6.46. Typical dependence of contact resistance (R) of the number of on/off cycles (N) during testing electroexplosive coatings for electroerosive resistance to arc erosion.

6.8. Conclusions

1. An electron-plasma combined method combining electroexplosive sputtering and subsequent irradiation with a high-intensity pulsed electron beam, multiphase coatings of the Mo–Cu, W–Cu, Mo–C–Cu, WC–Cu, W–Ni–Cu systems were first formed on the copper surface, Mo–Ni–Cu, Cr–C–Cu and TiB$_2$–Cu, characterized by high values of

nano and microhardness, Young's modulus and wear resistance.

2. The volume ratio of the matrix and the filler in the composite coatings is set at the EES stage and corresponds to their ratio in the composite electrically exploded conductor used for spraying.

3. The main phase of the coatings of the Mo–Cu and W–Cu systems formed in optimal conditions is a solid solution based on copper and particles of the second phases of molybdenum or tungsten. The pseudo-alloy coatings of the Mo–C–Cu and W–C–Cu systems are hardened by the wear- and electroerosion-resistant carbide phases of the composition Mo_2C and WC. In the coatings of the TiB_2–Cu system, a partial dissolution of the TiB_2 powder occurs upon irradiation with an electron beam and its re-isolation in the composition of Ti_2B_5.

4. The cross-sectional structure of the coatings of the Mo–Ni–Cu and W–Ni–Cu systems does not contain pores and is a copper-nickel matrix with molybdenum or tungsten inclusions, the sizes of which vary from 0.5 to 2.5 µm. Molybdenum (tungsten) and a copper-nickel binder are distributed approximately equally in the volume of coatings. During the EBT process of electroexplosive coatings, recrystallization with the formation of other compounds does not occur. Using transmission electron diffraction microscopy of thin foils, it was found that the coatings are formed by a solid solution based on Cu-Ni in the volume of which molybdenum or tungsten inclusions are randomly located with sizes from 5 to 150 nm.

5. In the electroexplosive coatings of the Mo–Cu, W–Cu, Mo–C–Cu, WC–Cu, W–Ni–Cu, Mo–Ni–Cu, Cr–C–Cu and TiB_2–Cu systems, the following dislocation forms after EBT substructures: cellular, strip, fragmented, subgrain, dislocation chaos or mesh. The preferred type of dislocation substructure for all coatings is the strip substructure, except for coatings of the W–C–Cu and Cr–C–Cu systems. For these systems, the predominant type of dislocation substructure is the subgrain substructure. An increase in the pulse duration of the electron beam from 100 to 200 µs and an increase in the number of pulses from 10 to 20 pulses.

Table. 6.7. Relative change of electroerosion resistance of electroexplosion coatings after EBT in the spark erosion conditions

System	W-Cu	W-C-Cu	W-Ni-Cu	TiB_2-Cu	Mo-Cu	Mo-C-Cu	Mo-Ni-Cu	Ti-B-Cu	Cr-C-Cu
	9.7	10.1	9.6	10.3	10.1	9.9	10.0	9.0	9.6

Note. m_e – the loss of mass of copper, taken as a standard at 10,000 test cycles, m – the loss of mass of the coating. The measurement error did not exceed 1%

contributes to the formation of a dislocation substructure with better subgrain boundaries, which contributes to increased wear and erosion resistance.

6. For coatings of the Cr–C–Cu system, when W increases from 3 to 5 • GW/m^2, the Cr(Cu) solid solution parameter increases from 0.2885 to 0.2890 nm. In this case, the parameter of the Cu(Cr) solid solution decreases from 0.36195 to 0.36125 nm. This is due to an increase in the degree of doping of the corresponding solid solution. The content of primary carbide Cr_7C_3 is greater, the lower the degree of alloying of a solid solution of Cr(Cu).

7. It has been established that EES leads to a simultaneous increase of several times the various operational properties of substrates – nano- and microhardness, first-order elastic modulus, wear resistance under conditions of dry sliding friction, electrical discharge resistance under conditions of arc and spark erosion. The maximum values of relative wear resistance have coatings of the W–Ni–Cu system on a copper substrate and amount to 8.1.

8. All coatings demonstrate an increase in electroerosion resistance during spark erosion to values of ~10 times. EBT of electroexplosive coatings leads to the fact that the EES in the conditions of a spark discharge increases by ~10%.

9. In the process of testing coatings of all systems with arc erosion, their resistance is in the range of 4.2...14 µOhm. In the range from 0 to 4000 on/off cycles, the resistance value of the coatings varies in the range of 4.2...8 µOhm. At 5000 cycles, the resistance increases to 11...14 µOhm due to the evaporation of the matrix under the influence of an electric arc and decreases to 8...12 µOhm to 6000 on/off cycles due to partial evaporation of the filler. Also, all coatings meet GOST testing for switching wear resistance. The electrical conductivity of electroexplosive coatings after EBT is in the range from 22 to 29 nS.

7

Use of work results

7.1. Use of the results of work in industry

The research results were used by introducing into the scientific and production activities of enterprises and organizations. Currently, the results of the work on the formation of wear- and electroerosion-resistant electrical explosive coatings of various systems and subsequent EBT are used at seven enterprises in Novokuznetsk, three in Krasnoyarsk and two in Yekaterinburg. The results are used in the development of a new generation of promising materials with improved characteristics for their application in the electrical and other high-tech industries. The scientific and technical products developed as part of the work are used in high-tech sectors of the economy in the manufacture of products from electrotechnical copper M00. Potential consumers of the proposed coatings are enterprises in the electrical industry. Table 7.1 presents the use of EES and EBT technology to strengthen specific details.

Pilot testing of the results for hardening of finger, socket and laminated contacts (Fig. 7.1, *a–c*) used in devices with voltages higher than 1000 V for various currents, as well as butt contacts (Fig. 7.9 *d*) for 110 kV and higher, was carried out. butt currents of not more than 1.0...1.5 kA. The results of use make it possible to recommend the EES of contacts in the production environment. Finger, end and socket contacts are used as workers and arrester, and plate contacts as workers. Contacts of this type are installed in relays, track switches, control buttons.

One of the important problems is the reduction of the transient resistance of the electrical contacts. This is due to the fact that it is the transition resistance that characterizes the amount of lost energy,

Table 7.1. Use of EES technology and EBT for hardening specific details

	Application region
1	Finger, socket and plate electrical contacts used in devices with voltages higher than 1000 V for various currents, end electric contacts for voltages of 110 kV and higher and currents of not more than 1.0...1.5 kA.
2	Cable lugs with electroexplosive composite coating
3	Recovery and hardening of electrical contacts of power mine equipment, namely the switching contacts of power controllers KS-304, KS-305
4	Contact hardening of vacuum switching devices, switches and relays of various type
5	A number of power contacts for magnetic starters PME 100, PME 200, PMA 3000, PMA 4000, PMA 5000, PMA 6000, PAE 300, PAE 400, PAE 500, PAE 600, hardened by the technology of electric explosion spraying
6	Mobile and fixed contacts in the contactors of the KT, KTPV, KPV, KPD, KTK, MK series, starters of the PME, PMA, PAE, PM series and command controllers of the KKT and KKP series
7	Standard contact elements, contacts to KT, KTPV, KPV, KPD, KPP, KTK, MK, PME, PMA, PAE, PM, KKT, KKP and other contacts to contactors, starters and command controllers, and also for non-standard contact elements.
8	Ejectors of conveying pipes, ejectors for feeding powders, heads of centrifugal distributors, etc.
9	PML series electromagnetic starters
10	Relays for protection of asynchronous motors of the RMZD series
11	Heavily loaded contacts of direct and alternating current, aviation relays of medium and heavy mode, automatic fuses, locomotive switches
12	High-frequency magnetic starters and contactors, household electrical appliance switches, drum switches, control buttons, high-voltage switches, centrifugal speed regulators for DC electric motors, contacts of powerful control transformers, power supplies for radio receivers, vibrators, starters, heavily loaded relays and switches of aircraft equipment

which is absorbed when the contacts are connected and passes into thermal energy by heating the contact. The rapidly forming oxide film on aluminum contacts also significantly increases the transient resistance. When an electric current flows through the contacts, they heat up. In this case, the highest temperature values are recorded on the contact surface due to the high transition resistance. Due to the heating of the contact, the specific resistance of the contact material increases, which in turn leads to an increase in the transition resistance. Also, an increase in the contact temperature

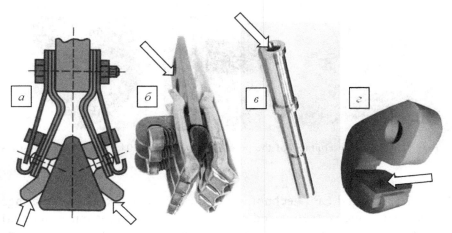

Fig. 7.1. Electrical contacts hardened by the EES and EBT method. *a* – finger, *b* – laminated, *c* – socket, *d* – butt. Arrows indicate contacts with sprayed coatings.

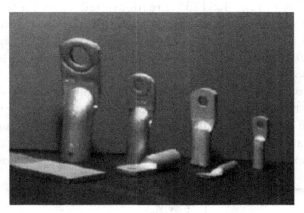

Fig. 7.2, Cable shoes and adapter plates with a protective coating formed by the EES and EBT method.

promotes the formation of oxides on its surface. It also increases the transient resistance. Despite the fact that with increasing temperature the contact material may soften due to an increase in the contact surface, but in general this process leads to the welding of contacts or their destruction. The transient electrical resistance of the electric explosive coatings obtained in this work varies from 40 to 50 μm.

Pilot tests of aluminium cable shoes with electrically explosive coatings (Fig. 7.2) showed their high durability compared to tinned cable lugs of the TML grade and are used to reduce transient electrical resistance.

224

Fig. 7.3. Switching contacts of the power controller KS-304, hardened by the EES method.

The EES and EBT technology of electroerosion-resistant coatings has been successfully used to restore and strengthen electrical contacts (Fig. 7.3) of power mine equipment, namely the switching contacts of power controllers KS-304, KS-305. Power controllers of the type KS-304, KS-305 are designed for electrodynamic braking and rheostatic start-up of traction motors for mine electric locomotives operating from a contact network with voltage of 250 V and direct current. These power controllers are widely used in mines and open pits of the Kemerovo region. A distinctive feature of the power controllers KS-304, KS-305 is a reinforced cam element. This design makes it possible for a current to flow through the cam element with greater force and for a longer time. Reinforcing the cam element creates an additional power reserve and extends the life of the controller. However, reinforcing the cam element is not possible

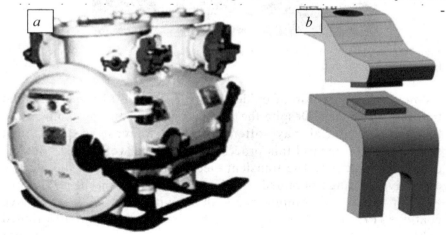

Figure 7.4. Starter used at Prommest company. *a* – starter brand PVI-320A, *b* - contacts of the starter, EES hardened.

Fig. 7.5. Ejector for feeding powders.

resistant coatings of the W–C–Cu, Mo–C–Cu, Cr–C–Cu, Ti–B–Cu and TiB_2–Cu systems. The coatings of these systems synthesize high-modulus high-hardness carbides of tungsten, molybdenum, chromium and titanium borides.

The results of the formation of nanocomposite electroerosion-resistant coatings are of practical interest and are used in the production of Prommest company for hardening the contacts of vacuum switching devices, switches and relays of various assortments, as well as contacts of starters made of PVI and PV grades.

Explosion- and spark-proof vacuum ignition starter PVI-320MV is used to stop and directly start asynchronous three-phase motors with a squirrel-cage rotor, as well as to protect against short-circuit currents and overloads in outgoing power circuits. PVI series starters operate in coal mines of the Kemerovo region and shale mine, hazardous in dust and gas. In accordance with safety rules in these mines, the use of electrical equipment with a protection level of RV is required.

Ejectors of conveying pipes, ejectors for feeding powders are used (Fig. 7.5), heads of centrifugal distributors with sprayed protective electro-explosive wear-resistant coatings of TiC–Mo, TiC–Ni, TiB_2–Mo and TiB_2–Ni systems. The ejector is designed to supply powder to the gun in a controlled, even and uniform flow. The maximum wear during operation of the ejectors is experienced by their internal nozzle. It is strengthened with the use of electric explosive coatings

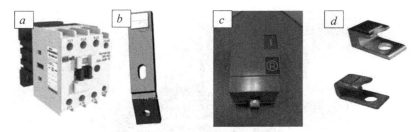

Fig. 7.6. Equipment, hardened by the EES and EBT method: *a* – contactor of the KM41P brand, *b* – contacts of contactors of the KM series, hardened by the EES method, *c* – PAE series starter, *d* - contacts of starters of the PAE series, hardened by the EES method.

The results were pilot tested during surface hardening (Fig. 7.6) of the contacts of the KM series contactors, as well as the contacts of the PAE series starters. The contacts strengthened by the EES and EBT methods showed an increase in the switching wear resource by 1.5...2.0 times in comparison with the original contacts.

Series KM electric contactors are special devices designed for switching sufficiently large AC or DC loads. They are used in AC electric networks with voltage up to 400 V and frequency 50 Hz; they are used for switching weakly inductive loads with rated current up to 63 A.

PAE series magnetic starters are designed for remote start and stop, as well as (if there is a relay) for protection against dangerous overloads of three-phase squirrel-cage asynchronous motors operating in a temperate climate with voltage up to 500 V, frequency 50 Hz, ambient temperature from −40° to +40°C. The starters are designed to operate in continuous, intermittent, continuous and intermittent modes with a frequency of 600 starts per hour with a duty cycle of

Fig. 7.7. Electrical equipment hardened by the EES and EBT method. *a* – KKT 61 brand controller; *b* – KKT brand 61 contact controller, EES hardened.

Fig. 7.8. Equipment hardened by electric explosive spraying and subsequent electron-beam processing. *a* – package transformer explosion-proof substation, *b* – contact of complete transformer explosion-proof substation, hardened by the EES and EBT method.

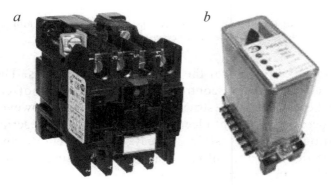

Fig. 7.9. Examples of the practical use of research results for hardening various devices. *a* – electromagnetic starter of the PML series; *b* – protection relay of asynchronous motors of the RMZD series.

40%. PAE starters are manufactured in open or closed design with or without a protected relay. Regardless of the starter's design, hardening of its electrical contacts by the method of spraying electroerosion-resistant coatings makes it possible to increase its service life.

Under the conditions of operation of the KKT 61, KKT 62, KKT 63, KKT 68 controllers (Fig. 7.7) at the shop of industrial billets OJSC Spetteplohimmontazh copper electrical contact surfaces hardened by the EES method showed an increased commutation wear resource by 1.5...2.0 times compared to the original contacts and are used.

The KKT series controllers are used to start, change the speed and reverse electric motors by changing the magnitude and resistance circuit. The controller is used only in AC circuits. The presence in the electrical circuit of the command controllers 12 electrical circuits

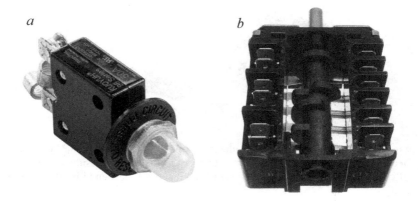

a   *b*

Fig. 7.10. Examples of the practical use of research results for hardening various devices; *a* – automatic fuse; *b* – locomotive switch.

allows you to flexibly control the current load conditions. The use of electrical contacts of the controller in various modes of current load leads to heterogeneous destruction of their surface. However, the use of electroerosion-resistant electroexplosive coatings described in this dissertation made it possible to create coatings with a uniform level of properties over the entire surface of the coating and thereby extend the life of the electrical contacts.

The EES and EBT technologies are used to strengthen standard contact elements, various contacts to contactors, starters and command controllers, as well as for non-standard contact elements with electroexplosive coatings.

In particular, complete transformer explosion-proof substations (Fig. 7.8) are designed to supply three-phase current to power receivers installed in underground mines hazardous in gas, methane and dust, as well as to protect low voltage lines of leakage outflows and maximum current protection.

In the test mode, the original and economical method for restoring the contacts of electromagnetic starters of the PML series (Fig. 7.9 *a*) due to the electroexplosive spraying of coatings of the CdO–Ag system was launched.

The contacts of the protection relay of asynchronous motors of the RMZD series (Fig. 7.9 *b*) are restored by electroexplosive spraying of SnO_2–Ag system coatings.

The technique for hardening the heavily loaded contacts of direct and alternating current, aviation relays of medium and heavy duty, automatic fuses, switches of diesel locomotives due to

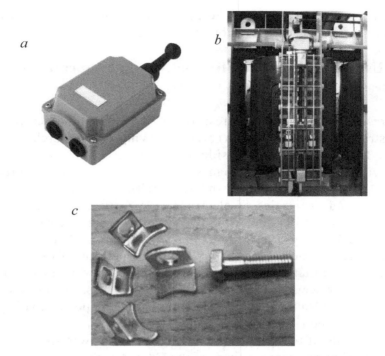

Fig. 7.11. Examples of the practical use of research results for hardening various devices. *a* – drum switch; *b* – contacts of a powerful control transformer; *c* – starter contacts

electroexplosive spraying of coatings of the CuO–Ag system has been tested and used (Fig. 7.10).

The application of the ZnO–Ag system of electric explosive spraying of coatings is implemented for hardening magnetic starters and contactors with a high switching frequency, household electrical appliance switches, drum switches, control buttons, high-voltage switches, centrifugal speed regulators of DC electric motors, contacts of powerful control transformers, power supplies for radio receivers, vibrators, starters, heavily loaded relays and switches of aircraft equipment (Fig. 7.11).

In addition to the presented examples of practical use, negotiations are underway on the use of the developed technology to strengthen electric contacts of the CJ200 grade with foreign companies.

Thus, the developed technologies of surface hardening of metals and alloys by creating electric explosive coatings with a certain set of properties on their surface are used in the conditions of the production activities of enterprises of the Russian Federation in order to increase the service life of electrical contacts and other parts in general, which ensures an economic effect.

7.2. Use of results in scientific activity and educational process

The results were used in the research activities of the Siberian State Industrial University (Russia) when carrying out research projects under the Grant of the President of the Russian Federation for state support of young Russian scientists – candidates of sciences MK-1118.2017.2 "Study of the regularities of formation of the structure and properties of electroerosion-resistant nanocomposite coatings of Ag–CdO and Ag–SnO$_2$ systems using environmentally friendly technology of electric explosive spraying and electron-beam processing, and the Russian Grant Fund competition 2018 'Carrying out research initiatives of young scientists', the President's program of research projects carried out by leading scientists, including young scientists 18-79-00013 'Electroexplosion nanocomposite coatings of high-power electrical networks switch contacts'.

The results of the study of the effect of EES of wear-resistant and electroerosion-resistant coatings of the CdO–Ag, SnO$_2$–Ag, CuO–Ag, and ZnO–Ag systems and subsequent electron-beam processing on the formation and evolution of the structure, phase composition, tribological properties, and nano- and microhardness of the copper substrate, obtained in the work are used in the educational process at the Department of Natural Sciences, named after Professor V.M. Finkel of the Siberian State Industrial University when performing laboratory work for students in the direction of undergraduate training 03/22/01 Materials science and materials technology (profile 'Nanomaterials and nanotechnologies') in the disciplines Methods of studying the structure and properties of materials, Computer modelling in materials science and for students in the direction of training of scientific and pedagogical personnel in graduate school 06/03/01 'Physics and Astronomy'.

Conclusion

As a result of the work, the physical laws of the formation of the structure and properties of electric explosive electroerosion-resistant coatings of the contacts of the switches of powerful electric networks with subsequent processing by a high-energy electron beam are established. *Main conclusions:*

1. The scientific problem of hardening the contacts of switches of powerful electric networks by electroexplosive spraying of wear- and electroerosion-resistant coatings of various compositions has been solved, which is of great economic importance.

2. Methods of modern physical materials science have revealed the regularities and nature of the formation of wear- and electroerosion-resistant coatings of various systems during electroexplosive spraying and subsequent electron-beam processing.

3. Methods of electro-explosive spraying of wear-resistant and electroerosion-resistant coatings of various systems on copper, aluminum and low-carbon steel with subsequent electron-beam processing have been developed. Methods of electroexplosive spraying of coatings of various systems are realized by means of an electric explosion of composite electrically exploded conductors of various compositions, the formation of explosion products into a plasma jet and their transfer to the treated surface, followed by high-speed crystallization of the coating. Subsequent electron-beam processing leads to homogenization of the surface layer of coatings to the maximum possible thickness without evaporation.

4. After electroexplosive spraying, the phase composition of the coatings is formed by strengthening wear- and electro-erosion-resistant phases – CdO, SnO_2, CuO, and ZnO oxides located in a silver matrix. After electron beam processing, the structure is transformed and the phase composition for the CdO–Ag system is represented by the phases Cu, Cd_3Cu_4, Ag_2O_3, CdO_2, Cd_3Cu_4; for the SnO_2–Ag system, by the phases SnO_2, Ag_3Sn, $Cu_{10}Sn_3$, Cu_3Sn, Cu_6Sn_5, Ag_4Sn, and CuO; for the CuO–Ag system, by the phases Cu_2O, $Cu_{64}O$; for the ZnO–Ag system, by the phases Ag, ZnO, Cu, CuZn, Ag_5Zn_8, Cu_2O, Ag_2O, $Cu_{0.67}Zn_{0.33}$, AgZn. In all systems, the effect of dispersion hardening of a copper layer adjacent to the coating, due to the formation of nanoscale phases of various compositions, was revealed.

5. Typical sizes of the first and second hierarchical levels of the structure were established for the CuO–Ag and ZnO–Ag systems, which, under the used spraying conditions, ranged from 2 to 5 nm and from 10 to 15 nm, respectively. A mechanism is proposed for the formation of hierarchical levels of the structure of electroexplosive coating systems. At the coating/substrate interface, surface periodic structures with a wavelength of 3 nm on average were detected. They represent the residual surface nanorelief that arose after the end of

the action of a pulsed plasma jet of electrical explosion products of conductors on the substrate and cooling of the surface.

6. Electroexplosive spraying of the surface of copper substrates by coatings of the CdO–Ag, SnO$_2$–Ag, CuO–Ag, and ZnO–Ag systems and subsequent electron beam treatment increase the wear resistance of the modified layer from 3.25 to 4.33 times; the friction coefficient in this case is $\approx$0.8...1.4 from the copper substrate. It has been established that the nanosolid hardness of sprayed coatings is up to 3.8 times greater than the hardness of annealed copper. All coatings increase the life of copper electrical contacts by 2 times and meet the requirements of tests for switching wear resistance.

7. The developed methods of electro-explosive spraying of wear-resistant and electroerosion-resistant coatings using electron-beam processing, protected by patents for inventions, are used to process parts used in engineering, electrical and mining industries. The total annual effect due to the saving of material and economic resources amounted to 8.3 million rubles, including the author's share of 3 million rubles. The results obtained in the work are implemented in the educational process.

8. The thickness h of the layers of electroexplosive coatings of various systems modified by the electron beam, depending on the surface energy density E_s, is linear. Its maximum value is observed for the TiB$_2$–Cu system. For coatings of other systems, it has intermediate values, which is explained by their thermophysical properties.

9. For coatings of the Cr–C–Cu system, with an increase in W from 3 to 5 $\cdot$ GW/m^2, the parameter of the Cr(Cu) solid solution increases from 0.2885 to 0.2890 nm. In this case, the parameter of the Cu(Cr) solid solution decreases from 0.36195 to 0.36125 nm. This is due to an increase in the degree of doping of the corresponding solid solution. The content of primary carbide Cr$_7$C$_3$ is greater, the lower the degree of alloying of a solid solution of Cr(Cu).

10. Regardless of the phase composition of the coating and the electron beam irradiation regime, the following dislocation substructures were revealed: cellular, strip, fragmented, subgrain, as well as grains with randomly distributed dislocations and dislocations that form networks. The randomly distributed dislocations and dislocations that form the grids are also detected in all the substructures indicated above. With an increase in the pulse duration of the beam from 100 to 200 μs and the number of pulses from 10 to 20, a dislocation substructure with more perfect boundaries

is predominantly formed. The predominant type of dislocation substructure (up to 37%) in coatings of W–Cu, Mo–Cu, Mo–C–Cu, WC–Cu, Ti–B–Cu, TiB_2–Cu, Mo–Ni–Cu, W–Ni–Cu and TiB_2–Al is a strip substructure, and in the coatings of the W–C–Cu and Cr–C–Cu systems, it is subgrain (up to 57%).

11. The morphological features of the surface of composite coatings of various systems formed after EBT have been established. In the EBT mode E_s = 60 J/cm^2, t = 100 μs, N = 10 pulses. The grain size of the polycrystalline structure varies from 3 to 40 μm. An increase in the pulse duration to 200 μs and their number to 20 pulses. leads to the formation of a more uniform grain structure with a grain size of 10 to 20 μm. In the volume of grains, regardless of the energy density of the electron beam, a cellular crystallization structure is observed that is characteristic of a material cooled at high speeds. The cell size ranges from 0.25 to 0.5 μm.

12. The basis of structure formation in electric explosive powder coatings is the dynamic rotation of the sprayed particles, which form a vortex structure both in the coating and in the upper layers of the substrate. This causes the dispersion of all structural elements of the coating, their mutual penetration into each other and the blurring of the interface between the dynamic rotations and the coating matrix, which helps to improve the properties of the coating.

13. Electroexplosive composite coatings with the filled structure of all systems after EBT are a metal matrix with reinforcing compounds located in it with phase particle sizes from 20–150 nm to 0.1–5 microns. Ultrafine (with characteristic sizes of 20–150 nm) particles of the hardening phases are formed during the dissolution of powder particles and subsequent crystallization of the coating. Particles with characteristic sizes of 0.1–5.0 μm are particles of powders used for spraying.

14. The dependence of the thickness of the mixing zone of coatings with a copper substrate on the heat flux density is linear when the absorbed power density changes from 4.1 to 5.3 GW/m^2. In this case, the highest values of h are achieved using tungsten powder, and the lowest – titanium diboride powder.

15. When spraying the coatings, which is accompanied by the synthesis of hardening phases of tungsten carbides and molybdenum, titanium borides, their content increases from 30 to 50% with an increase in heat flux density within the range of q from 5.5 to 7.6 GW/m^2. This is due to the fact that the formation reactions of carbides and borides proceed to the end.

16. It has been established that the surface roughness of the sprayed coatings is affected by the material of the exploding conductor. The highest roughness Ra = 2.4 μm is found in coatings sprayed with foils with powder samples placed on them. The roughness of coatings sprayed using foils and composite electrically explosive materials have similar values and are less by 12% compared to the maximum. In all cases, the roughness parameter Ra of the surface of coatings after EBT decreases by 40–50% and does not exceed 1.2 μm.

17. The thickness of single layers sprayed with foils and foils with powders placed on them is proportional to the mass of the exploding conductor and varies from 10 to 40 μm with a change in the mass of the exploding conductor from 75 to 300 mg. When using a composite electrically explosive material, the thickness of the coatings is proportional to the number of unit layers and varies from 50 to 200 μm when their number changes from 1 to 4.

References

1. Cho, W. C. A classification of electrical component failures and their human error types in South Korean NPPs during last 10 years / W. C. Cho, T. H. Ahn // Engineering and Technology. – 2019. – Vol. 51. – P. 709–718

2. Gu, L. Coupled numerical simulation of arc plasma channel evolution and discharge crater formation in arc discharge machining / L. Gu, Y. Zhu, G. He et al. // International Journal of Heat and Mass Transfer. – 2019. – Vol. June 2019. – P. 25–28

3. Yang, H. Influence of reciprocating distance on the delamination wear of the carbon strip in pantograph–catenary system at high sliding-speed with strong electrical current / H. Yang, B. Hu, Y. Liu et al. // Engineering Failure Analysis. – 2019. – Vol. 104. – P. 887–897

4. Zabeo, A. Value of information analysis for assessing risks and benefits of nanotechnology innovation / A. Zabeo, J. M. Keisler, D. Hristozov et al. // Environmental Sciences Europe. – 2019. – Vol. 31. – P. 11

5. Sun, Z. M. Progress in research and development on MAX phases: A family of layered ternary compounds / Z. M. Sun // International Materials Reviews. – 2011. – Vol. 56. – P. 143–166

6. Peng, L. Fabrication and properties of Ti3AlC2 particulates reinforced copper composites / L. Peng // Scripta Materialia. – 2007. – Vol. 56. – P. 729–732

7. Zhang, P. Arc erosion behavior of Cu-Ti3SiC2 cathode and anode / P. Zhang, T. L. Ngai, A. Wang, Z. Ye // Vacuum. – 2017. – Vol. 141. – P. 235–242

8. Liu, M. Ag/Ti$_3$AlC$_2$ composites with high hardness, high strength and high conductivity / M. Liu, J. Chen, H. Cui et al. // Materials Letters. – 2018. – Vol. 213. – P. 269–273

9. Ding, J. Arc erosion behavior of Ag/Ti3AlC2 electrical contact materials / J. Ding, W. B. Tian, P. Zhang et al. // Journal of Alloys and Compounds. – 2018. – Vol. 740. – P. 669–676

10. Li, H. Material transfer behavior of AgTiB$_2$ and AgSnO$_2$ electrical contact materials under different currents / H. Li, X. Wang, X. Guo et al. // Materials and Design. – 2017. – Vol. 114. – P. 139–148

11. 11. Ray, N. Effect of WC particle size and Ag volume fraction on electrical contact resistance and thermal conductivity of Ag-WC contact materials / N. Ray, B. Kempf, T. Mützel et al. // Materials and Design. – 2015. – Vol. 85. – P. 412–422

12. Ray, N. Novel processing of Ag-WC electrical contact materials using spark plasma sintering / N. Ray, B. Kempf, G. Wiehl et al. // Materials and Design. – 2017. – Vol. 121. – P. 262–271

13. Afonin, M. P. Effect of structural anisotropy on contact properties in a silver-Graphite composite / M. P. Afonin, A. V. Boiko // Powder Metallurgy and Metal Ceramics. – 2005. – Vol. 44. – P. 84–87

14. Vinaricky, E. Switching behavior of silver/graphite contact material in different atmospheres in regard to contact erosion / E. Vinaricky, V. Behrens // Electrical Contacts, Proceedings of the Annual Holm Conference on Electrical Contacts. – 1998.

236

– P. 292–300

15. Behrens, V. Test results of different silver/graphite contact materials in regard to applications in circuit breakers / V. Behrens, Th. Honig, A. Kraus et al. // Electrical Contacts, Proceedings of the Annual Holm Conference on Electrical Contacts. – 1995. – P. 393–397

16. Chen, Y. L. A novel process for fabricating electrical contact SnO2/Ag composites by reciprocating extrusion / Y. L. Chen, C. F. Yang, J. W. Yeh et al. // Metallurgical and Materials Transactions A: Physical Metallurgy and Materials Science. – 2005. – Vol. 36. – P. 2441–2447

17. Wu, C. P. Influence of alloy components on arc erosion morphology of Ag/MeO electrical contact materials / C. P. Wu, D. Q. Yi, W. Weng et al. // Transactions of Nonferrous Metals Society of China (English Edition). – 2016. – Vol. 26. – P. 185–195

18. Wang, D. Anisotropic properties of Ag/Ti3AlC2 electrical contact materials prepared by equal channel angular pressing / D. Wang, W. Tian, A. Ma et al. // Journal of Alloys and Compounds. – 2019. – Vol. 784. – P. 431–438

19. Ding, J. Corrosion and degradation mechanism of Ag/Ti3AlC2 composites under dynamic electric arc discharge / J. Ding, W. Tian, D. Wang et al. // Corrosion Science. – 2019. – Vol. 156. – P. 147–160

20. Ding, J. Microstructure evolution, oxidation behavior and corrosion mechanism of Ag/Ti$_2$SnC composite during dynamic electric arc discharging / J. Ding, W. Tian, D. Wang et al. // Journal of Alloys and Compounds. – 2019. – Vol. 785. – P. 1086–1096

21. Wang, X. Effect of sintering temperature on fine-grained Cu/W composites with high copper / X. Wang, S. Wei, L. Xu et al. // Materials Characterization. – 2019. – Vol. 153. – P. 121–127

22. Li, B. Fabrication of fine-grained W-Cu composites with high hardness / B. Li, Z. Sun, G. Hou et al. // Journal of Alloys and Compounds. – 2018. – Vol. 766. – P. 204–214

23. Guo, Y. Field-assisted solid phase sintering of W-20 wt.% Cu nanocomposites prepared by co-precipitation method / Y. Guo, D. Guo, S. Wang et al. // Materials Express. – 2018. – Vol. 8. – P. 547–554

24. Wen, X. Electric arc-induced damage on electroless Ag film using ionic liquid as a lubricant under sliding electrical contact / X. Wen, F. Yuwen, Z. Ding et al. // Tribology International. – 2019. – Vol. 135. – P. 269–276

25. Huang, W. Electrical Sliding Friction Lubricated with Ionic Liquids / W. Huang, L. Kong, X. Wang // Tribology Letters. – 2017. – Vol. 65. – P. 65:17

26. Wang, Y. Controlled friction behaviors of gradient porous Cu-Zn composites storing ionic liquids under electric field / Y. Wang, G. Zhang, W. Wang et al. // AIP Advances. – 2018. – Vol. 8. – P. 115020

27. Lin, Z. Excellent anti-arc erosion performance and corresponding mechanisms of a nickel-belt-reinforced silver-based electrical contact material / Z. Lin, S. Fan, M. Liu et al. // Journal of Alloys and Compounds. – 2019. – Vol. 788. – P. 163–171

28. Lin, Z. Morphology-controllable synthesis and thermal decomposition of Ag and Ni oxalate for Ag-Ni alloy electrical contact materials / Z. Lin, S. Liu, J. G. Li et al. // Materials and Design. – 2016. – Vol. 108. – P. 640–647

29. Zhang, K. Preparation of Ag-Ni-Cu Composite Material by Ultrasonic Arc Spray Forming and Accumulative Roll Bonding and the Evolution of Its Microstructure / K. Zhang, G. Y. Qin, S.Y. Xu et al. // Metallurgical and Materials Transactions A: Physical Metallurgy and Materials Science. – 2015. – Vol. 46. – P. 880–886

30. Zhang, X. Thermal deformation behavior of the Al2O3-Cu/(W, Cr) electrical con-

tacts / X. Zhang, Y. Zhang, B. Tian et al. // Vacuum. – 2019. – Vol. 164. – P. 361–366

31. Zhang, X. Arc erosion behavior of the Al2O3-Cu/(W, Cr) electrical contacts / X. Zhang, Y. Zhang, B. Tian et al. // Composites Part B: Engineering. – 2019. – Vol. 160. – P. 110–118

32. Li, W. J. Air arc erosion behavior of CuZr/Zn2SnO4 electrical contact materials / W. J. Li, W. Z. Shao, N. Xie et al. // Journal of Alloys and Compounds. – 2018. – Vol. 743. – P. 697–706

33. Zhou, Y. X. Failure analysis of arc ablated tungsten-copper electrical contacts / Y. X. Zhou, Y. L. Xue, K. Zhou // Vacuum. – 2019. – Vol. 164. – P. 390–395

34. Biyik, S. Effect of polyethylene glycol on the mechanical alloying behavior of Cu-W electrical contact material / S. Biyik // Acta Physica Polonica A. – 2018. – Vol. 134. – P. 208–212

35. Zhou, K. W-Cu composites reinforced by copper coated graphene prepared using infiltration sintering and spark plasma sintering: A comparative study / K. Zhou, W. G. Chen, J. J. Wang et al. // International Journal of Refractory Metals and Hard Materials. – 2019. – Vol. 82. – P. 91–99

36. Veazey, R. A. Modeling the influence of two terminal electrode contact geometry and sample dimensions in electro-materials / R. A. Veazey, A. S. Gandy, D. C. Sinclair, J. S. Dean // Journal of the American Ceramic Society. – 2019. – Vol. 102. – P. 3609–3622

37. Welzl, A. Microelectrodes for local conductivity and degradation measurements on Al stabilized Li7La3Zr2O12 garnets / A. Welzl, R. Wagner, D. Rettenwander et al. // Journal of Electroceramics. – 2017. – Vol. 38. – P. 176–181

38. Shen, L. Preparation and characterization of Ga and Sr co-doped Li7La3Zr2O12 garnet-type solid electrolyte / L. Shen, L. Wang, Z. Wang et al. // Solid State Ionics. – 2019. – Vol. 339. – P. 114992

39. Daocharoenporn, S. Prediction of the pantograph/catenary wear using nonlinear multibody system dynamic algorithms / S. Daocharoenporn, M. Mongkolwongrojn, S. Kulkarni, A. A. Shabana // Journal of Tribology. – 2019. – Vol. 141. – P. 051603

40. Kulkarni, S. Pantograph/Catenary contact formulations / S. Kulkarni, C. M. Pappalardo, A. A. Shabana // Journal of Vibration and Acoustics, Transactions of the ASME. – 2017. – Vol. 139. – P. 011010

41. Chen, G. Pantograph/Catenary contact formulations / G. Chen, Y. Yang, Y. Yang // Prediction of dynamic characteristics of a pantograph-catenary system using the displacement compatibility. – 2017. – Vol. 19. – P. 5405–5420

42. Ying, Z. Study on electrical properties of AgSnO2 contact materials doped with rare-earth La, Ce, and Y / Z. Ying, W. Jingqin, K. Huiling // IEEE Transactions on Components, Packaging and Manufacturing Technology. – 2019. – Vol. 9. – P. 864–870

43. Zhang, Y. Simulation and experimental study on the properties of Fe, Y co-doped AgSnO2 contact materials / Y. Zhang, J. Wang, H. Kang // IEEJ Transactions on Electrical and Electronic Engineering. – 2019. – Vol. 14. – P. 990–995

44. Jingqin, W. Study on properties of AgSnO2 contact materials doped with rare earth Y / W. Jingqin, Z. Ying, K. Huiling // Materials Research Express. – 2018. – Vol. 5. – P. 085902

45. Poljanec, D. Effect of polarity and various contact pairing combinations of electrographite, polymer-bonded graphite and copper on the performance of sliding electrical contacts / D. Poljanec, M. Kalin // Wear. – 2019. – Vol. 426–427. – P. 1163–1175

46. Kalin, M. Influence of the contact parameters and several graphite materials on the

tribological behaviour of graphite/copper two-disc electrical contacts / M. Kalin, D. Poljanec // Tribology International. – 2018. – Vol. 126. – P. 192–205

47. Poljanec, D. Influence of contact parameters on the tribological behaviour of various graphite/graphite sliding electrical contacts / D. Poljanec, M. Kalin, L. Kumar // Wear. – 2018. – Vol. 406-407. – P. 75–83

48. Wu, M. High oxidation resistance of CVD graphene-reinforced copper matrix composites / M. Wu, B. Hou, S. Shu et al. // Nanomaterials. – 2019. – Vol. 9. – P. 498.

49. Li, S. CVD synthesis of monodisperse graphene/Cu microparticles with high corrosion resistance in Cu etchant / S. Li, B. Hou, D. Dai et al. // Materials. – 2018. – Vol. 11. – P. 1459

50. Li, S. Preparation, properties and application of graphene/Cu composite materials / S. Li, A. Li, D. Dai et al. // Gongneng Cailiao/Journal of Functional Materials. – 2017. – Vol. 48. – P. 09043–09051

51. Bahramian, A. Enhancing the corrosion resistance of Cu/Ni-P/Au electrical contacts by electropolymerized poly (methyl methacrylate) / A. Bahramian, M. Eyraud, S. Maria et al. // Corrosion Science. – 2019. – Vol. 149. – P. 75–86

52. Bahramian, A. Cu/Ni/Au multilayers by electrochemistry: A crucial system in electronics - A critical review / A. Bahramian, M. Eyraud, F. Vacandio, P. Knauth // Microelectronic Engineering. – 2019. – Vol. 206. – P. 25–44

53. Bahramian, A. Improving the corrosion properties of amorphous Ni-P thin films using different additives / A. Bahramian, M. Eyraud, F. Vacandio, P. Knauth // Surface and Coatings Technology. – 2018. – Vol. 345. – P. 40–52

54. Mohammadhosein, M. Online Assessment of Contact Erosion in High Voltage Gas Circuit Breakers Based on Different Physical Quantities / M. Mohammadhosein, K. Niayesh, A. A. Shayegani-Akmal et al. // IEEE Transactions on Power Delivery. – 2019. – Vol. 34. – P. 580–587

55. Mohammadhosein, M. Impact of Surface Morphology on Arcing Induced Erosion of CuW Contacts in Gas Circuit Breakers / M. Mohammadhosein, K. Niayesh, A.A.S. Akmal, H. Mohseni // Electrical Contacts, Proceedings of the Annual Holm Conference on Electrical Contacts. – 2019. – Vol. 2018. – P. 99–105

56. Bagherpoor, A. Online condition assessment of interruption chamber of gas circuit breakers using arc voltage measurement / A. Bagherpoor, S. Rahimi-Pordanjani, A. A. Razi-Kazemi, K. Niayesh // IEEE Transactions on Power Delivery. – 2017. – Vol. 32. – P. 1776–1783

57. Ravelo, B. Multiphysics analysis of pin-socket electrical dynamic contact susceptibility under vibration stress / B. Ravelo // IEEE Transactions on Electromagnetic Compatibility. – 2019. – Vol. 61. – P. 344–351

58. Cholachue, C. Fast S-Parameter TAN Model of n-Port lumped structures / C. Cholachue, B. Ravelo, A. Simoens, A. Fathallah // IEEE Access. – 2019. – Vol. 7. – P. 72505–72517

59. Xu, Z. Analysis of multilayer interconnects distributed energy-per-bit and power integrity with Kron-Branin formalism / Z. Xu, Y. Liu, B. Ravelo, O. Maurice // 32nd General Assembly and Scientific Symposium of the International Union of Radio Science. – 2017. – Vol. 2017. – P. 1–4

60. Cui, R. Investigation of the structure and properties of electrodeposited Cu/graphene composite coatings for the electrical contact materials of an ultrahigh voltage circuit breaker / R. Cui, Y. Han, Z. Zhu et al. // Journal of Alloys and Compounds. – 2019. – Vol. 777. – P. 1159–1167

61. Chen, W. Synergistic enhancing effect for mechanical and electrical properties of tungsten copper composites using spark plasma infiltrating sintering of copper-coat-

ed grapheme / W. Chen, L. Dong, J. Wang et al. // Scientific Reports. – 2017. – Vol. 7. – P. 17836

62. Kurapova, O. Yu. Structure and microhardness of two-layer foils of nanotwinned copper with graphene nanoinclusions / O. Yu. Kurapova, V. G. Konakov, A. S. Grashchenko et al. // Materials Physics and Mechanics. – 2017. – Vol. 32. – P. 58–73

63. Li, H. Effect of Ni addition on the arc-erosion behavior of AgTiB2 contact material / H. Li, X. Wang, Y .Xi et al. // Vacuum. – 2019. – Vol. 161. – P. 361–370

64. Xi, Y. Material transfer behavior of AgTiB2 contact under different contact forces and electrode gaps / Y. Xi, X. H. Wang, Z. J. Zhou et al. // Transactions of Nonferrous Metals Society of China (English Edition). – 2019. – Vol. 29. – P. 1046–1056

65. Li, H. Effect of strengthening phase on material transfer behavior of Ag-based contact materials under different voltages / H. Li, X. Wang, Y. Liu, X. Guo // Vacuum. – 2017. – Vol. 135. – P. 55–65

66. Zhang, X. Arc erosion behavior of the Al2O3-Cu/(W, Cr) electrical contacts / X. Zhang, Y. Zhang, B. Tian et al. // Composites Part B: Engineering. – 2019. – Vol. 160. – P. 110–118

67. Wang, S. L. Influence of thermal shock behavior on microstructure and mechanical properties of IN718 superalloy / S. L. Wang, Y. R. Sun, L. J. Du et al. // Applied Surface Science. – 2019. – Vol. 484. – P. 1282–1287

68. Liu, J.M. Ultrasonic modulation of phase separation and corrosion resistance for ternary Cu-Sn-Bi immiscible alloy / J. M. Liu, W. H. Wu, W. Zhai, B. Wei // Ultrasonics Sonochemistry. – 2019. – Vol. 54. – P. 281–289.

69. Ivanov, L.I. Impact alloying of metals with chemically non-interacting elements with them using concentrated pulsed energy flows / L.I. Ivanov, A.I. Dedyurin, I.V. Borovitskaya et al. // Perspective. materials. - 2006. - No. 5. - S. 79–83

70. Ivanov, L.I. Highly adhesive compound of chemically noninteracting metals using concentrated pulsed energy flows / L.I. Ivanov, A.I. Dedyurin, I.V. Borovitskaya, etc. // Perspective. materials. Specialist. vol., sept. 2007. - T. 1. - S. 158–161

71. Ivanov, L. I. Creation of copper coatings on tungsten using high-temperature pulsed plasma flows / L.I. Ivanov, I.V. Borovitskaya, G.G. Bondarenko et al. // Prospect. Materials. - 2009. - No. 3. - P. 77–81

72. Grechaniuk, NI. Condensed from the vapor phase composite materials based on copper and molybdenum for electrical contacts. Structure, properties, technology. Current state and prospects of applying the technology of electron beam high-speed evaporation-condensation to obtain materials of electrical contacts. Communication 1 / N.I. Grechanyuk, V.A. Osokin, I.N. Grechanyuk, R.V. Minakova // Sovremen. electrometallurgy. - 2005. - No. 2. - S. 28–35

73. Grechaniuk, N. I. Fundamentals of electron beam technology for producing materials for electrical contacts. Their structure, properties. Communication 2 / N.I. Grechanyuk, I.N. Grechanyuk, V.A. Osokin, etc. // Sovremen. electrometallurgy. - 2006. - No. 2. - S. 9–19

74. Grechanyuk, I. N. Current state and prospects of high-speed electron-beam evaporation and subsequent vacuum condensation of metals and nonmetals to produce electric contacts and electrodes / N. I. Grechanyuk, R. V. Minakova, G. E. Kopylova // Powder Metallurgy and Metal Ceramics. - 2013 .-- Vol. 52. - P. 228–236

75. Khomenko, E. V. Microstructural evolution of Cr-Cu composites in liquid-phase sintering / E. V. Khomenko, R. V. Minakova, N. D. Lesnik // Powder Metallurgy and Metal Ceramics. - 2013 .-- Vol. 52. - P. 20–31

76. Bogdan, M. The actual state and prospects of a high power electron beam technology for metallic and non-metallic compositions used in electric contacts and elec-

trodes / M. Bogdan, H. Marcin, I. N. Grechanyuk et al. // Advanced Materials Research. - 2014 .-- Vol. 875-877. - P. 1437-1448

77. Bukhanovsky, V. V. Production technology, structure and properties of Cu-W layered composite condensed materials for electrical contacts / V. V. Bukhanovsky, N. I. Grechanyuk, R. V. Minakova et al. // International Journal of Refractory Metals and Hard Materials. - 2011 .-- Vol. 29. - P. 573–581

78. Bukhanovsky, V. Vapor-phase condensed composite materials based on copper and carbon / V. Bukhanovsky, M. Rudnytsky, M. Grechanyuk et al. // Materiali in Tehnologije. - 2016. - Vol. 50. - P. 523–530

79. Romanov, D. A. Experience and prospects of using the EVU 60/10 electric explosive installation for surface modification of materials / D. A. Romanov, E. A. Budovsky, Yu. D. Zhmakin, V. E. Gromov // Izv. university. Ferrous metallurgy. - 2011.– No. 6. - S. 20–24. (Romanov, DA Surface modification by the EVU 60/10 electroexplosive system / DA Romanov, EA Budovskikh, YD Zhmakin, VE Gromov // Steel in translation. - 2011. - Vol. 41. - No. 6. - P. 464– 468)

80. Romanov, D. A. Surface relief and structure of electric explosive composite surface layers of the molybdenum-copper system / D. A. Romanov, E. A. Budovsky, V. E. Gromov // Surface. X-ray, synchrotron and neutron studies. - 2011. - No. 11. - S. 95–100. (Romanov, DA Surface Relief and Structure of Electroexplosive Composite Surface Layers of the Molybdenum – Copper System / D. A. Romanov, EA Budovskikh, VE Gromov // Journal of Surface Investigation. X-ray, Synchrotron and Neutron Techniques. - 2011. - Vol. 5. - No. 6. - P. 1112–1117)

81. Romanov, D. A. Surface relief and structure of composite surface layers of W-Cu and Mo-Cu systems formed by the electric explosion method / D. A. Romanov, E. A. Budovskikh, V. E. Gromov // Physics and Chemistry processing materials. - 2011. - No. 5. - P. 51–55

82. Romanov, D. A. Surface relief and structure of pseudo-alloy coatings of the molybdenum-copper system formed by the electric explosion method / D. A. Romanov, E. A. Budovsky, V. E. Gromov // Hardening technologies and coatings. - 2011. - No. 10. - S. 19–21

83. Romanov, D. A. Formation of the electrical contact surface layers of the WC-Cu system using a modernized EVU 60 / 10M explosive installation / D. A. Romanov, Yu. D. Zhmakin, E. A. Budovsky and others // Fundamental problems modern materials science. - 2011. - T. 8. - No. 2. - S. 19–23

84. Romanov, D. A. Electrocontact coatings of the Mo-C-Cu system obtained by electric explosion spraying / D. A. Romanov, E. A. Budovsky, V. E. Gromov // Prospective materials. - 2012. - No. 6. - P. 75–78.

85. Romanov, D. A. Electric blasting spraying of electroerosion-resistant coatings of the Ti-B-Cu system / D. A. Romanov, E. A. Budovsky, A. V. Ionina, V. E. Gromov // Fundamental problems of modern materials science. - 2011. - T. 8. - No. 4. - S. 60–64

86. Romanov, D. A. Surface relief and structure of electric explosive composite surface layers of the titanium-boron-copper system / D. A. Romanov, E. A. Budovsky, V. E. Gromov // Hardening technologies and coatings. - 2012. - No. 9. - P. 30–33

87. Romanov, D. A. Structure and phase composition of electroerosion-resistant coatings of the TiB_2 - Cu system formed by electric explosion spraying / D. A. Romanov, E. A. Budovsky, V. E. Gromov et al. // Metal Processing: Technology , equipment, tools. - 2012. - No. 3. - P. 87–91

88. Budovskikh, E. A. The mechanism of formation of high adhesion of electric explosive coatings with a metal base / E. A. Budovskikh, V. E. Gromov, D. A. Romanov

// Reports of the Academy of Sciences. - 2013. - T. 449. - No. 1. - S. 25–27. (Budovskikh, EA The Formation Mechanism Providing High-Adhesion Properties of an Electric-Explosive Coating on a Metal Basis / EA Budovskikh, VE Gromov, DA Romanov // Doklady Fiz.. - 2013. - Vol. 58. - No. 3. - P. 82–84)

89. Panin, V. E. Physical foundations of structure formation in electric explosive coatings / V. E. Panin, V. E. Gromov, D. A. Romanov and others // Doklady of the Academy of Sciences. - 2017. - T. 472.– No. 6. - S. 650–653. (Panin V. E. The Physical Basics of Structure Formation in Electroexplosive Coatings / V. E. Panin, V. E. Gromov, D. A. Romanov et al. // Doklady Fiz.. - 2017. - Vol. 62. - No. 2. - P. 67–70)

90. Molotkov, S. G. Analysis of the structural features of electric explosive coatings at the border with the base / S. G. Molotkov, D. A. Romanov, E. A. Budovsky, A. F. Sofroshenkov // Izv. Univ. Chern. Metall. - 2012. - No. 2. - S. 69–70

91. Romanov, D. A. Formation of globular structural features of electric explosive coatings / D. A. Romanov, E. A. Budovsky, V. E. Gromov // Fundamental problems of modern materials science. - 2016. - T. 13. - No. 3. P. 355–357

92. Romanov, D. A. Model of electroerosive destruction of composite electric explosive coatings under conditions of spark erosion / D. A. Romanov, E. V. Protopopov // Izv. university. Ferrous metallurgy. - 2018. - T 61. - No. 2. P. 143–147

93. Romanov, D. A. The structure and properties of electroerosion-resistant coatings formed by electric explosion spraying / D. A. Romanov, O. A. Olesyuk, E. A. Budovsky and others // Metal processing: technology, equipment, tools. - 2013. - No. 1. - P. 53–57

94. Romanov, D. A. Features of the structure and properties of electroerosion-resistant coatings formed by electric explosive spraying / D. A. Romanov, E. A. Budovsky, V. E. Gromov // Izv. universities. Powder metallurgy and functional coatings. - 2014. - No. 2. - P. 58–62

95. Romanov, D. A. Structure of electro-explosion resistant coatings consisting of immiscible components / D. A. Romanov, V. E. Gromov, A. M. Glezer et al. // Materials Letters. - 2017 .-- Vol. 188. - P. 25–28

96. Romanov, D. A. Formation of the structure, phase composition and properties of electroerosion-resistant coatings obtained by electric explosion spraying / D. A. Romanov, E. A. Budovskikh, V. E. Gromov // Procurement in mechanical engineering. - 2013. - No. 1. - P. 36–43

97. Romanov, D. A. The structure of electroexplosive composite coatings of immiscible components of the Cu – Mo system after electron beam processing / D. A. Romanov, O. V. Olesyuk, E. A. Budovsky and others // Metal processing: technology, equipment, tools. - 2014. - No. 1. - P. 54-60

98. Romanov, D. A. The structure of composite coatings of immiscible components of the Cu - Mo system obtained by electric explosive spraying and subsequent electron-beam processing / D. A. Romanov, O. V. Olesyuk, E. A. Budovskikh et al. / / Bulletin of the Siberian State Industrial University. - 2014. - No. 1. - S. 7-10

99. Romanov, D. A. The structure of composite coatings of the W - C - Cu system obtained by electric explosive spraying and subsequent electron-beam processing / D. A. Romanov, O. V. Olesyuk, S. V. Konovalov, etc. // Promising materials. - 2014. - No. 4. - P. 64–69

100. Romanov, D. A. Structure of electroexplosive composite coatings of the TiB2 - Cu system after electron-beam processing / D. A. Romanov, O. V. Olesyuk, E. A. Budovsky and others // Physics and Chemistry of Materials Processing. - 2015. - No. 1. - P. 73–78

101. Romanov, D.A. Structural-phase state of the Cu - Cr electroerosion coating formed

on copper by the combined method / D. A. Romanov, E. N. Goncharova, E. A. Budovsky and others // Hardening technologies and coatings. - 2016. - No. 7. - S. 25–29.

102. Romanov, D. A. Structural phase states and tribological properties of electroexplosive composite coatings on copper after electron-beam processing / D. A. Romanov, O. V. Olesyuk, E. A. Budovsky and others // Surface. X-ray, synchrotron and neutron studies. - 2015. - No. 7. - P. 50–56. (Romanov, DA Structural-Phase States and Tribological Properties of Electroexplosive Composite Coatings on Copper after ElectronBeam Treatment / DA Romanov, OV Olesyuk, EA Budovskikh et al. // Journal of Surface Investigation. X-ray, Synchrotron and Neutron Techniques. - 2015 . - No. 7. - P. 50–56)

103. Olesyuk, O. V. Influence of electron-beam processing on the tribological properties of electric explosive electroerosion-resistant coatings / O. V. Olesyuk, S. V. Konovalov, D. A. Romanov // Modern problems of science and education. - 2014. - No. 2. [Electronic resource]. URL: http://www.science-education.ru/116-12659. (Date accessed: 08/14/2019).

104. Romanov, D. A. Formation of Structure, Phase Composition and Properties of Electro Explosion Resistant Coatings Using Electron-Beam Processing / D. A. Romanov, K. V. Sosnin, V. E. Gromov et al. // International Conf. on Physical Mesomechanics of Multilevel Systems. - 2014. - P. 523–526

105. Arzamasov, B. N. Material Science: a textbook for high schools / B. N. Arzamasov / Under the general. ed. B. N. Arzamasova, G. G. Mukhina. - M.: MSTU. N.E. Bauman, 2002 .-- 648 p.

106. Pat. 2478732 RF. IPC C23C 14/32. Composite Electrically Explosive Conductor for Electroexplosive Spraying of Coatings or Electroexplosive Alloying of the Surface of Metals and Alloys / D. A. Romanov, E. A. Budovskikh, V. E. Gromov; Federal State Budgetary Educational Institution of Higher Professional Education "Siberian State Industrial University". - No. 2011137782/02, declared 09/13/2011; publ. 04/10/2013. Bull. Number 10

107. harlamov, Yu. O. Construction of mathematical models of technological processes for gas thermal spraying of coatings / Yu. O. Kharlamov, M. Yu. Kharlamov // Vestn. East nat. University of them. Vladimir Dahl. - 1999. - No. 3 (18). - S. 211–219

108. Kharlamov, Yu. O. Model of the outflow of a pulsed heterogeneous jet from a combustion chamber / Yu. O. Kharlamov, A.N. Tsyapa, M. Yu. Kharlamov, O.N. Druz // Vestn. East nat. University of them. Vladimir Dahl. - 1999. - No. 4 (20). - S. 176–184

109. Andrievsky, R. A. Nanocomposites based on refractory compounds: state of development and prospects / R. A. Andrievsky // Materials Science. - 2006. - No. 4. - P. 20–27

110. State diagrams of double metal systems: a reference book in 3 vols. T. 1 - 3. / Under. total ed. N.P. Lyakisheva. - M .: Engineering, 1996 - 2000. - 992 p .; - 1024 s .; - 448 p.

111. Drits, M. E. Double and multicomponent systems based on copper: a Handbook / M. E. Drits, N. R. Bochvar, L. S. Guzey, etc. - M .: Nauka, 1979. - 248 p.

112. Fedorov, V.N. Phase Diagrams of Metallic Systems / V. N. Fedorov, O. E. Osintsev, E. T. Yushkina // Acad. Sci. USSR. - 1964-1982. - Vol. 26. - P. 149–150

113. Gebhardt, E. The Constitution of the System Ag-Cu-Sn / E. Gebhardt, G. Petzow // Metallkd. - 1959. - Vol. 50. - P. 597–605

114. Zhmakin, Yu. D. Automated electric blasting plant for improving the operational characteristics of materials / Yu. D. Zhmakin, D.A. Romanov, E.A. Budovsky and others // Industrial Energy. - 2011. - No. 6. P. 22–25

115.   Filimonov, S. Yu. Development of a combined method for surface modification of steel 45 / S. Yu. Filimonov, Yu. F. Ivanov, V. Ye. Gromov et al. // Scientific Bulletins. Math series. Physics. - 2011. - No. 5. Issue. 22. - S. 195–200

116.   Evstigneev, V.V. Mathematical modeling of heating the contact surface of the base - the sprayed layer during the detonation-gas deposition of protective coatings / V.V. Evstigneev, V. Yu. Filimonov, K. B. Koshelev, etc. // Fundam. problems are modern. materials science. - 2005. - No. 6. - S. 98–102

117.   Engel, L. Scanning electron microscopy. Destruction: Ref. ed. / L. Engel, G. Klingele; trans. with him. - M.: Metallurgiya, 1986.- 232 p.

118.   Krishtal, M.M. Scanning electron microscopy and X-ray spectral analysis / M.M. Krishtal, I.S. Yasnikov, V.I. Polunin, etc.

119.   Romanov, D. A. The structure of the coating composition SnO2 – Ag formed on copper by the electric blasting method / D. A. Romanov, S. V. Moskovsky, S. Yu. Pronin et al. // Prospective materials. - 2018. - No. 6. - S. 46–53

120.   Romanov, D. A. Structure of SnO2-Ag coating formed on copper by electroexplosion / D. A. Romanov, S. V. Moskovskii, K. V. Sosnin et al. // IOP Conference Series: Materials Science and Engineering - 2018 .-- Vol. 447.– P. 012077

121.   Romanov, D. A. Structure of SnO2-Ag coating formed on copper by electroexplosion method / D. A. Romanov, S. V. Moskovskii, K. V. Sosnin et al. // IOP Conference Series: Journal of Physics: Conf. Series - 2018 .– Vol. 1115. - P. 032079.

122.   Romanov, D. A. Structural and phase state of the SnO2-Ag coating formed on copper by the electroexplosive method / D. A. Romanov, S. V. Moskovskii, V.E. Gromov et al. // AIP Conference Proceedings - 2018 .-- Vol. 2051. - P. 020255

123.   Romanov, D. A. Structural-phase state of the system "CdO-Ag coating / copper substrate" formed by electroexplosive method / D. A. Romanov, S. V. Moskovskii, E. A. Martusevich et al. // Metalurgija - 2018 .-- Vol. 57. - No. 4. - P. 299–302

124.   Romanov, D. A. Structure and electrical discharge resistance of copper electrical contacts modified by the electric explosion method / D. A. Romanov, S. V. Moskovsky, V. E. Gromov et al. // Fundamental problems of modern materials science. - 2019.- T 16. - No. 1. S. 62–70

125.   Kroupa, A. COST531 project - Study of the advanced materials for lead free soldering / A. Kroupa, A. T. Dinsdale, A. Watson et al. // Journal of Mining and Metallurgy, Section B: Metallurgy - 2007. - Vol. 43. - P. 113–123

126.   Marjanovic, S. Calculation of thermodynamic properties for ternary Ag – Cu – Sn system / S. Marjanovic, D. Manasijevic, D. Zivkovic et al. // RMZ - Materials and Geoenvironment - 2009. - Vol. 56. - No. 56. - P. 30–37

127.   Thomas, G. Transmission electron microscopy of materials / G. Thomas, M.J. Goring. - M .: Nauka, 1983 .-- 320 p.

128.   Ivanov, Yu. F. Electron microscopic analysis of nanocrystalline materials / Yu. F. Ivanov, A.V. Paul, N.A. Koneva, E.V. Kozlov // FMM. - 1991.– No. 7. P. 206–208

129.   Ivanov, Yu. F. Electron-microscopic diffraction analysis of ultrafine materials / Yu. F. Ivanov, A.V. Paul, E.V. Kozlov, L.N. Ignatenko // Factory Laboratory. - 1992.– No. 12. P. 38–40

130.   Matthews, M. Composite Materials. Mechanics and technology / M. Matthews, R. Rawlings. - M .: Technosphere, 2004 .-- 408 p.

131.   Romanov, D. A. Physical foundations of electric explosive spraying of wear- and electroerosion-resistant coatings / D. A. Romanov, E. A. Budovsky, V. E. Gromov et al. - Novokuznetsk: Izd. Center of SibGIU, 2018 .-- 321 p.

132.   Koneva, N. A. The nature of substructural hardening / N. A. Koneva, E. V. Kozlov // News of universities. Physics. - 1982.– No. 8. P. 3–14

133. Koneva, N. A. Physics of substructural hardening / N. A. Koneva, E. V. Kozlov // Vestnik TGASU. - 1999.– No. 1. P. 21–35

134. Kozlov, E.V. Evolution of a dislocation substructure and thermodynamics of plastic deformation of metallic materials / E.V. Kozlov, V.A. Starenchenko, N.A. Koneva // Metals. - 1993.– No. 5. P. 152–161

135. Gorelik, S. S. Recrystallization of metals and alloys / S. S. Gorelik. - M.: Metallurgiya, 1978. - 568 p.

136. Hessner, F. Recrystallization of metallic materials / F. Hessner. - M.: Metallurgy, 1982. - 352 p,

137. 137. Larikov, L. N. The mechanism of recrystallization of deformed metals / L. N. Larikov, E. E. Zasimchuk. - In the book: Study of defects in the crystal structure of metals and alloys - Kiev: Naukova Dumka, 1966. P. 70–84

138. Koretsky, Yu. V. Handbook of Electrotechnical Materials / Yu. V. Koretsky, VV Pasynkov, B. M. Kireev. T.3. - L .: Energoatomizdat, 1988 .-- 728 p.

139. GOST 2933-83. Test for mechanical and switching wear resistance. Devices are electric low-voltage test methods. - M .: Publishing house of standards, 1983. - 26 p.

140. Romanov, D. A. Structure and electrical erosion resistance of an electro-explosive coating of the CuO – Ag system / D. A. Romanov, S. V. Moskovskii, K. V. Sosnin et al. // Materials Research Express - 2019 .-- Vol. 6.– P. 055042

141. Romanov, D. A. Effect of electron-beam processing on structure of electroexplosive electroerosion resistant coatings of CuO-Ag system / D. A. Romanov, S. V. Moskovskii, K. V. Sosnin et al. // Materials Research Express - 2019 .-- Vol. 6.– P. 085077

142. Romanov, D.A., Structure and electroerosion resistance of an Ag – CuO coating obtained by electric explosive spraying on copper electrical contacts / D. A. Romanov, S. V. Moskovsky, V. E. Gromov et al. // Deformation and destruction of materials. - 2019. - No. 6. - S. 22–25. (Romanov, DA Structure and Electroerosion Resistance of the Ag – CuO Coating Prepared by Electroexplosive Sputtering on Copper Electrical Contacts / DA Romanov, SV Moskovskii, VE Gromov et al. // Russian Metallurgy (Metally). - 2019. - Vol. 2019 - No. 10. - P. 1036–1039)

143. Romanov, D. A. Phase composition, structure, and wear resistance of the electric explosive coating of the CuO – Ag system after electron beam processing / D. A. Romanov, S. V. Moskovsky, A. M. Glezer et al. // Bulletin of the RAS . The series is physical. - 2019.- T 83. - No. 10. - S. 1389–1393. (Romanov, DA Phase Composition, Structure, and Wear Resistance of Electric-Explosive CuO – Ag System Coatings after Electron Beam Processing / DA Romanov, SV Moskovskii, AM Glezer et al. // Bulletin of the Russian Academy of Sciences: Physics. - 2019. - Vol. 83 - No. 10. - P. 1270–1274)

144. Romanov, D. A. Influence of electron-beam processing on the structure and electroerosion resistance of electric blasting coatings of the CuO-Ag system / D. A. Romanov, S. V. Moskovsky, K. V. Sosnin et al. // Fundamental problems of modern materials science. - 2019.- T. 15 - No. 16. - S. 361–369

145. Romanov, D. A. Structure and properties of the electromagnetic starter's contacts with the electro-explosive CuO-Ag coating / D. A. Romanov, S. V. Moskovskii, V. E. Gromov // Journal of Physics: Conference Series. - 2019 .-- Vol. 1347. - P. 012123

146. Romanov, D. A. Structure and Electrical Erosion Resistance of An Electro-Explosive Coating of the ZnO-Ag System / D. A. Romanov, S. V. Moskovskii, K. V. Sosnin // IOP Conference Series: Materials Science and Engineering. - 2019 .-- Vol. 582. - P. 012006

147. Romanov, D. A. Effect of electron beam processing on structure of electroexplosion

electroerosion-resistant ZnO-Ag coating / D. A. Romanov, S. V. Moskovskii, V. E. Gromov et al. // AIP Conference Proceedings. - 2019 .-- Vol. 2167. - P. 020295

148. Romanov, D. A. Effect of electron beam processing on structure of electroexplosion coating of ZnO-Ag system / D. A. Romanov, S. V. Moskovskii, K. V. Sosnin // IOP Conference Series: Materials Science and Engineering. - 2019 .-- Vol. 681. - P. 012036

149. Romanov, D. Improvement of copper alloy properties in electro-explosive spraying of ZnO-Ag coatings resistant to electrical erosion / D. Romanov, S. Moskovskii, S. Konovalov et al. // Journal of Materials Research and Technology. - 2019 .-- Vol. 8 - No. 6. - P. 5515–5523

150. Romanov, D. A. Improving the properties of copper electrical contact due to its processing by plasma formed during an electric explosion of silver foil with a weight of zinc oxide powder / D. A. Romanov, S. V. Moskovsky, K. V. Sosnin, etc. . // Procurement in engineering. - 2019. - No. 11. - S. 511-517.

151. Pat. 2699486 RF. IPC C23C 4/10, C23C 4/12, H01H 1/02. The method of applying electroerosion-resistant coatings based on copper and silver oxide on copper electrical contacts / D. A. Romanov, S. V. Moskovsky; Federal State Budgetary Educational Institution of Higher Professional Education "Siberian State Industrial University". - No. 2018142200, declared 11/29/2018; publ. 09/05/2019. Bull. Number 25

152. Pat. 2699487RF. IPC C23C 4/10, C23C 4/12, H01H 1/02. The method of applying electroerosion-resistant coatings based on zinc oxide and silver on copper electrical contacts / D. A. Romanov, S. V. Moskovsky; Federal State Budgetary Educational Institution of Higher Professional Education "Siberian State Industrial University". - No. 2018142202, declared 11/29/2018; publ. 09/05/2019. Bull. Number 25

153. Moatimid, G. M. Kelvin-Helmholtz instability for flow in porous media under the influence of oblique magnetic fields: A viscous potential flow analysis / G. M. Moatimid, M. H. Obied Allah, M. A. Hassan // Physics of Plasmas. - 2013 .-- Vol. 20. - P. 102111

154. Wang, M. Simulation of femtosecond laser ablation sapphire based on free electron density / M. Wang, W. Mei, Y. Wang // Optics & Laser Technology. - 2019 .-- Vol. 113. - P. 123–128

155. Mallick, C. Plasma characterization of a microwave discharge ion source with mirror magnetic field configuration / C. Mallick, M. Bandyopadhyay, R. Kumar // Review of Scientific Instruments. - 2018 .-- Vol. 89. - P. 125112

156. 156. Venkata Krishna Rao, R. Conductive silver inks and their applications in printed and flexible electronics / R. Venkata Krishna Rao, K. Venkata Abhinav, P. S. Karthik, S. P. Singh // Review of Scientific Instruments. - 2015. - Vol. 5. - P. 77760–90

157. Bugayev, A. Lattice dynamics and electronic Grüneisen parameters of femtosecond laser-excited bismuth / A. Bugayev, H. E. Elsayed-Ali // Journal of Physics and Chemistry of Solids. - 2019 .-- Vol. 129. - P. 312-316

158. Qin, Y. Deep Modification of materials by thermal stress wave generated by irradiation of high-current pulsed electron beams / Y. Qin, C. Dong, Z. Song et al. // Journal of Vacuum Science and Technology A: Vacuum, Surfaces and Films - 2009 .-- Vol. 27.– P. 430–435

159. Zinenko, V. I. Lattice dynamics of BiFeO3 under hydrostatic pressure / V. I. Zinenko, M. S. Pavlovskii // Physics of the Solid State. - 2009. - Vol. 51. - P. 1404–1408

160. Hirsch, P. Electron microscopy of thin crystals / P. Hirsch, A. Howie, R. Nicholson and others. - M .: Mir, 1968. - 574 p.

161. Ivanov, Yu.F. Structural-phase states and hardening mechanisms of deformed steel / Yu. F. Ivanov, V. E. Gromov, N. A. Popova et al. - Novokuznetsk: Polygraphist,

246

2016. - 510 p.

162. Babichev A.P. Physical quantities: Reference book / A.P. Babichev, N.A. Babush-kina, A.M. Bratkovsky, etc. - M.: Energoatomizdat, 1991. - 1232 p.

163. Romanov, D.A. Formation of the electrical contact surface layers of the WC-Cu system using the modernized EVU 60 / 10M explosive installation / D. A. Romanov, Yu. D. Zhmakin, E. A. Budovsky and others // Fundamental problems Modern Materials Science - 2011 - T. 8 - No. 2 - P. 19–23.

164. Romanov, D. A. Experience and prospects of using the EVU 60/10 electric explosive installation for surface modification of materials / D. A. Romanov, E. A. Budovsky, Yu. D. Zhmakin, V. E. Gromov // Izv. university. Ferrous metallurgy - 2011.– No. 6 - S. 20–24. (Romanov, D. A. Surface modification by the EVU 60/10 electroexplosive system / D. A. Romanov, E. A. Budovskikh, Y. D. Zhmakin, V. E. Gromov // Steel in translation - 2011 - Vol. 41 - No. 6 - P. 464-468).

165. Romanov, D. A. Surface relief and structure of electric explosive composite surface layers of the molybdenum-copper system / D. A. Romanov, E. A. Budovsky, V. E. Gromov // Surface. X-ray, synchrotron and neutron studies - 2011 - No. 11 - P. 95–100. (Romanov, DA Surface Relief and Structure of Electroexplosive Composite Surface Layers of the Molybdenum – Copper System / D. A. Romanov, EA Budovskikh, VE Gromov // Journal of Surface Investigation. X-ray, Synchrotron and Neutron Techniques - 2011 - Vol 5 - No. 6 - P. 1112–1117).

166. 166. Romanov, D. A. Surface relief and structure of composite surface layers of W-Cu and Mo-Cu systems formed by the electric explosion method / D. A. Romanov, E. A. Budovskikh, V. E. Gromov // Physics and Chemistry material processing - 2011 - No. 5 - P. 51–55.

167. Romanov, D. A. Surface relief and structure of pseudo-alloy coatings of the molybdenum-copper system formed by the electric explosion method / D. A. Romanov, E. A. Budovsky, V. E. Gromov // Strengthening technologies and coatings - 2011 - No. 10 - S. 19-21.

168. Romanov, D.A. Electroexplosive spraying of electroerosion-resistant coatings of the Ti-B-Cu system / D.A. Romanov, E.A. Budovsky, A.V. Ionina, V.E. Gromov // Fundamental Problems of Modern Materials Science - 2011 -VT. 8 - No. 4 - S. 60–64.

169. Romanov, D. A. The structure and phase composition of electroerosion-resistant coatings of the TiB2 - Cu system formed by electric explosion spraying / D. A. Romanov, E. A. Budovsky, V. E. Gromov et al. // Metal Processing: Technology , Equipment, Tools - 2012 - No. 3 - P. 87–91.

170. Romanov, D. A. Surface relief and the structure of electric explosive composite surface layers of the titanium-boron-copper system / D. A. Romanov, E. A. Budovsky, V. E. Gromov // Hardening technologies and coatings - 2012 - No. 9 - S. 30–33.

171. Romanov, D. A. Electrocontact coatings of the Mo-C-Cu system obtained by electric explosion spraying / D. A. Romanov, E. A. Budovsky, V. E. Gromov // Promising materials - 2012 - No. 6 - C . 75–78.

172. Romanov, D. A. Formation of the structure, phase composition and properties of electroerosion-resistant coatings obtained by electric explosion spraying / D. A. Romanov, E. A. Budovsky, V. E. Gromov // Procurement in mechanical engineering - 2013 - No. 1 - S. 36–43.

173. Romanov, D. A. The structure and properties of electroerosion-resistant coatings formed by the method of electric explosive spraying / D. A. Romanov, O. A. Olesyuk, E. A. Budovsky and others // Metal processing: technology, equipment, tools - 2013 - No. 1 - S. 53–57.

174. Budovskikh, E. A. The mechanism of formation of high adhesion of electric explo-

sive coatings with a metal base / E. A. Budovsky, V. E. Gromov, D. A. Romanov // Reports of the Academy of Sciences - 2013 - T. 449 - No. 1 - S. 25–27. (Budovskikh, EA The Formation Mechanism Providing High-Adhesion Properties of an Electric-Explosive Coating on a Metal Basis / EA Budovskikh, VE Gromov, DA Romanov // Doklady Physics - 2013 - Vol. 58 - No. 3 - P. 82– 84).

175. Olesyuk, O. V. The structure of wear-resistant coatings of TiB2-Al and TiC-Mo systems obtained by electric explosive spraying / O. V. Olesyuk, D. A. Romanov, E. A. Budovsky, V. E. Gromov // Fundamental Problems of Modern Materials Science - 2013 - V. 10 - No. 3. P. 417–423.

176. Romanov, D. A. Features of the structure and properties of electroerosion-resistant coatings formed by electric explosion spraying / D. A. Romanov, E. A. Budovskikh, V. E. Gromov // Izv. universities. Powder Metallurgy and Functional Coatings - 2014 - No. 2 - P. 58–62.

177. Romanov, D.A., Structure and phase composition of wear-resistant coatings of the TiB2-Al system obtained by electroexplosive spraying, D.A. Romanov, O.V. Olesyuk, E.A. Budovsky and others // Izv. universities. Powder Metallurgy and Functional Coatings - 2014 - No. 3 - P. 60–65.

178. Romanov, D. A. Formation of Structure, Phase Composition and Properties of Electro Explosion Resistant Coatings Using Electron-Beam Processing / D. A. Romanov, K. V. Sosnin, V. E. Gromov et al. // International Conf. on Physical Mesomechanics of Multilevel Systems - 2014 - P. 523–526.

179. Romanov, D. A. Structure of electro-explosion resistant coatings consisting of immiscible components / D. A. Romanov, V. E. Gromov, A. M. Glezer et al. // Materials Letters - 2017 - Vol. 188.– P. 25–28.

180. Panin, V. E. Physical foundations of structure formation in electric explosive coatings / V. E. Panin, V. E. Gromov, D. A. Romanov et al. // Reports of the Academy of Sciences - 2017 - V. 472.– No. 6 - S. 650–653. (Panin V. E. The Physical Basics of Structure Formation in Electroexplosive Coatings / V. E. Panin, V. E. Gromov, D. A. Romanov et al. // Doklady Physics - 2017 - Vol. 62 - No. 2 - P. 67–70).

181. 181. Pat. 2404493 RF. IPC H01R 11/00. Electrical connecting product / E. A. Budovsky, D. A. Romanov - No. 2009146451/07; declared 12/14/2009; publ. 11/20/2010. Bull. Number 32.

182. Pat. 2422555 RF. IPC C23C 4/12, C23C 24/08. The method of electric explosive deposition of metal coatings on contact surfaces "/ E. A. Budovsky, D. A. Romanov - No. 2009146449/02; declared 12/14/2009; publ. 06/27/2011. Bull. Number 18.

183. Pat. 2438217 RF. IPC H01R 11/11. Electric tip / D.A. Romanov, E.A. Budovsky, V.E. Gromov; State educational institution of higher professional education "Siberian State Industrial University" - No. 2010142630/07, decl. 10/18/2010; publ. 12/27/2011. Bull. Number 36.

184. Pat. 2436863 RF. IPC C23C 14/32, C23C 14/14. The method of applying a pseudo-alloy molybdenum-copper coating on a copper contact surface / E. A. Budovsky, V. E. Gromov, D. A. Romanov; State educational institution of higher professional education "Siberian State Industrial University" - No. 2010107718/02, decl. 03/02/2010; publ. 12/20/2011. Bull. Number 35.

185. Pat. 2436864 RF. IPC C23C 14/32, C23C 14/14. The method of applying a composite laminate molybdenum-copper coating on a copper contact surface / E. A. Budovsky, D. A. Romanov, V. E. Gromov ,; State educational institution of higher professional education "Siberian State Industrial University" - No. 2010112760/02, decl. 04/01/2010; publ. 12/20/2011. Bull. Number 35.

186. Pat. 2451110 of the Russian Federation. IPC C23C 14/24, C23C 14/16. The method

of applying to the contact surface of electroerosion-resistant tungsten-copper composite coatings with a filled structure / D. A. Romanov, E. A. Budovsky, V. E. Gromov - No. 2011103427/02, decl. 01/31/2011; publ. 05/20/2012. Bull. Number 14.

187. Pat. 2451111 of the Russian Federation. IPC C23C 14/32, C23C 14/16. A method of applying electroerosion-resistant molybdenum-copper composite coatings with a filled structure to the contact surfaces / D. A. Romanov, E. A. Budovsky, V.E. Gromov - No. 2011103419/02, declared 01/31/2011; publ. 05/20/2012. Bull. Number 14.

188. Pat. 2451112 of the Russian Federation. IPC C23C 14/32, C23C 14/16, B32B 15/01. The method of applying electroerosion-resistant wram-fram-copper composite coatings with a layered structure to the contact surfaces / D. A. Romanov, E. A. Budovskikh, V.E. Gromov - No. 2011103424/02, declared 01/31/2011; publ. 05/20/2012. Bull. Number 14.

189. Pat. 2456369 RF. IPC C23C 4/10, C23C 4/12. The method of forming titanium-boron-copper coatings on copper contact surfaces / D. A. Romanov, E. A. Budovskikh, V.E. Thunders; State educational institution of higher professional education "Siberian State Industrial University" - No. 2010145406/02, decl. 11/08/2010; publ. 07/20/2012 Bull. Number 20.

190. Pat 2455388 of the Russian Federation. IPC C23C 14/32, C23C 14/16. The method of applying electroerosion-resistant molybdenum-copper composite coatings with a layered structure to the contact surfaces / D. A. Romanov, E. A. Budovsky, V.E. Gromov - No. 2011103422/02, declared 01/31/2011; publ. 07/10/2012. Bull. Number 19.

191. Pat. 118792 of the Russian Federation. IPC H01H 33/664. Contact of a vacuum interrupter chamber / D. A. Romanov, E. A. Budovsky, V. E. Gromov; Federal State Budgetary Educational Institution of Higher Professional Education "Siberian State Industrial University" - No. 2012108422/07, decl. 03/05/2012; publ. 07/27/2012. Bull. No. 21..

192. Pat. 2464354 RF. IPC C23C 14/32, C23C 14/16. The method of forming tungsten-carbon-copper coatings on copper contact surfaces / D. A. Romanov, E. A. Budovsky, V. E. Gromov; State educational institution of higher professional education "Siberian State Industrial University" - No. 2011116157/02, decl. 04/22/2011; publ. 10/20/2012. Bull. Number 29.

193. Pat. 2470089 RF. IPC C23C 4/08, C23C 4/12. The method of forming molybdenum-carbon-copper coatings on copper contact surfaces / D. A. Romanov, E. A. Budovsky, V. E. Gromov; Federal State Budgetary Educational Institution of Higher Professional Education "Siberian State Industrial University" - No. 2011136322/02, decl. 08/31/2011; publ. 12/20/2012. Bull. Number 35.

194. Pat. 2489515 RF. IPC C23C 14/32, C23C 14/14. The method of electric explosive spraying of composite coatings of a system, TiB2-Cu on copper contact surfaces / D. A. Romanov, E. A. Budovsky, E. S. Vashchuk, V. E. Gromov; Federal State Budgetary Educational Institution of Higher Professional Education "Siberian State Industrial University" - No. 2012104941/02, decl. 02/13/2012; publ. 08/10/2013. Bull. Number 22.

195. Pat. 2497976 of the Russian Federation. IPC C23C 4/12, C23C 4/04, C23C 14/34. The method of electric explosive spraying of composite coatings of the Al-TiB2 system on aluminum surfaces / D. A. Romanov, E. A. Budovsky, V. E. Gromov; Federal State Budgetary Educational Institution of Higher Professional Education "Siberian State Industrial University" - No. 2012144704/02, decl. 10/19/2012; publ. 11/10/2013. Bull. Number 31.

196. Romanov, D. A. Electroexplosive spraying of electroerosion-resistant coatings: the formation of the structure, phase composition and properties of electroerosion-resistant coatings by the method of electric explosive spraying / D. A. Romanov, E. A. Budovsky, V. E. Gromov - Saarbrucken: LAP LAMBERT Academic Publishing GmbH & Co. KG, 2012 - 170 s.

197. Electroexplosive spraying of wear-resistant and electroerosion-resistant coatings / D. A. Romanov, E. A. Budovsky, V. E. Gromov, Yu. F. Ivanov - Novokuznetsk: Publishing House LLC Polygraphist, 2014 - 203 p.

198. Physical foundations of electric explosive alloying of metals and alloys: monograph. / A. Ya. Bagautdinov, E. A. Budovsky, Yu. F. Ivanov, V. E. Gromov - Novokuznetsk: SibGIU, 2007 - 301 p.

199. Vaschuk, E. S. Features of pulsed electron-beam surface treatment of electric explosive alloying of steel 45 and titanium / E. S. Vaschuk, A. V. Vostretsova, E. A. Budovsky and others // Structural-phase states of promising metallic metals . / Ans. ed. V.E. Gromov - Novokuznetsk: NPK Publishing House, 2009. P. 28–41.

200. Kharlamov, Yu. O. Compact detonation-gas installation for powder coating / Yu. O. Kharlamov, L. L. Gorb // Svaroch. pr-in - 1991 - No. 1 - S. 18–19.

201. Safonov, L. I. Electric rectangular connectors. Friction and wear in contact pairs of electrical connectors / L. I. Safonov, A. L. Safonov // Technologies in electron. prom-sti - 2003 - No. 8 - S. 34–39.

202. Fundamentals of physico-chemical analysis / V. Ya. Anosov, M.I. Ozerova, Yu. Ya. Fialkov., M.: Nauka, 1976.

203. Meshcheryakov, Yu. I. Dynamic rotations in crystals / Yu. I. Meshcheryakov, S. A. Atroshenko // Izv. Univ.. Fizika - 1992 - No. 4 - S. 105–123.

204. Pat. 2473712 of the Russian Federation. IPC C23C 14/32. Device for electric explosive surface treatment of materials // Yu. D. Zhmakin, D.A., Romanov E.A. Budovsky and others; State educational institution of higher professional education "Siberian State Industrial University". - No. 2011128986/02, declared 07/12/2011; publ. 01/27/2013, Bull. Number 3.

205. Panin, V. E. Solitons of curvature as generalized wave structural carriers of plastic deformation and fracture / V. E. Panin, V. E. Egorushkin // Phys. Mesomechanics - 2013 - T. 16 - No. 3 - S. 7–26.

206. Panin, V.E. Physical mesomechanics of a deformable solid as a multilevel system. II. The phenomenon of mutual penetration of particles of heterogeneous solids without disruption of continuity under the influence of concentrated energy flows / V.E. Panin, A.V. Panin, D. D. Moiseenko, etc. // Fiz. Mesomechanics - 2006 - T. 9 - No. 4 - S. 5–13.

207. Bobylev, A. V. Mechanical and technological properties of metals: a reference book / A. V. Bobylev - M .: Metallurgiya, 1987 - 208 p.

208. Meshcheryakov, V. P. Electric arc of high power in circuit breakers. Part I / V.P. Meshcheryakov - Ulyanovsk: Contactor OJSC, 2006 - 344 p.

209. Meshcheryakov, V. P. An electric arc of high power in circuit breakers. Part II / V.P. Meshcheryakov - Ulyanovsk: Contactor OJSC, 2006 - 429 p.

210. Romanov, D. A. The structure of electroexplosive composite coatings of immiscible components of the Cu - Mo system after electron beam processing / D. A. Romanov, O. V. Olesyuk, E. A. Budovsky and others // Metal processing: technology, equipment, tools - 2014 - No. 1 - P. 54-60.

211. Romanov, D. A. The structure of composite coatings of the W - C - Cu system obtained by electric explosive spraying and subsequent electron-beam processing / D. A. Romanov, O. V. Olesyuk, S. V. Konovalov, etc. // Prospective materials - 2014

- No. 4 - S. 64–69.

212.   Romanov, D. A. The structure of composite coatings of immiscible components of the Cu - Mo system obtained by electric explosive spraying and subsequent electron-beam processing / D. A. Romanov, O. V. Olesyuk, E. A. Budovskikh et al. / / Bulletin of the Siberian State Industrial University - 2014 - No. 1 - P. 7–10.

213.   Romanov, D. A. Formation of Structure, Phase Composition and Properties of Electro Explosion Resistant Coatings Using Electron-Beam Processing / D. A. Romanov, K. V. Sosnin, V. E. Gromov et al. // International Conf. on Physical Mesomechanics of Multilevel Systems - 2014 - P. 523–526.

214.   Romanov, D.A., Structure of electroexplosive composite coatings of the TiB2 - Cu system after electron beam processing / D.A. Romanov, O.V. Olesyuk, E.A. Budovsky and others // Physics and Chemistry of Materials Processing - 2015 - No. 1 - S. 73–78.

215.   Romanov, D. A. Structural phase states and tribological properties of electroexplosive composite coatings on copper after electron-beam processing / D. A. Romanov, O. V. Olesyuk, E. A. Budovsky and others // Surface. X-ray, synchrotron and neutron studies - 2015 - No. 7 - P. 50–56. (Romanov, DA Structural-Phase States and Tribological Properties of Electroexplosive Composite Coatings on Copper after ElectronBeam Treatment / DA Romanov, OV Olesyuk, EA Budovskikh et al. // Journal of Surface Investigation. X-ray, Synchrotron and Neutron Techniques - 2015 - No. 7 - P. 50–56).

216.   Olesyuk, O. V. Influence of electron-beam processing on the tribological properties of electric explosive electroerosion-resistant coatings / O. V. Olesyuk, S. V. Konovalov, D. A. Romanov // Modern problems of science and education - 2014 - No. 2. [Electronic resource]. URL: http://www.science-education.ru/116-12659. (Date of treatment: 12/11/2017).

217.   Romanov, D.A. Structural-phase state of the Cu – Cr electroerosion coating formed on copper by the combined method / D. A. Romanov, E. N. Goncharova, E. A. Budovsky and others // Strengthening technologies and coatings - 2016 - No. 7 - C. 25–29.

218.   Pat. 2537687 of the Russian Federation. IPC C23C 4/12, C23C 14/32, C23C 14/16, H01H 1/02. The method of applying electroerosion-resistant coatings based on carbon molybdenum, molybdenum and copper to copper electrical contacts / D. A. Romanov, O. V. Olesyuk, E. A. Budovsky, V. E. Gromov; D. A. Romanov - No. 2013155789/02, declared 12/16/2013; publ. 01/10/2015. Bull. Number 1.

219.   Pat. 2539138 of the Russian Federation. IPC C23C 4/12, C23C 14/14, C23C 4/10, C23C 14/32, H01H 1/02. The method of applying electroerosion-resistant coatings based on titanium and copper diboride to copper electrical contacts / D. A. Romanov, O. V. Olesyuk, E. A. Budovskikh, V. E. Gromov; D. A. Romanov - No. 2013155793/02, declared 12/16/2013; publ. 01/10/2015. Bull. Number 1.

220.   Pat. 2546940 RF. IPC C23C 4/12, C23C 14/32, C23C 14/16, H01H 1/02. The method of applying electroerosion-resistant coatings based on carbon tungsten, tungsten and copper on copper electrical contacts / D. A. Romanov, O. V. Olesyuk, E. A. Budovskikh, V. E. Gromov; D. A. Romanov - No. 2013155791/02, declared 12/16/2013; publ. 04/10/2015. Bull. Number 10.

221.   Pat. 2546939 RF. IPC C23C 4/12, C23C 14/32, C23C 14/16, H01H 1/02. The method of applying electroerosion-resistant coatings based on tungsten and copper on copper electrical contacts / D. A. Romanov, O. V. Olesyuk, E. A. Budovskikh, V. E. Gromov; D. A. Romanov - No. 2013155790/02, declared 12/16/2013; publ. 04/10/2015. Bull. Number 10..

222. Pat. 2545852 RF. IPC C23C 4/08, C23C 4/12. The method of applying electro-erosion-resistant coatings based on molybdenum and copper on copper electrical contacts / D. A. Romanov, O. V. Olesyuk, E. A. Budovskikh, V. E. Gromov; D.A. Romanov - No. 2013155792/02, declared 12/16/2013; publ. 04/10/2015. Bull. Number 10.

223. Pat. 2478732 RF. IPC C23C 14/32. Composite Electrically Explosive Conductor for Electroexplosive Spraying of Coatings or Electroexplosive Alloying of the Surface of Metals and Alloys / D. A. Romanov, E. A. Budovskikh, V. E. Gromov; Federal State Budgetary Educational Institution of Higher Professional Education "Siberian State Industrial University" - No. 2011137782/02, decl. 09/13/2011; publ. 04/10/2013. Bull. Number 10.

224. Pat. 161731 of the Russian Federation. IPC H01H 1/00. Detachable electrical contact / D. A. Romanov, E. A. Budovsky, V. E. Gromov, L. R. Bakhrieva; Federal State Budgetary Educational Institution of Higher Professional Education "Siberian State Industrial University" —№ 2015147885/07, decl. 11/06/2015; publ. 05/10/2016. Bull. Number 13.

225. Pat. 170539 RF. IPC H01H 1/06. Electrical contact / D. A. Romanov, V. E. Gromov, L. R. Bakhrieva; Federal State Budgetary Educational Institution of Higher Professional Education "Siberian State Industrial University" —№ 2016121763, decl. 06/01/2016; publ. 04/28/2017. Bull. Number 13.

226. Mogutnova, N. N. Alloys of molybdenum / N. N. Mogutnova, B. A. Klypin, V. A. Boyarshinov et al. - M.: Metallurgy, 1975 - 392 p.

227. Glezer, A. M. Nanomaterials: structure, properties, application / A. M. Glezer, V. E. Gromov, Yu. F. Ivanov et al. - Novokuznetsk: Inter-Kuzbass Publishing House, 2010 - 423 pp.

228. Shmakov, A.M. Problems of powder materials science. Part VI. Plasma-laser coatings / Shmakov A. M., Antsiferov V. N., Bulanov V. Ya., Khanov A. M - Yekaterinburg: Ural Branch of the Russian Academy of Sciences, 2006 - 587 p.

229. Brandon, D. Microstructure of materials. Research and control methods / D. Brandon, W. Kaplan - M .: Technosphere, 2006 - 384 p.

230. Utevsky, L. M. Diffraction electron microscopy in metal science / L. M. Utevsky - M.: Metallurgiya, 1978 - 584 p.

231. Ivanov, Yu. F. Hardened structural steel: structure and hardening mechanisms / Yu. F. Ivanov, E.V. Kornet, E.V. Kozlov - Novokuznetsk: ed. SibGIU, 2010 - 174 p.

232. Golovin, Yu. I. Nanoindentation and mechanical properties of solids in submicro-volumes, thin surface layers and films (Review) / Yu. I. Golovin // FTT - 2008 - V. 50 - Issue. 12 - S. 2113–2142.

233. Berezin, V. B. Handbook of electrical materials: 3rd ed. / V. B. Berezin, N. S. Prokhorov, G. A. Rykov, A. M. Khaikin - M .: Energoatomizdat, 1983.

Index

A

C